REPORT 2008

A MAN'S GUIDE TO WOMEN

REPORT 2008

A MAN'S GUIDE TO WOMEN

Get the Sex You Want—and Make Her Beg for More—
with Hundreds of Tricks, Tips, and Techniques

RODALE

Notice

This book is intended as a reference volume only, not as a medical manual. The information given here is designed to help you make informed decisions about your health. It is not intended as a substitute for any treatment that may have been prescribed by your doctor. If you suspect that you have a medical problem, we urge you to seek competent medical help.

Mention of specific companies, organizations, or authorities in this book does not imply endorsement by the author or publisher, nor does mention of specific companies, organizations, or authorities imply that they endorse this book, its author, or the publisher.

© 2008 by Rodale Inc.

Internet addresses and telephone numbers given in this book were accurate at the time it went to press.

All rights reserved. No part of this publication may be reproduced or transmitted in any form or by any means, electronic or mechanical, including photocopying, recording, or any other information storage and retrieval system, without the written permission of the publisher.

Printed in the United States of America
Rodale Inc. makes every effort to use acid-free ♾, recycled paper ♲.

ISBN 13: 978–1–59486–698–2
ISBN 10: 1–59486–698–8

2 4 6 8 10 9 7 5 3 1 hardcover

RODALE
LIVE YOUR WHOLE LIFE™

We inspire and enable people to improve their lives and the world around them

For more of our products visit **rodalestore.com** or call 800-848-4735

SEX AND VALUES AT RODALE

We believe that an active and healthy sex life, based on mutual consent and respect between partners, is an important component of physical and mental well-being. We also respect that sex is a private matter and that each person has a different opinion of what sexual practices or levels of discourse are appropriate. Rodale is committed to offering responsible, practical advice about sexual matters, supported by accredited professionals and legitimate scientific research. Our goal—for sex and all other topics—is to publish information that empowers people's lives.

CONTENTS

INTRODUCTION

You're holding in your hands the tool to help you get the sex that you want. What does that mean to you? If you're like most people, *a lot*. *Men's Health* and *Cosmo* magazine teamed up and surveyed 6,000 men and women about sex, finding that more than one-third—of both men and women—want sex two or three times a week.

In order to help advance that worthy goal, we interviewed dozens and dozens of experts. They shared with us their best tips and techniques for this book.

The first section of this book, "Get Noticed," shines a light on you, to help you remake yourself to be more attractive to women. You'll learn the 18 little things that add up to make you a better man. You'll discover how to speak the foreign language of emotion that women seem so fluent in. And you'll find out what thousands of women said when we asked for advice on fixing men's biggest style mistakes.

In our "Understand Women" section, you'll find 10 simple tips to push her over the edge to O, my. You'll uncover her deepest fantasies, and then find out how to make each and every one of them come true. And you'll pick up some tricks to get her to show some skin.

Next, in the "Date Great" section, seize five forgotten holidays to keep her hot all year long. Plan an unforgettable trip together with our runaway strategies. And fan the flames to keep your fire burning bright long past the first passion-packed week.

The "Enhance Sex" section offers plenty of advice to do just that. You'll read one woman's guide to avoiding common bedroom mistakes made by men. Then you'll discover how to make the most of her favorite sex toy. (Hint: It's at the end of your arm.) And you'll see how to heat her up by switching it up with our sex position playbook.

In the "Get Better" section, we discuss the problems that come up in relationships. We offer the lowdown on oils and lubricants for sex. Prepare for the pitfalls of cohabitation with our shacking-up survival guide. And discover how sex experts solved five couples' common sex problems.

Lastly, in the "Survive Relationships" section, you'll find seven incendiary strategies to keep your home fires burning. You'll learn how to battle-proof your relationship. You'll discover how to arouse her interest, anytime, anywhere, with just the touch of your hand. And much, much more.

Each part of this book also includes some Quickies—which are short takes on the topic at hand—questions and answers from our lovely Girl Next Door, and the very latest research on the Science of Sex.

It's our hope that all of this information comes together to make this the year you'll have the best sex of your life!

PART 1

GET NOTICED

On one hand, getting noticed seems like the hardest part of connecting with women. So often they seem like creatures from, or even on, another planet. But on the other hand, getting noticed is the part of the equation that's most within your own control. Small choices that you make every day—from how you part your hair, to the jeans that you wear, to the words that you use—add up to the total package that other people see. How will it get you noticed?

In this section, you'll learn the 18 little things that will all add up to make you a better man. You'll discover how to speak the language women seem to know from birth—the language of emotion. And you'll read the hard-won lessons of a serial monogamist who ventured back into the market after a decade-long absence. You'll fix your biggest style mistakes with advice we gleaned from thousands of women. And perhaps most important, you'll learn how to be a gentleman, or at least look like one.

THE LITTLE THINGS

TAKE THE TIME FOR THESE 18 THINGS.
THEY'LL ADD UP TO MAKE YOU A BETTER MAN

BY DUANE SWIERCZYNSKI

1. **PAYING ATTENTION—REAL ATTENTION—TO A SMALL CHILD.** I still remember the adults who did that when I was a kid. They also happen to be my role models.

2. **THE LID ON A JAR OF PICKLES.** It's not that women really need your help twisting it loose from the jar. They could use a hammer. But they like to make you appear strong, even if you are built like Mick Jagger.

3. **A BREATH MINT.**

4. **A BROWN BAG.** Pack a turkey-on-wheat most of the workweek and you'll save enough for a plasma TV by year's end.

5. **A LUNCHTIME RESERVATION—ONE THAT DOESN'T INVOLVE A DRIVE-THRU.** All those sack lunches earn you a fine meal in a steak house every couple of weeks. Life ain't a gulag.

6. **A 50-MINUTE CPR CLASS.**

7. **GRATITUDE.** It takes 15 seconds to thank someone for their time or gift. It takes 15 years for them to forgive you when you don't.

8. **A SINGLE GLANCE.** *That* glance. If you have to ask, it's been too long since you've given it.

9. **FIVE DEGREES.** Go easy on the thermostat overnight this winter and you'll save 5 percent on heat. Mother Nature thanks you. So does Al Gore.

10. **CHECKING YOUR SPELLING.** Because the difference between Public Relations and Pubic Relations could be your job.

11. **LISTENING—REALLY LISTENING—TO YOUR GRANDFATHER WHEN HE TELLS YOU, FOR THE NINTH TIME, ABOUT THAT SEAFOOD SHOP BACK IN SOUTH PHILLY THAT SOLD LITTLENECK CLAMS FOR A PENNY EACH.** Forget the clams. He's trying for a little bit of immortality by passing along the story to you.

12. **A HANDWRITTEN NOTE.** I landed myself a hot redhead because I sent her a goofy Far Side card with a dashed-off question along the lines of, "So, how have you been?" Ten years later, we have a house and two kids.

13. **RETHINKING THAT LAST DRINK.** If you're drunk enough to absolutely need it, you absolutely don't.

14. **THE RIGHT TO REMAIN SILENT.** People never remember you for being quiet. They remember you for a stupid joke about a venereal disease, your boss, and a transvestite hooker.

15. **GETTING OFF YOUR ASS.** Time was, you stood up when being introduced to someone new. Meet people eye-to-eye and shake, which is a small way of saying, "I'm not above or below you."

16. **GETTING OFF YOUR ASS, PERIOD.** Even 10 minutes of activity a day can drop your blood pressure, boost your mood, and prevent you from forming a covalent bond with your couch.

17. **A SINGLE DETAIL.** About someone else. Could be a wife's name, a kid's sport, or the gum disease their hound had. Wield details wisely, and you'll be a charm machine. Flub them, and you'll make people feel like they're interchangeable cogs in a cosmic mishmash.

18. **A SINGLE DATE.** I have it easy. My wedding anniversary is September 11. Plant a Post-it, set an Outlook alert, or write it on your hand in permanent marker. A Sharpie fades. Her memory doesn't.

EMOTION 101

FOR MANY MEN, EMOTION IS A FOREIGN LANGUAGE. BUT IF YOU WANT
TO MAX OUT ON SEX, LOVE, SUCCESS, AND HAPPINESS—AND PRODUCE
A FEW HEIRS WHILE YOU'RE AT IT—LEARN TO SPEAK IT

BY LAURENCE ROY STAINS

With a sigh of relief, you pull into your driveway at the end of another 12-hour day.

You're ready to unwind. Already, your blood pressure is falling. But inside your house, your personal life is waiting. Maybe you have a girlfriend or wife who craves your companionship, and children who demand your attention. When you walk through that door, you may be thinking in terms of haven and escape. But in these next few hours, you're really undergoing a transition. You're going to make the switch from work to love, from ambition to emotion, from power to intimacy.

This transition is a big job—and the ramifications are bigger than ever. So you need to handle it well.

What if you don't? Hey, no harm done. You'll simply join the legions of the angry and depressed, with half your money gone to your ex-wife, your kids mad at you, your few friends slowly drifting away, and a vague sense of shame that keeps you from making social connections. Not that I'm speaking from personal experience or anything.

Okay? Now you can loosen your tie. But don't open the car door just yet. I want to talk to you for a while longer.

I'm not that crazy about the word "intimacy." I bet you're not, either. It's a department-store word. (Third floor: Intimate Apparel.) And, come to think of it, I'm never happy to hear the word "emotion." It means that pretty soon I'll be hearing the word "feelings," as in I've hurt her feelings or I don't seem to have any feelings, unless team X comes from behind to beat team Y. When men hear about "emotion," we're usually about to be scolded.

I'm being more than a little defensive, but you and I both know that our apparent difficulty with the whole feelings thing bothers women. And, further, they grow testy over the fact that it bothers them more than it bothers us. But how's this for an idea? Men should stop being defined by what we lack. Instead, let's take a clear-eyed look at emotions, the unique ways in which we experience them, and their role in who we are today. Wouldn't it be cool if we understood that, and why we are the way we are? Wouldn't it be cool if we could finally explain ourselves to women—if only so they'd stop asking us to?

Fortunately for all of us, some serious scientific and psychological discoveries of the past decade can help us do just that. So let's push beyond the gauzy metaphor of Mars and Venus. Yes, men and women are different, but it's no longer enough to categorize men by the words they fail to say.

And let's concede one point straight off: Men are not as emotionally articulate as women are. It's not out of spite; we don't stubbornly refuse to spend hours talking about feelings. We just can't do it. That is, the inner architecture of our brains just can't do it. New technology, such as functional magnetic-resonance imaging (better known by its abbreviation, fMRI), allows neuroscientists to virtually open up the skull and see what's happening inside. This means you can show people photos of mutilated bodies, for example, and watch their brains react. It may sound cruel, but that's exactly what a team of Stanford scientists did. They showed brutal images to 12 men and 12 women. In the women, nine different areas of the brain showed higher activity, both when viewing the pictures and when recalling them 3 weeks later. Nine different areas! In the men, only two areas lit up. The comparison says it all.

Thanks to neuroscience, we now know that the amygdala, a small, almond-shaped region deep in the brain, plays a key role in both emotional reactions and emotional memories. And, wouldn't you know it, the female amygdala is far more efficient. That's why women can recall more emotional memories more quickly (have you noticed?), and their memories are richer and more intense. (No wonder she still remembers that hurtful remark you made last Christmas.) The amygdala may also play a role in women's greater tendency to engage in what scientists call ruminative thinking, the repetitive focus on negative feelings and events. (You've noticed that, as well.) Psychologists now know that a lot of rumination actually confuses people about how they really feel, but you won't want to tell her that when she's ruminating.

There are other key brain differences. The female brain has a better connection between its left hemisphere, which is involved in speech, and its

DEAL WITH THE BIG ISSUES

"Unless you're the one in 10 million families that's perfect, you'll face some land mines," says William Pollack, PhD, director of the Center for Men and Young Men at McLean Hospital and an assistant clinical professor of psychology at Harvard. We went to the bomb-sweeping experts for strategies.

The land mine: Your passions have taken a backseat to your children's.

The fix: Stoke your own interests so you don't have to live vicariously through theirs. Nobody wants that. "It's time for men to reclaim the good things about being a dad," says Chris Erskine, a *Los Angeles Times* columnist and the author of *Man of the House.* "Yes, you can watch two NFL games on a Sunday afternoon. Kids don't need to be entertained all the time, or held hostage to all these organized activities. Hey, Dad, get a life. Give the kids a little space."

The land mine: The kids (or the wife) think that you're playing favorites.

The fix: "We used to drag Eli to so many of Cooper and Peyton's games, I thought he might grow up to not even like sports," says NFL Hall-of-Famer Archie Manning, the patriarch of a QB dynasty and one of the reigning Father's Day/Mother's Day Council's Fathers of the Year. "You try your best to make it to everything your kids do, but sometimes it just isn't possible," he says. Swap spectator duties with your wife so all your kids feel the love from the stands.

The land mine: Your desire to have one of the kids follow in your footsteps is straining the relationship.

right hemisphere, which is involved in emotion. (That connective tissue is called the corpus callosum, and females have more of it than we do, in relation to total brain size.) When most women talk, both sides of their brains are activated; men use only their left hemispheres for speech. It's emerging details like this that are leading scientists to theorize that, yes indeed, women seem to have a greater built-in facility for talking about their feelings.

By simply observing little kids' behavior, we get the picture that our differences are innate. A whole slew of psychological studies have gathered data on

The fix: Drop the self-centered desire to raise a Mini-Me. Let them grow. "I can't force my kid to play the drums," says Zakk Wylde, front man for the heavy-metal group Black Label Society and lead guitarist for Ozzy Osbourne. "I told him, 'If you want to play drums, I'll give you the sticks. If not, I'll throw them in the garbage.' Watch—my youngest son is going to be into basket weaving and ballet. They're going to find what their love is anyway."

THE LAND MINE: Your son is assuming your bad habits.

The fix: Don't pretend to be infallible. "My son asked me about steroids. I said, 'Nick, I can tell you the right thing to do even if I didn't lead by example,'" says Hulk Hogan, wrestling great and star of *Hogan Knows Best*. "I used steroids, but we didn't understand them in the '80s. Now we've been re-educated. I made a mistake; I don't want him to do the same. Be a parent first, a friend later."

The land mine: The new face in the family has you feeling overwhelmed.

The fix: "Don't take it personally that absolutely everyone peripheral to the birthing process will ignore you," says Rob Corddry, formerly of *The Daily Show* and a first-time father. You're a supporting actor in this show, so be the best husband and father you can—but don't expect an Oscar nomination. "This isn't about you, you selfish jerk," says Corddry.

—MATT GOULDING

the habits of preschoolers, and here's a sampling: By age 1, girls make more eye contact than boys do. A couple of years later, paintings made by young girls will almost always contain one or two people; little boys' renderings commonly depict rocket ships, bicycles, and cars. At play, boys were 50 times more competitive over toy sharing, while girls were 20 times more likely to take turns.

Could a horribly sexist culture be to blame for those differences? No—at least not entirely, says Simon Baron-Cohen, PhD, a psychologist at Cambridge University. In multiple studies, he has looked at the amount of testosterone babies are exposed to in the womb, and then looked at them at 12 months, 18 months, 2 years, and 4 years of age.

The results have been startling.

The higher the baby's level of fetal testosterone, regardless of gender, the less eye contact the child makes at age 1 and the smaller his or her vocabulary is at 18 months. By age 4, those with the highest fetal-testosterone levels score the lowest on a test of social skills and the highest on a test showing deep interest in a narrow range of topics.

Testosterone in the womb could be the big key to our interests and behavior as adults. "More specifically," Baron-Cohen writes in his latest book, *The Essential Difference,* "the more you have of this special substance, the more your brain is tuned in to systems and the less your brain is tuned in to emotional relationships."

There's the taproot of the male condition.

Baron-Cohen has marshaled all this evidence into a grand theory, which he lays out in his book. There are basically two kinds of brains—the empathizing brain and the systemizing brain. If you have an empathizing brain, you're exquisitely good at understanding how someone else might feel, and furthermore you want to alleviate their distress. You're good at identifying people's inner emotions simply by looking at their facial expressions. (Baron-Cohen and his colleagues have catalogued 412 discrete emotions. Oy.) You're good at relationships, and you maintain those healthy relationships by sharing feelings. And you have a flair for language, so you can express all 412 of those emotions.

If you have a systemizing brain, says Baron-Cohen, you're driven to understand systems—anything from plumbing fixtures to the NBA rule book, from patent law to the bond market. Systemizers specialize in events with predictable consequences, so that when you act, you can be pretty darn

WHISPER SO THEY DON'T SCREAM

If Cesar Millan, TV's Dog Whisperer, can penetrate the canine psyche and calm a ferocious pooch, then you should be able to regain control of your two-legged progeny. Influence your problem child with these subtle psychological tricks.

The Clingy Student

The problem: Your kid clings to Mom every morning when she drops him off at school. A 2-minute no-brainer becomes a 20-minute ordeal.

The whisper: Start taking your kids to school yourself. "Children tend to separate more easily from the dad, because the child is usually used to his leaving for work every morning," says Gail Reichlin, coauthor of *The Pocket Parent*.

The Absentminded Dresser

The problem: The morning dash out the door is invariably stalled by missing shoes, mittens, and backpacks.

The whisper: Teach your kids to be more responsible with their belongings by taking them shopping for closet organizers. "When the child is involved in making a plan to solve the problem, you'll get more cooperation next time," says Reichlin. Once they can remember that the Spider-Man backpack goes on the Spider-Man coat hook and their shoes go on the shelf shaped like a frog, you'll fly off to work like Superman.

The Budding Pugilist

The problem: Your kids fight, and fight, and fight, and fight—and fight.

The whisper: Even if one child is clearly the instigator, never take sides. "Rather than singling one child out, teach them problem-solving skills, so they learn to listen to each other and work together," says Mary Sheedy Kurcinka, author of *Kids, Parents, and Power Struggles.* If one child is hitting the other one, pull the hitter away but say, "You both need to stop fighting right now."

—DENNY WATKINS

certain of the result. Such systems can take a long time to learn, but if you have a systemizing brain, that doesn't bother you—you can spend endless hours observing all the details, to the exclusion of everything (and, oops, everybody) else in your life. You're more interested in organizing principles than in the social world. You're good with mechanical things, not people. You cultivate an expertise. And you love sports, because they're a combination of four systems: an organizing system (E-A-G-L-E-S!), a system of rules ("He was nowhere near the end zone!"), a motoric system (". . . a 43-yard touchdown pass . . ."), and a statistical system (". . . that keeps their wild-card hopes alive if Green Bay loses, the Falcons win, and the Giants get lost on the way to the Meadowlands!").

In the past, systemizers have been good at tool making, hunting, and trading. Now they're good at engineering, inventing, coaching, computer programming, and leading a corporation along a "critical path" toward "key metrics." In their daily lives, these people tend to be independent, driven, successful individuals who do well in business because of their expertise and their ability to take decisive action. They do well socially, not because of their power to empathize, but because they've reduced the pecking order to a system of rules and know how to manipulate their way through it. If they're men, as they often are, they're very attractive to women—the very same women who, after a few years, wonder why these guys aren't better empathizers.

Sound like anyone you know?

You don't have to be male to have a systemizing brain—but it helps. (Remember, your fetal testosterone level helped shape your brain.) Baron-Cohen has come up with 60-question tests to identify people as empathizers or systemizers, and from the thousands he's administered to date, he figures that 44 percent of women have empathizing brains, 17 percent have systemizing brains (which accounts for the many brilliant female scientists), and 35 percent have brains that are roughly balanced between the two poles. Four percent exhibit an "extreme female brain" type.

Baron-Cohen says that 53 percent of men have systemizing brains,

17 percent have empathizing brains, and 24 percent are roughly balanced. The remaining 6 percent have an extreme male brain—and these men, he theorizes, exhibit behavior that's labeled autistic.

But just because your brain isn't tuned in to emotional relationships doesn't mean you can blow them off. Rather, it means you have to pay attention to emotions—those of others, and your own. Otherwise, when the chips are down, you'll find yourself sitting at the table alone, with no one to help you and no idea how to help yourself.

The psychologist Ronald F. Levant, EdD, has spent 2 decades conducting research in the field of men and their emotions. Having grown up in South Central Los Angeles, an area "that was tough and is tough," as he says, he experienced firsthand the ways in which traditional cultures teach men to

ESTABLISH SOLITARY REFINEMENT

"Nearly everyone will have to live alone at some point in his life," says Michael Broder, PhD, author of *The Art of Living Single.* "You can either fall into a state of isolation or learn how to perfect the lifestyle." These two tips can make living alone less alienating.

Let there be light (and color). "A room full of gray can be sterile and cold, unless some warm touches are added," says Leatrice Eiseman, executive director of the Pantone Color Institute and author of *More Alive with Color.* So ditch those $15 lamps that you've had since college and invest in floor lamps with more personality. (Check out those from Design Within Reach, www.dwr.com.) They'll brighten up your apartment while showing that you possess the one thing money can't buy: good taste.

Stick together. Bachelorhood isn't an excuse for isolation and ramen-noodle subsistence. Once a week, gather around the table with a few of your friends—single or not. Rotate houses from one meal to the next; whoever hosts cooks the main course, but guests are in charge of salads, side dishes, appetizers, and beverages. And when your turn to host comes around, don't even think of dialing Domino's.

—BRIAN MCCLINTOCK

stifle their emotions. As a researcher, he knew of a clinical condition called alexithymia (uh-lexa-THIGH-me-uh), which literally means the inability to put emotions into words. It was originally applied to the severe emotional constriction of drug-dependent post-traumatic stress disorder patients. But in his counseling practice, he saw a more "garden-variety" form of alexithymia. His male patients often exhibited an inability to know what they were feeling—especially if those feelings were in the tender and vulnerable vein.

As a professor of psychology at the University of Akron, Levant has devoted his research to showing that a mild-to-moderate form of alexithymia is widespread in our society. As he says, "It's normative for many men in our society to be genuinely unaware of some of their emotions."

He gives one quick example: In his practice, he saw a man who had been caught cross-dressing—by his grown children. So the man came to a therapy session with his wife. Levant asked him how he felt at the moment he was discovered. And the man turned to his wife and asked, "How did I feel?"

Levant believes we experience emotion on three different levels: the neural, biochemical level, expressed in heartbeat and breathing patterns; the physical and behavioral level, revealed in facial expression and body language; and finally the level of conscious awareness. Typically, alexithymic men lack the third level, and may even lack an awareness at the second level.

Whether this emotional checkout is hardwired or pounded into you, it can be crippling. Levant believes that the cost of repressing your emotions—or, worse, dissociating from them completely—leads to alcohol abuse, anger and aggression, thrill-seeking behaviors, and psychosomatic illness. To avoid these fates, it isn't required that you become a master of emotional fluency; awareness by itself is sufficient. But this is not just about making sure you don't wind up in a wheelchair. If you know how to feel, you know how to act. "It helps us live better lives," says Levant. "It enables us to respond more quickly and more appropriately to events that arise in our lives, both at work and at home."

In my own marriage, I suspect that my wife uses emotions to avoid action.

RESET THE TABLE

Nearly 15 percent of meals in this country are eaten behind steering wheels; another 42 percent, in front of televisions. A recent Cornell University study links time-related stress to a surge in fast-food consumption and a marked decrease in family meals. "They mean more than nutrition and simply eating at the table; it's about communication and bonding," says Carol Devine, PhD, an associate professor of nutritional sciences at Cornell University and the lead author of the study. Here are four simple ways to bring your family back to the table and make dinner meaningful again.

Make them your sous-chefs. Rather than giving your family (or friends) menial tasks like grating cheese or peeling potatoes, have them work on dishes they can "own" from start to finish. For example, give the kids a few cookbooks and have them hunt for a recipe for a side dish or salad. Have them taste it, adjust the seasonings to their liking, and bring their masterpiece triumphantly to the table.

Forget about today. "How are you?" is only one step removed from discussing the weather. If something great happened, they'll offer it up naturally; otherwise, don't try to pry the past out of them. Instead, stoke the conversational fires with, "Tell me about something cool you have coming up." It eliminates one-word answers and focuses on some positive event in the future.

Change the seating arrangement. Dinner can be deadly if you're stuck with the same layout every night. So try to change things up with an alternate outdoor table or impromptu picnic dinners in some local park, or by rotating seating positions. If you're creative, you'll encourage family members to think of that time together as an adventure and opportunity, rather than just an obligation.

Go to the source. Show your kids that not all food comes shrink-wrapped. "I'll go out for the day to the coast, stop at a fish shop, and have them pick what they want, even if it's something they've never eaten," says Pino Maffeo, chef at Restaurant L in Boston. "They love the adventure." Take them apple picking, to a local dairy farm, or to the farmers' market, and let them select the building blocks for dinner.

—MATT GOULDING

(I told her that. You can imagine how well it went over.) I suspect a lot of guys think of emotions that way, as the opposite of action. Wasn't that Hamlet's problem?

But emotions are not useless. They can motivate us to action. Did you see Tiger Woods, a few months after the death of his father, annihilating all challengers in the final nine holes at Hoylake at this year's British Open? On the last fairway, with victory nearly secured, his caddy said to him, "This one's for Pops." And Tiger was wracked with big, gutsy sobs. Then, more to the point, he blubbered in the arms of his beautiful blonde wife.

Remember, Hamlet didn't get the girl or the claret jug. But Tiger did. Be glad it's 2008.

Emotions are now part of the manly formula for success: acting with head and heart and hands. Or, in the words of Harvard psychologist Daniel Gilbert, PhD, "Emotion is a compass that tells us what to do."

You have a lot to cram into these next few hours. If you're going to nourish your rich personal life, you have some ground to cover. At any given moment tonight, the American male will be juggling the following:

FRIENDS. As men, we commonly base our friendships on shared activities. It's a pattern established in late boyhood, when we made friends on the basis of common interests, such as skateboarding or heavy metal. It's how we do intimacy. It's good fun, and it's good for our health: In his 2000 book, *Bowling Alone,* Harvard University political scientist Robert Putnam lists the many

>> A MAN'S GUIDE POLL

With which notorious party animal would you most like to go out on the town?

Tommy Lee	33%
John Belushi	25%
Dean Martin	23%
Babe Ruth	10%
Benjamin Franklin	9%

health benefits of having friends and concludes that not having a posse is as big a health risk as smoking.

PARENTS. If you've gotten closer to your parents recently, you're not alone. According to the Family Caregiver Alliance, up to 7 million Americans are caring for elderly people, and the number of men providing the primary care may be on an upswing. One report documents the number of males becoming primary caregivers as rising 50 percent between 1984 and 1994. With the aging of the boomers and the parents who sired them, that number can only keep rising.

CHILDREN. By their early forties, 78 percent of American men have fathered at least one child, according to the 2002 National Survey of Family Growth. And among men ages 15 to 44 who haven't had children yet, another 78 percent say it would bother them at least a little if they never had a child. Clearly, children are important to us—so important that, in the same study, more men than women say a man's kids should come before his career! And, for many divorced men, their kids are their only family. (Ditto gay divorced cowboys, like Heath Ledger's character in *Brokeback Mountain*.) Sociologist Paul Amato, PhD, of Pennsylvania State University, has analyzed 63 studies dealing with divorced dads and their kids. He found that if the kids felt close to their fathers and if the dads provided authoritative parenting, the children did well in school and were less likely to get into trouble after school.

WIVES—OR GIRLFRIENDS WHO MIGHT ONE DAY BECOME WIVES. By age 35, 70 percent of us have gotten married. So marriage is important to most of us. Unfortunately, marriage is becoming less important to women. The latest evidence comes from the same survey. The 12,000 men and women who participated were asked to agree or disagree with the statement "It is better to get married than go through life single." Two-thirds (66 percent) of men agreed—but only 51 percent of women did. In other words, one in two women thinks marriage isn't such a sweet deal for her. Maybe your wife.

So where are you going to find the time to rekindle old friendships, look in on your parents, help your kids with their homework . . . oh, and do something that'll cause your wife to thank her lucky stars she married you? There's the problem: Time is scarce. You don't have the time. Experts blithely refer to this universal modern bind as "work-family conflict." And it's not just a girl thing. "Work and family is almost always viewed as a women's issue," says Joseph Grzywacz, PhD, an associate professor at Wake Forest University school of medicine. "It's equally important for men."

Grzywacz's most recent research focuses on the opposite effect, what he calls "positive spillover" from work to home, and vice versa. Your home life helps your work when you can talk about job problems and seek advice about solving them; it also helps if you can relax and recharge at home, and if you aren't interrupted by family disruptions at work. Conversely, work helps the family by making you a more interesting person and by providing a good salary and benefits that the entire family wants to protect. "That's the best mental-health scenario," says Grzywacz.

The worst scenario is when work conflicts with family, and vice versa. That conflict leads to a greater likelihood of depression, anxiety, and problem drinking, he found upon analyzing the results of 3,032 responses to the 1995 National Survey of Midlife Development.

And, apparently, how men handle that pent-up frustration has everything to do with their ability to recover from it. Emotional spills, surprisingly, may not be the answer. Marc Schulz, PhD, a clinical psychologist and professor at Bryn Mawr College, conducted a study of 42 married couples with young children; the men worked an average of 43 hours a week, and the women averaged 25 hours a week. Among those with the happiest marriages, the man would withdraw after a bad day—and his wife would let him. "They need time to unwind," says Schulz. "Some evidence supports the idea that men are far from unemotional—that in fact they're exquisitely sensitive to emotions. They might in fact feel them too strongly. And so they just need some space when they're filled with negative feelings. There's something about good marriages that gives each partner the space to do what he or she wants to do."

As you've gathered by now, marriage is the linchpin of a happy life for most men. But to succeed in it, you'll have to balance a man's two greatest needs:

BIG LESSONS ON SMALL SCREENS

Teach your family something valuable while you're all being entertained around the electronic campfire. "Parental mediation can mold the messages children take from certain programs, even if the programs are horrible," says Elizabeth Vandewater, PhD, director of the Center for Interactive Technology, Television, and Children at the University of Texas. Here's your prime-time lesson plan.

On Being a Brother: *My Name Is Earl* (NBC)

The premise: Lottery winner Earl Hickey's (Jason Lee) quest to gain karmic retribution by righting every wrong he's ever committed is repeatedly helped in unexpected ways by his man-child younger brother, Randy (Ethan Suplee).

The lesson: Bickering siblings can learn to appreciate each other's differences, lest karma catch up with them, too.

On Applied Science: *Mythbusters* (Discovery Channel)

The premise: Hollywood special-effects experts devise elaborate experiments to test urban legends and explain scientific principles.

The lesson: If watching a fireball engulf a toilet doesn't inspire a child to learn the quadratic formula, nothing will.

On Facing New Situations: *The Amazing Race* (CBS)

The premise: Two- or four-person teams circle the globe Carmen Sandiego–style, finding clues to their next destination. Some handle this feat with finesse, but others apply notoriously American brashness.

The lesson: The best moments reveal how stress brings out the worst in people, and how not to be a stranger in a strange land.

On Sexual Dynamics: *The Office* (NBC)

The premise: Workplace drudgery and madness, leavened by an earnest flirtation between office prankster Jim (John Krasinski) and Pam (Jenna Fischer), a cute receptionist.

The lesson: A relationship isn't built on low-rise jeans and high-end lingerie alone.

—DENNIS WATKINS

the need for power and the need for intimacy. So says psychologist Gordon M. Hart, PhD, in his new book, *Power and Intimacy in Men's Development.*

A common male mistake, he says, is to seek power and avoid intimacy. Some men just work and work and work—and never switch gears. We spend all day honing our lightning-fast problem-solving abilities, and then we take those skills home with us and try them out on the wife and kids: Hey, I get props all day for doing this stuff! Why aren't you guys impressed? Or we get scrappy with our wives in the same way we'd spar with a rival manager at work: No, I'm not selling my motorcycle! We reflexively approach everything as a power struggle: She's not going to tell me what to do. But she may think of it as an intimacy issue: I can't be your partner if you've splattered yourself on the highway.

Hart notes that in the average office environment, we have to keep our emotions in check, "otherwise we're seen as vulnerable. If we're seen as emotional, we're seen as out of control—and of course that's the kiss of death." But unless we trade in our emotional distancing for emotional responsiveness when we get home, we will lose that home. The guys who have figured out the secret of modern masculinity will come home and "take off the emotional armor," as Hart puts it.

Or they won't, and they'll get divorced. Roughly two out of every three divorces are initiated by women. Sanford L. Braver, PhD, a professor of psychology at Arizona State University, surveyed hundreds of divorced men and women for his book *Divorced Dads.* The top reason women gave for a divorce was "losing a sense of closeness."

Marital researchers are saying lately that emotional closeness is the only thing the contemporary marriage has left. If she doesn't feel connected to you, is there any reason for her to stick around? Most women would say no. Not practically, not morally, not financially. She had better feel close to you. If not, there's the door, and a lawyer is propping it open for her. When she goes, the children will follow.

Ironically, women still start out their marriages thrilled to be Mrs. You. Then comes Junior in a baby carriage, which nobody's ready for. According to a University of Washington study of newlyweds, nearly two-thirds of wives suffer a big decline in marital satisfaction within about 2 years after a baby is born—despite what you see in the Huggies commercials. After year 10, satisfaction rises again—but only for men; it takes women 15 years to see a bump in satisfaction.

Men are rather famous for coming on strong before marriage and putting our feet up afterward. Marriage researcher Howard J. Markman, PhD, co-author of *Fighting for Your Marriage,* once told me that, after men get married, a sort of "benign neglect" sets in, as they turn their attention to other things. "It's the biggest error men make," he said. "The man just starts taking the relationship for granted. He's assuming it's going to take care of itself." But, clearly, it doesn't.

We've had a nice little chat, sitting out here in your driveway. Now, before you go into the house, tell me: What are you going to do differently?

First off, you're going to take charge of this transition. If you need 20 minutes to decompress, take it. If you need 20 minutes sitting quietly with your wife in the den with a glass of wine and absolutely no children, do that. (My friend Kathy made that a house rule. She's still on her first marriage.) Whatever you need, man, just make it happen. "Nobody has to be a victim," says Marianne J. Legato, MD, author of *Why Men Never Remember and Women Never Forget.* "Eventually, people learn to wait a minute."

Okay, your 20 minutes are up. Let the games begin. Your wife wants a word with you. Sit down. Listen. Let her talk. You don't have to match her level of emotional intensity. "If other things start cropping up—like all your offenses for the past 15 years—just stop and say, 'This doesn't help. What is the issue today?' Stop a discussion that is counterproductive," Dr. Legato says. But do it respectfully. And be patient. "Gently guide her to the issues she really wants to talk about. Give her room to calm down." In short, let her feel close to you.

A recent major study of 5,010 couples found that women are happiest in their marriages when they get their husbands' attention. The single most important factor in a woman's happy marriage is her husband's emotional engagement. What does that mean, exactly? I put that question to

Steven L. Nock, PhD, a University of Virginia sociologist and the study's coauthor. He says it simply means "men showing interest in the routines of their wives' lives—the routine, mundane things that men normally don't talk about." Granted, it's not most men's style to do this, an acknowledgment Nock makes personally and professionally.

"I don't know about you, but for me it doesn't come naturally," he says. He wonders how many men find it perfectly natural, after several years of marriage, to sit down every day and say, "Tell me about your day." "It is an effort," he says.

Nock is sympathetic, but adamant: "Get over it," he says. Your marriage is important to you. You earn more money because of it, you live longer, you're in better health all around, your chances of having an active sex life are way better, and your standard of living is higher. If your marriage is happy, you're more productive at work than if your marriage is unhappy.

Plus, there's a more intangible but nonetheless important benefit: "Marriage is a standard of masculinity for guys," Nock says. It shows the world that you've grown up, that you're a stand-up guy. In short, marriage is a better deal for men than it is for women. He comes to this conclusion after years of studying marriages and writing academic books like *Marriage in Men's Lives*. His bottom line to you: "If a guy is smart, he's going to realize he's getting a great deal, and he's going to put in a lot of effort to keep his wife happy and keep those benefits flowing."

One of the biggest trends in marriage studies during the past 30 years is videotaping couples talking and fighting. Researchers draft a bunch of undergraduate work-study grunts to watch these tapes and write down what they see, and 5 years later, they follow up with the couples to see who's divorced. Well, guess what? The couples who got divorced are those who clearly ignored each other or were downright hostile. It's not the couples in which the guy actually listened to his wife when she spoke—listened and showed interest and affection. Five years later, those marriages are okay.

Five years from now, will your marriage be okay?

Now you're ready to walk in the door.

BACK IN THE SADDLE

HEED THESE LESSONS ONE SERIAL MONOGAMIST LEARNED
WHEN HE VENTURED BACK INTO THE DATING GAME
FOR HIS FIRST TIME IN A DECADE

BY STEPHEN RODRICK

My marriage ended with a whimper, not a bang. In 2002, after 9 years together, my wife and I split up in the parking lot of a Gap in suburban Boston. Not that I didn't see it coming. There had been couples counseling, crying jags, and final chances. She wanted to raise kids in an insular seaside town.

I wanted kids, too: just in New York or L.A. At least that's what we said the issue was. We were two emotional Marxists, incapable of compromise, heading toward mutually assured destruction.

"It's just not working," she said.

For once in my life, I said nothing. My first thought was, "A Gap parking lot? Sitting in a Nissan Sentra? C'mon, you can do better than that!"

We rode home in silence. At the house, I threw some clothes into two duffel bags and laughed bitterly at the wallpaper I'd been peeling off our bedroom walls, prep work for a renovation that now would never happen. I tossed my CDs into a crate and packed up my 1991 Honda Accord for my move to New York City. I was fine for a while, then flopped on the kitchen floor, bawling uncontrollably. My wife wondered if she should call the paramedics.

Finally, I gathered myself and drove away. Five minutes later, she called me.

"Aha," I deduced. Second thoughts already!

"Hey, you forgot your laptop."

I waited at a gas station where I used to make goofy faces at her while filling up the Sentra.

A few minutes later, she arrived, handed me my computer bag, and was gone. I threw it on the passenger side, took a breath, and steeled myself for a long drive and the first day of the rest of my life.

Then it hit me. "Damn it!" I screamed. Not on account of her. I had just remembered that my car's CD player had been swiped the week before. I was about to be left alone with my thoughts for hundreds of miles on the interstate.

God, being divorced was going to suck.

Or maybe not.

At first, I found being single again at age 36 daunting. During nearly a decade in the matrimonial cocoon, much had happened. Bill and Monica, Internet dating, and insta-communication had altered the way men and women paired off. Could you flirt endlessly with a pretty girl via e-mail and text messages now? Yes! Could the same girl show up at a party with a never-before-mentioned boyfriend? Yes!

As Bill Murray's character experiences in *Groundhog Day,* massive repetition led to gradual enlightenment. Well, enlightenment might be the wrong word. I still give thanks to Jesus, Allah, and Zeus for the moment when a spunky makeup artist told me we could "hook up" whenever I was in LA.

I thought this meant, uh, we could have a night of dinner and dancing. She set me straight: "Hooking up" meant we could call each other whenever I was in LA and have sex. But like Murray, who is forced to relive the worst day in his life over and over again until he changes, I came to realize that as a single man, I had no one to blame but myself if my life blew chunks. My character was my karma, and if I wanted to change my life or to be happy or to find whatever your vision of enlightenment is, the responsibility was mine.

Forty-three percent of first marriages end in divorce, and a cottage industry has sprung up to advise men on their journey through Denial, Rage, and Acceptance. My stages of grief could more aptly be described as Fear, More Fear, and Ultimate Fear. So take your pick: Read a namby-pamby self-help book or follow me on an NC-17 journey that includes stops in the garden of earthly delights and Candy Land's Molasses Swamp. All I ask is, don't judge me. Mistakes were made. Dignity was misplaced. I was flying without instruments. Count yourself lucky; at least you have a navigator.

THE FIRST DATE

Unlike some of my pasty-white buddies who broke up with their wives and got all gangsta, blasting "women are nothing but hos and bitches" from the stereos of their Subaru Foresters, I didn't sour on love. Quite to the contrary, I truly thought I might fall in love again soon. How soon? I didn't know—maybe on my first date in 9 years?

She was an editor at a women's magazine who seemed, via e-mail and a brief phone chat, nice and nonthreatening. We arranged to meet at a Greenwich Village bar. And then I began a disconcerting ritual I call first-date prep. In short, Rodrick Industries closes for business the day of a first date. Gentlemen, don't try this at work: It will get you fired. But I'm a writer, and my days are permanent grad school; there's rarely anything that can't be pushed back in the service of freaking myself out.

For Kelly, the troops began mobilizing the night before. I debated when to shave so I'd have enough stubble to look cool but not enough to look like a vagrant. Unfortunately, the dull razor left a possible-suicide-attempt-gone-awry gouge on my neck. I bought condoms and debated whether to put one in my wallet; that lasted 3 or 4 hours. Eventually, I realized "carrying" might give off the aura that I'm a player. That's not me! But why did I spend the rest of the afternoon making a mix CD in case of a triumphant return?

That night, I approached the rendezvous point right on time. As Coldplay played at a volume even Chris Martin would disapprove of, I saw a woman who matched the description of Kelly, my set-up girl. With the melodic mope rock strumming away in my ears, I mouthed "Kelly" in her direction. She nodded yes; we embraced and agreed to head out for quieter climes. So far, I was rocking the party that rocks the party.

But as we nursed a second drink and made excruciatingly awkward conversation, I gamely asked how long she had known Francis, our mutual friend and matchmaker. "I don't know any Francis," she said. The room spun a bit.

"Is your name Kelly?" I asked.

"No, it's Karen. Are you Scott?"

On my first date in 9 years, I'd managed to leave the bar with the wrong woman. I returned to the scene of the crime with Karen, hoping to make a prisoner exchange. I found Kelly and Scott drinking at the bar. He was bald and hairy. Kelly looked like a beautiful blonde bank hostage waiting for the right moment to crawl to safety.

Kelly and I ended up hanging out for a few instructive weeks. After our second or third date, she invited me back up to her apartment, pulled the quilt off her bed, sat down, and started showing me family pictures. She sat very close to me. Her knee collided with mine. Repeatedly. I looked at the photos for about a half hour and then got up, kissed her on the cheek, and left. She looked baffled.

Later, I related the incident to a buddy.

"She invites you up and sits on her bed?" he asked, his eyes popping out of his head. He then spoke to me slowly, as if I was in a special-ed class. "Do. You. Know. What. That. Means?"

I swirled the ice in my glass and gave him a perplexed look. "No, what?"

"Uh, dude, she wanted to have sex with you."

"Ohhh."

When I tried to act upon this intel, I learned about the modern phenomenon known as c-ck blocking. The next week, I took Kelly to the US Open tennis tournament. My best friend, Sam, went separately with another date. Afterward, we met up for a drink. He clamped his hand on my shoulder.

"You know, I was at the same match as you and Kelly," he said. "I was watching the two of you through binoculars. It's clear you two don't have chemistry. You shouldn't waste your time on her."

Sam had been my best man during my first trip down the aisle, so I took his advice and stopped seeing Kelly. Sam and I drifted apart for a few months. I then heard through a mutual friend that he was in a hot and heavy relationship with—wait for it—Kelly. A year later, they married. I was invited to the wedding but, in a final indignity, wasn't allowed to bring a date. I never got them a wedding present.

Clearly, I had a lot to learn.

After my first Christmas alone and the finalizing of an amicable divorce, I became a nihilist and carried an "all we are is dust in the wind" philosophy into my dating forays. I'd never really been single since I was 17, swinging from vine to vine in four monogamous relationships. Now I was unattached and high on a lethal combination of making up for lost time, not giving a crap, and knowing that women found me attractive. Filling my head with this psychological cocktail was like giving a borderline-retarded kid an eight ball and the combination to the nuclear football.

When I told a couple of co-workers that a very engaged beauty had shot me a couple of come-hither looks, they laughed in my face. Sufficiently challenged, I embarked on Operation Remove the Ring. There were candlelit dinners where she told me, "Mathematically, you have a beautiful face," and some torrid make-out sessions. The last one took place in front of the home of her very tall, very large fiancé. I didn't close the deal, but I also managed not to get my jaw broken, so let's call it a draw.

Sure, there were the nights of Veuve Clicquot and terry-cloth robes in luxury hotels, but there were also Bible-black ones when introspection came calling. The deeper I got into my life as a "re-single," the more I realized that there was self-destructive behavior going on here. It was one thing to get my mojo back; it was another to distance myself from the good women I met so I could chase after the ones who were guaranteed to make me miserable.

For a few months, I dated Laura, a 35-year-old sweet and kind comedy executive with an extraordinary Gramercy Park apartment. However, the sex was ordinary—it's never a good sign when, in week 2, you look away as she gets out of bed—and I sabotaged it by obsessing over her tragic Talbots-heavy wardrobe. This was followed by systematic belittlement, a long-standing character flaw that often left my ex-wife searching for a carving knife. On a summer night, Laura organized a charity boat cruise featuring performances by her comedian friends. She slaved for hours on the event and, at the end of the night, asked me what I thought. In my most bored voice, I quipped, "The funniest thing was when two of your comics missed the boat."

Don't worry, I paid for my callowness: I then met Melissa, a 27-year-old who had done lots of acid, attended four colleges, and forwarded my introductory e-mail to all our coworkers as her idea of hilarity. With Melissa, whom my guy friends eventually dubbed "crazy girl," there were moments of happiness, but they were always followed by behavior that left me believing she'd have burned my house down were it not made of brick. Once, I received an out-of-nowhere e-mail announcing, "Hi! I'm in Mexico. I didn't want you to worry. I love you and miss you." Only later did I find out that she was there with one of my best friends, whom she had been seeing off and on behind my back. Eventually, Melissa showed up on my doorstep, begging forgiveness. She told me she wanted to move in with me and buy a dog. "I want us to be a team," she insisted. In reality, she just wanted to turn the emotional terrorism up to 11. A week later, she changed her mind again. I was left feeling that if I'd broken up with her 6 months earlier, I'd be 5 years younger.

Every newly divorced man eventually reaches a similar fork in the road. After a few months of getting laid, he can shut out the little self-critical voice in his head, crank up Modest Mouse's "The Good Times Are Killing Me," and skate through years of Malibu weekends with girls whose names are instantly forgotten until he's the creepy old guy at the kegger. Or he can embark on a more difficult path and examine why he's alone.

TAKING STOCK

It took hours of therapy, and more hours drinking vodka cranberries with friends, to figure out why I was in this sexually rewarding yet emotionally draining downward cycle. And the answer is that I was addicted to charismatic, unstable, and emotionally unpredictable women. This was nothing new. My pilot father died in a plane crash when I was 13, leaving me in the care of my mom, a charismatic, unstable, and emotionally unpredictable woman. Left alone with three kids, she struggled mightily, particularly with me, the only boy.

I learned to keep her happy and smiling by apologizing for things I hadn't done wrong, coddling her, and subsuming my own wishes in order to keep the peace. All you shrinks out there won't be surprised that I lugged that steamer trunk of emotional baggage into my romantic relationships. From my 20-year-old film-auteur-wannabe college girlfriend to my wife, I had liaisons with tremendously talented and sometimes sweet women who demanded unconditional appeasement from me. I was more than happy to be their Neville Chamberlain.

In taking responsibility for always picking the impossible girl over the sweet woman, I also had to accept my less-charming characteristics. My snide boat-side comment to Laura was not an anomaly. If cutting remarks and impatience were virtues, I'd be spooning with Joan of Arc. Every woman I have ever loved has endured withering sarcasm and condescension, an ugly side of me that I didn't fully realize until I watched a dear friend mock his sweet girlfriend for not being able to name any members of the Ramones. I thought to myself, "God, is that what I'm like?"

I try every day to be a little less of a prick, but some days I fail. And you realize that not every dream girl you meet is going to sign up for that. I try to be a better man and approach every date with optimism. Still, dating fatigue kicks in. You reach a point where you have told your life story so many times, you feel like a bad comedian on an endless tour. When the Chardonnay arrives on the table, I'll open tonight's monologue with the self-deprecating anecdote about being the only white guy at a former heavyweight champ's wedding. If it's a good audience, I'll save the death of my father for dessert.

Not long ago, I met a woman for dinner at Lucky Strike, a New York bistro I cherish like a dependable friend. But that evening was a classic disaster; a pal had oversold a friend of hers, telling me that Karen could be Mary-Louise Parker's twin. Not quite. We didn't hit it off, and when she excused herself for the ladies' room, I recalled how many women I'd brought here for dinner. By the time she returned with a bright smile and said, "You were telling me about a story you did in Colombia."

I was up to 12 or 13.

It was all I could do not to start crying. I was enveloped in the grim thought that maybe I had exhausted my lifetime supply of "the ones." In the bistro mirrors, I could see my hair graying, my crow's-feet crawling, and the circles under my eyes darkening. I felt old, and the Leonard Cohen line, "I ache in the places where I used to play," ran through my head on an endless loop.

I quickly got the check, said good night, and decided to walk the 4 miles home. A fall storm whipped debris through the canyons of Manhattan as I made my way toward the Brooklyn Bridge at midnight. My mind wandered to a December night in the last year of my marriage. My wife was away in Pakistan covering the aftermath of 9/11, and I was in New York on business. After a long day, I sat in a sleek black leather chair in my hotel room, watching snow grudgingly fall onto 43rd Street, and played Bruce Springsteen's "Valentine's Day" over and over again. Our relationship by then was irrevocably troubled, but that night I longed for nothing more than to have her back in my arms.

As I crossed the bridge, passing couples whispering like happy conspirators, I realized I missed the missing, the feeling that to one human you mean

≫He Said/She Said

ANATOMY OF A FLING

Women looking for a one-night stand are attracted to a hot body above all else—just as men are—according to a study from the University of Texas. Runner-up: a good smile, which says you're outgoing, honest, and smart.

HE SAID		SHE SAID
48%	Body	34%
6.5%	Smile	14%
13%	Face	9%
9%	Hair	9%
7%	Height	7%
5%	Eyes	7%
0%	Skin	1%

more than the Earth and the sky. I wasn't lusting after another conquest; no, I was a craving an intimacy that comes only after you've told someone all your stupid self-promotional stories and she loves you anyway. It was a craving for a woman who becomes more interesting the more you understand the lines on her face. A craving for a woman who appreciates the man you are and roots for the man you could become.

LOOKING GREAT IN HER EYES

FIX YOUR BIGGEST STYLE MISTAKES

BY BRIAN BOYÉ

When we asked some style-savvy women to cite the most common fashion mistakes that men make, they were perhaps a little too eager. But we listened, and we're better for it. Better dressed, anyway.

44 PERCENT OF WOMEN SAY OUR SWEATERS ARE TOO BULKY

THE SOLUTION: Err on the side of snug when choosing a sweater. Women told us they want a hint of what lies beneath, not a saggy, shapeless tent.

55 PERCENT OF WOMEN SAY OUR JEANS ARE TOO BAGGY

THE SOLUTION: Remember, sizing in the seat and thigh are most important. The waist can always be taken in. Another thing that made women roll their eyes: We pick the wrong cut for our rears. Try on several labels—and take her along. She knows what she likes.

47 PERCENT OF WOMEN SAY OUR BUSINESS-CASUAL LOOK IS BORING

THE SOLUTION: Casual does not mean lazy, women told us. You have pants that aren't khaki, you have shirts that aren't blue. Think creative layers: a textured sweater, a surprising color, a striking watch. And lose the pleats— 40 percent of our women said they can't stand that blunder.

  TIP: Invest in a few solid shirts, a cashmere V-neck, and a textured cardigan. Maximum options, minimum boredom.

55 PERCENT OF WOMEN SAY WE NEED TO HIDE OUR GADGETS

THE SOLUTION: It's totally acceptable—necessary, even—for men to carry a messenger-style bag to manage the modern clutter of a PDA, an MP3 player, a phone, files, pens, mints, scripts, business cards, and magazines. Call it fashion math: Subtract several dorky items and add one cool one of quality (preferably leather). This equals style, cubed.

NUMBER OF WOMEN WHO THINK THEIR GUY COULD USE A STYLE MAKEOVER:

1 in 4

34 PERCENT OF WOMEN SAY WE TEND TO UNDERDRESS FOR PARTIES

THE SOLUTION: Don't even ask her, "What should I wear?" Strike an effortless balance between casual and dressy with a leather sport coat worn with jeans or trousers. Shoes are crucial: 63 percent of women say we blow the effect with out-of-date, scuffed shoes. Yes, they care. So should you. Loosening the tie will relax the look—and you.

30 PERCENT OF WOMEN THINK WE DON'T WEAR ENOUGH COLOR

THE SOLUTION: If women want color, let's give it to them—our way. Some women (23 percent) said we pick wrong for our skin tone, and some (25 percent) said we can't match colors. So simplify. Subtle surprise can work: One woman told us pink done right looks "yummy and supermasculine."

TIP: Color needn't shout. Consider a slate-blue leather jacket and a pale pink-and-gray striped sweater. Quiet confidence says plenty.

37 PERCENT OF WOMEN THINK OUR SUITS AREN'T TAILORED PROPERLY

THE SOLUTION: An expensive suit that isn't tailored well looks cheap, and an inexpensive one that fits correctly looks more expensive. Almost any suit can benefit from a few minutes more on the tailor's platform. The tie, a woman told us, is crucial: "your badge and defining moment." They hate cheap fabrics. Choose well, and don't scrimp.

TIP: Bring a dress shirt to your suit fitting, to ensure that the sleeve length of the jacket is just right. Ask the tailor to nip the jacket's waist so there's visible space between the arm and the body.

THE MAN'S GUIDE GROOMING AWARDS

STOP BEING A TOILETRY TESTER. WE FOUND THE BEST FOR YOU

BY MATT BEAN AND BRIAN BOYÉ

You are how you groom. Behind every blinding smile, careful coiffure, and neatly trimmed nostril fringe lies the daily routine that defines you. The way you leave the bathroom says a lot about how you'll tackle each day.

We're waxing philosophical about pomade for a reason: Good grooming has the power to make you a better man—and snag a better woman. The advice that follows, along with some of our favorite grooming products, can help you impress women with your polish—no matter what kind of groomer you are.

Are you out of the shower before the curtain is wet? We'll help you speed up your daily regimen even more. Do you set time aside for specific image upgrades? We'll give you quick, all-day solutions to the biggest grooming problems men face. Enjoy polishing your image, no matter how long it takes? We'll give you salon secrets to develop a more luxurious routine.

Each type of man has something to teach the others, of course, and that's why you should consider this your à la carte reference guide. Choose the products and tips that suit you, and start grooming for improvement.

TIME-SAVERS

FRESHEN YOUR FACE FASTER. Wash your face anywhere but the shower, and you're wasting time—the steam-rich environment opens your pores for a deeper cleaning. Begin with an exfoliating face scrub, using soft, circular motions to spread the sandlike grains over your mug. (We like the resurfacing scrub from Aramis Lab Series for Men.) Exfoliation frees ingrown hairs and wipes away dead skin cells that would otherwise prevent your facial cleanser (or soap) from reaching the layers below, says Paul Jarrod Frank, MD, coauthor of *Turn Back the Clock without Losing Time.* Dab your face halfway dry when you leave the shower, then put on moisturizer.

"When you exfoliate, you're stripping good oils as well as dead skin, so it's important to hydrate right away," says Denise Vitiello, director of the fitness center and spa at the Mandarin Oriental Hotel in New York City.

CHANGE THE WAY YOU SHAVE. It doesn't matter if your razor has 60 blades. If you rush, you won't get a close shave. "That's a piece of steel you're scraping across your face. You have to respect that," says John Allan, founder of John Allan's Club salons. His advice: Make the shave a before-bedtime ritual. "After my kids are asleep, I'll go in the bathroom and shave for half an hour. I'll enjoy a glass of scotch, read the paper, and talk with my wife. It's a great way to calm down and get ready for bed." The trick is to shave thoroughly enough to ensure that your face is still smooth in the morning. Allan's advice: Lather with a bristle brush, working the shaving cream into your beard with firm, circular strokes to lift the follicles off the skin. Give your

BE YOUR OWN BARBER

Here's our three-step guide to giving yourself a last-minute ear-lowering.

Step 1: Trim your fringe. "Shaggy hair shows in the sideburns," says Vaughn Acord, a stylist and grooming specialist at Bumble and Bumble in New York City. Dampen and comb your 'burns forward toward your face and, using a straight, upward cut with a pair of scissors, chop off the fur that sticks out. Comb toward your ears and snip again.

Step 2: Dampen the hair above your ears. Then, with your ear pushed against your head, make a C-shaped pass to cut the strands that hang over your ear, stopping when you get to 3 o'clock behind it.

Step 3: Shave the back of your neck. "The secret is to lift your hair up so you don't cut into it," says Paul Labrecque, owner of the Paul Labrecque Salon in New York City. Cup your hair in one hand and, with a wet razor, shave from the base of your neck to your hairline using gentle strokes.

DETAIL YOUR DIGITS

Unkempt hands and feet can send women running. Three steps to a softer touch.

Step 1: Think straight. Start with a simple horizontal clip across each nail. "Cutting at an angle trains the nail to grow that way," says Denise Vitiello, director of the fitness center and spa at the Mandarin Oriental Hotel in New York City. Round off corners with a medium-grit emery board—never a harsh metal file—filing in one direction only.

Step 2: Thin your skin. Massage the pads of your palms and the sides of your heels and feet with an exfoliating scrub, using firm, circular strokes with your thumbs. This breaks down thickened areas of skin, which can develop into corns or fissures, says Cary Zinkin, DPM, a spokesperson for the American Podiatric Medical Association.

Step 3: Kill the fungi. Dry your dogs, then hit them with a cold-air blast from a hair dryer to evaporate any remaining moisture, which could harbor the fungi that cause athlete's foot. Then slather a thick moisturizer on your hands and feet after you leave the shower. (We like the Acqua di Parma product on page 43.) "Everyone forgets the feet," says Dr. Zinkin. "But they're even more important to moisturize because of all the rubbing in the shoes."

beard time to soften—at least 5 minutes—and make an initial pass, shaving with the grain. Then reapply shaving cream and make a second pass, against the grain.

MOISTURIZE NOW, AGE LATER. Applying moisturizer in response to dry skin treats the symptom but not the disease. The skin's internal scaffolding—a network of elastin and collagen fibers—has already started to loosen and unravel, and letting your skin dry out worsens the decline, causing the lipid-secreting glands of the face to atrophy and rob your mug of its natural lubrication. The result: premature wrinkling. Moisturizing every day, however, can delay wrinkles for years. "Apply it after you leave the shower in the morning, midway through your day, and after you hit the gym," suggests Vitiello. Look for nutritive compounds in the lotion—like the biopeptides in

Biotherm Homme's Age Refirm lotion—that can perk up your besieged oil glands and collagen networks.

SOFTEN YOUR HARD EDGES. Baby-soft skin is the province of the fairer sex—your outer dermis is thicker and therefore more likely to form blemishes and capture ingrown hairs as dead cells resist eviction. Hot showers, heavy sweating during exercise, and air-conditioning make it even harder for the 600,000 cells you shed each hour to break free, but the occasional exfoliating scrub can release the cellular logjam. "For such a quick grooming move, body scrubs pay off in a huge way," says James Whittall, president of the grooming site www.menessentials.com. "Your skin will feel better under clothing, and

TAME YOUR MANE

Whether hirsute or practically hairless, a man's body parts often need a trim. Here's how to do it without feeling like a girl.

Step 1: Define your borders. "I love chest hair," says Nicole Beland, the *Men's Health* Girl Next Door, "but an armpit-to-armpit shag carpet is too much of a good thing." So take a weed whacker—a scissors, tweezers, or electric trimmer—to the fringe areas, pruning back the bridges that spring up between your chest hair and armpits or happy trail.

Step 2: Stop strays. Waxing your back is a major life decision—we'll leave it up to you. But there's one part of manscaping that's mandatory: nixing errant hairs. The brain is trained to scan for visual distractions from a pattern—which makes stray nose, ear, and chest hairs easy to spot. "And if you have one thick black hair in a tuft of lighter hairs, that has to go, too," says Beland, "or we'll wonder if you're about to pull a *Teen Wolf.*"

Step 3: Trim with care. Whatever length you choose, make sure your main patch of chest hair passes the cheek test. "As much as women dislike excess fur," says Beland, "a shaved chest that feels like a bed of nails is worse." If you're just doing a trim, make sure it's longer than half an inch. And if you're taking it all off, make sure you shave at least three times a week to prevent stubble.

your rough elbows, knees, and ankles won't itch anymore." In the shower, gently rub the scrub (we like the one from Malin + Goetz) over your entire body, then focus on rough spots—knees, elbows, hands, feet—for about 30 seconds each. Follow with a thick moisturizer.

PROBLEM SOLVERS

FLURRY-FREE YOUR SCALP. Dandruff comes in several forms, but the most common cause is an overgrowth of *Pityrosporum ovale,* says Amy Wechsler, MD, a dermatologist at the State University of New York Downstate Medical Center. This yeast occurs naturally on all scalps, but in 20 percent of the population—those with the oiliest skin—it spreads much faster. Excessive *P. ovale* inflames your scalp, accelerating the turnover of scalp cells from once a month to once every 10 days. Result: the buildup of dead skin cells, or dandruff. Some dandruff shampoos do nothing more than wash away flakes and the oil that the yeast feeds on, so look for one with an antifungal drug such as zinc pyrithione or ketoconazole.

LOSE YOUR BAGGAGE. Aging wears away the skin around your eye sockets, which, at 0.00079 inch, is already the thinnest on your body. Eventually, the blood vessels beneath show through, and the waterlogged fat sponges around your eyes start to sag, causing dark circles and bags. A pearl-sized dollop of eye cream or serum, dabbed under each eye before bed, can take years off your peepers. Most creams, like the soothing gel from B. Kamins, contain topical anti-inflammatories—chemicals like caffeine that dehydrate tissue, tightening the skin into a taut, dense layer to hide the dark circles. Serums add antioxidants, such as vitamins A, C, and E, to reverse cellular damage from the sun. Both also moisturize the skin to minimize existing crinkles.

COVER UP WITHOUT COMBING OVER. "The longer your hair, the easier it is to see what's not there," says Martial Vivot, a stylist at Paul Labrecque Salon. The lesson: If your hair is thinning, keep it short. And skip strong gels and mousses in favor of pastes or clays with a light or medium hold. (We like the lightweight styling wax from ZIRH.)

(continued on page 44)

POTENT PRODUCTS

Best Face Cleanser

Mario Badescu Skin Care Seaweed Cleansing Soap: With grains of bladder wrack, it exfoliates while it cleans ($12/www.mariobadescu.com).

Best Face Scrub

Aramis Lab Series for Men Skin Refinisher: Facial scrubs strip away dead skin cells with fine grains of an abrasive, revealing fresher skin and freeing ingrown hairs. This one uses two types of grit for a cleansing and resurfacing touch, and adds a high-tech wrinkle: a water-activated heating agent that opens the pores for even deeper cleaning ($30/www.labseries.com).

   Best Deal: Anthony Sport Face Scrub ($15/www.anthonysport.com).

Best Face Mask

Bullie Refinement Normal/Oily Skin Peel-Off Mask: Face masks might seem emasculating, but they're one of the only ways to strip away blackhead-causing pore blockers without disrupting the skin's oil balance. This one acts like a vacuum, adhering lightly to the face and drawing out pore-clogging dirt. It's best for anyone who spends a lot of time in a sooty environment or whose skin is oilier than Dick Cheney's résumé ($40/www.bulliecare.com).

   Best Deal: Grassroots Get Grounded Skin Purifying Clay Mask ($14/www.kohls.com).

Best Moisturizer with Sunscreen

Jack Black Double-Duty Face Moisturizer SPF 20: This moisturizer's not all defense—in addition to blocking UVA- and UVB-spectrum sunlight, it encourages collagen production, which keeps your skin taut and wrinkle-free ($26/www.getjackblack.com).

   Best Deal: Nivea for Men Sensitive Lotion with SPF 4 ($6/www.drugstore.com).

Best Niche Skin Product

MD Skincare One-Step Daily Facial Pads: These do-it-all pads shrink pores, reduce razor bumps, and moisturize, making them the most efficient face-fixing system we've seen yet. The green-tea extract, an antioxidant, may even prevent skin cancer by deactivating cell-damaging free radicals, says Corey Hartman, MD, a dermatologist at the University of Alabama at Birmingham ($40/www.mdskincare.com).

Best Deal: Neutrogena Advanced Solutions At Home MicroDermabrasion System ($40/www.drugstore.com).

Best Face-Cleansing Duo

L'Oréal Men's Expert Power Buff Exfoliator and Power Clean Anti-Dullness Facial Wash: Alcohol-based products strip your face of oils, causing skin to overproduce its natural lube. The result: clogged pores and blackheads. These products strip dirt away and boost skin's defenses with vitamin A, retinol, and carotene ($7 each/www.cvs.com).

Best Splurge: Bobbi Brown Lathering Tube Soap ($22/www.bobbibrown.com).

Best Eye Cream or Gel

Clarins Men Undereye Serum: Blends into the skin quicker than most ($27/www.clarinsmen.com).

Best Deal: Nivea for Men Revitalizing Eye Cream Q10 ($9/www.drugstore.com).

Best Face Moisturizer

Clinique Skin Supplies for Men M Lotion: Soothes dryness, reduces irritation, and works equally well on oily or dry skin ($19/www.cliniqueformen.com).

Best Deal: Lumene Skin Tech Advanced C-Energy ($13/www.cvs.com).

Best Electric Razor

Philips Norelco SmartTouch-XL: The built-in shocks are a big improvement over previous models, which allowed flex only in the cutting heads. Bonus: The noise-dampening insulation knocks 28 decibels off previous models' levels ($200/www.philips.com/norelco).

Best Aftershave Lotion or Balm

Nivea for Men Sensitive After Shave Balm: An everyday, postshave product ($6/www.drugstore.com).

Best Splurge: Billy Jealousy Shaved Ice After-Shave Balm ($25/www.billyjealousy.com).

Best Shaving Cream

The Art of Shaving Shaving Cream Lavender Essential Oil Tube: Delivers a super-smooth shave and smells great, too ($14/www.theartofshaving.com).

(continued)

POTENT PRODUCTS (*cont.*)

Best Preshave Oil

Clinique Skin Supplies for Men Soothing Shave Oil: Preshave oils give the razor a slicker surface to skate across, and bring your whiskers to attention. That means reduced razor burn and longer razor life, says Vaughn Acord, a stylist and grooming specialist at Bumble and Bumble in New York City ($14/www.cliniqueformen.com).

Best Steal: Anthony Sport Pre-Shave Oil ($15/www.anthonysport.com).

Best Shave Gel

King of Shaves MagnaGel MME Shaving Gel: Gels lather less than creams, so it's easier to maintain goatees and beards, says Vivot. This one adds vitamin E, grape-seed oil, and aloe to cut irritation, while magnetic particles within cling to the blade, helping it glide over your skin's surface ($7/www.shave.com).

Best Steal: Gillette Fusion HydraGel ($3.50/www.drugstore.com).

Best Splurge: Acqua di Parma Collezione Barbiere Shaving Gel ($35/www. neimanmarcus.com).

Best Body Tool

Philips Norelco Bodygroom BG2020: Sixty-five percent of the men we surveyed perform some form of below-the-belt manscaping. This is the first trimmer designed to tackle the follicles below your beard. It's easy to control and safe to use in the shower, and played John Deere on our tester's body with nary a nick ($40/www. philips.com/norelco).

Best Manual Razor

Gillette Fusion Power: The latest salvo in the shave wars, this five-bladed tech-de-force acts like a quintet of tiny handsaws, clear-cutting your beard while leaving the skin beneath unharmed. Our tester loved the built-in sideburn trimmer on the back ($12/www.drugstore.com).

Best Hairstyling Product

Bumble and Bumble Styling Wax: It's medium-grip, so it's great for almost everyone ($17/www.bumbleandbumble.com).

Best Conditioner

Kiehl's Olive Fruit Oil Nourishing Conditioner: Conditioners work like drywall mud, patching the gaps in your hair's keratin to boost elasticity, says Vivot. This, in turn, means better body without resorting to buildup-causing products. The olive oil in this conditioner makes it perfect for thick or coarse hair ($19/www.kiehls.com).

Best Deal: Citré Shine Fresh Fusion Moisture Replenish Conditioner ($4/www. drugstore.com).

Best Body Wash

John Allan's Body Wash: Cleans, exfoliates, and leaves your skin baby-glute soft ($21/www.johnallans.com).

Best Deal: Axe Reload Shower Gel with Revitalizing Oxygen ($5/www.drugstore.com).

Best Body Moisturizer

Acqua di Parma Blu Mediterraneo Arancia di Capri: Only 19 percent of the men we surveyed told us they moisturize their entire body. What they're missing: the best way to keep skin soft and acne-free after sweat-drenched gym sessions or on multiple-shower days. "A good body lotion soaks easily into the skin, doesn't leave a heavy residue, and isn't overly fragranced," Vivot says. The orange extracts in this one please the nose without activating the gag reflex, and our tester loved the easy-access, scoop-and-slather container ($60/www.neimanmarcus.com).

Best Deal: Vaseline Intensive Care Total Moisture Dry Skin Lotion ($7/www. drugstore.com).

Best Shampoo

Frédéric Fekkai & Company Sensitive Scalp Shampoo: A supple scalp sheds less dandruff. This subtle honey-and-lavender mixture keeps your dome flake-free with the chemical panthenol, which metabolizes into vitamin B_3 when it hits the head. "That helps with circulation in your scalp and follicles," says Tim Rogers, editorial stylist for the Charles Worthington London salon. Our tester likened it to a boxer's robe: "Silky smooth, yet all man, baby" ($20/www.sephora.com).

Best Deal: Garnier Fructis Body & Volume Fortifying Shampoo ($4/www. garnierfructis.com).

(continued)

POTENT PRODUCTS (*cont.*)

Best Body Scrub

Malin + Goetz Peppermint Body Scrub: The bamboo and pumice in this scrub help scrape away dead skin cells, while the peppermint extract acts as a mild antiseptic and cleanser. Our tester liked the telltale tingle, but warned, "It's intense. Make sure you keep it away from your candy cane" ($30/www.malinandgoetz.com).

Best Deal: Grassroots Seeds of Perfection Invigorating Body Exfoliator ($13/www.kohls.com).

Best Styling Product

ZIRH Control Lightweight Styling Wax: Styling products fall on a viscosity continuum, ranging from watery—lightweight, little hold—to liquid nails. This barely there wax helps hair hold its shape without strong-arming it into place. "It's like handcuffs, not solitary," says Rogers. Translation: Your strands stay in place, without the helmet feel ($19/www.zirh.com).

Best Deal: Anthony Sport Styling Pomade ($16/www.anthonysport.com).

FINISHING TOUCHES

MANAGE YOUR OIL RESERVES: The larger your pores, the more oil they collect. The more oil in your skin, the more likely you are to develop blackheads. Get the picture? Good. Now, does a once-a-week facial mask—once a month, if oily skin isn't a concern—seem so bad?

Masks pull embedded grime from your pores, then tighten them. But first, you need to coax your pores to release their gunk. Prepare a bowl of hot, steaming water and set it on a flat surface. Drape a towel over your head and lean over the bowl so that the edges of the towel fall just outside the lip. Let the steam dilate your pores for at least 5 minutes, then apply the mask. "Do it right and your skin will look brighter and feel smoother," says Eric Ruimy, owner and founder of Nickel Spa SF for Men.

Bonus: Unlike harsh astringents, clay masks don't interfere with the

Best Fragrance

Calvin Klein Eternity for Men: Subtle, masculine—a smart choice for most occasions ($50/www.calvinklein.com).

Best Day Scent

Nautica Voyage ($60/www.nauticafragrance.com).

Best Date Scent

Armani Code ($35/www.giorgioarmanibeauty.com).

Best Evening Scent

Fresh Cannabis Santal Eau de Parfum ($75/www.fresh.com).

Best Whitening Product

GoSmile Advanced Formula B1: Four to 10 shades whiter in 1 week. 'Nuff said ($90/www.gosmile.com).

moisture-producing glands that naturally lubricate your skin.

PEEL AWAY GRIME: Facial peels work like paint thinner, chemically dissolving the adhesive bonds between cells to strip away blemished, blotchy, or uneven skin and reveal the virgin layers below. One hurdle: "If you use the wrong peel," Dr. Wechsler says, "it can throw off the chemical balance of your face." Dry skin responds best to peels containing lactic or glycolic acids, which also act as humectants, grabbing moisture from the air and depositing it one-tenth of an inch below the skin's surface. Trichloracetic and salicylic acid peels, however—like the Bullie Refinement mask—strip away moisture, making them best for oily complexions.

Most at-home peels contain only 2 to 3 percent acid, compared with the 20 percent-and-up formulas used by dermatologists—but it's best to avoid shaving and other forms of exfoliation on the same day.

WATCH YOUR WHITES: First-time users of tooth whiteners often experience sensitive teeth, says Richard Price, DMD, of the American Dental Association. Salvation: A study in the *Journal of Clinical Dentistry* reports that people who brush with potassium nitrate toothpaste for 2 weeks before starting at-home whitening are less likely to feel increased sensitivity. Our favorite: Tom's of Maine natural toothpastes.

Just as important: knowing when to stop your whitening routine—like if your chompers start to turn blue around the edges. "This signals a break-down of dentin," says Jonathan Levine, DMD, founder of GoSmile, "which is the substance beneath the tooth enamel that's being whitened."

SMELL GOOD FROM THE GROUND UP: Cologne evaporates upward once it's warmed by the body. That means a spritz or two on the conventional pulse points—the neck, chest, and wrists—could simply float toward the ceiling instead of wooing a nearby member of the fairer sex. Rochelle Bloom, president of the Fragrance Foundation, suggests spritzing your ankles, as well. The fragrance will rise throughout the day, delivering soft, surprising wafts of scent.

SOCIAL GRACES FIT FOR A KING

LEARN HOW TO BE A GENTLEMAN, OR AT LEAST LOOK LIKE ONE

BY LARRY SMITH

A gentleman doesn't shove sheep intestines into his mouth willy-nilly. Especially not in Scotland, in a castle, where I'm dressed in my best black suit, adorned with a blue cravat, and seated at a formal dining table with a fire blazing in the background. The host is serving haggis, and taking a mouthful is not easy. It's not because I'm grossed out, which I am. (The many parts of a sheep that constitute this dish are boiled in the animal's stomach before it lands on my plate.) It's because I am trying to become a gentleman and don't want to mess up before the first bite.

Twenty-four miles northwest of Aberdeen, in the farming and fishing village of Oyne, eight men are in training to eat the local dish in a manner that would befit the Queen of England. I am one, having submitted myself to an intensive 3-day finishing school for gentlemen. Picture an upper-class boot camp, with the role of Louis Gossett Jr. played by a fleet of fancy British women, and you're getting warm.

A lot has to occur before a true gentleman can dig into his dinner. For starters, he must wait for the host to sit down and start eating—this is your cue. But not so fast: First, a gentleman must offer water to the people to his immediate left and right. Next, he should inquire whether anyone in his vicinity needs bread, salt, pepper, or other relevant condiments. Then and only then can he hold his fork tine-side down, employ his knife to gracefully slide some of the dish onto the end of the fork, and bring the cutlery to his mouth, rather than his mouth to the cutlery, as I have a habit of doing.

"Oh, my," says Diana Mather, the founder and a managing director of the program, called the Finishing Academy—Teaching Life's Essentials. "We're going to have to work on you and that fork."

I didn't travel thousands of miles to argue with British aristocracy. But what I realize at this moment—and what she surely senses—is that we're going to have to work on a lot more than forks.

I was not raised by wolves; just loud, ungraceful, though loving, Jews. I do not talk with my mouth full. I give up my seat on the bus to the elderly, the pregnant, and the good-looking. I stopped spitting in public years ago. I rarely walk empty-handed into a home to which I have been invited. I am, by and large, good to my mother.

TIPS FOR EXTRAORDINARY GENTLEMEN

Here are the answers to the questions we all have about dinner parties.

Can I uncork the wine before people arrive? Yes, but reds only. Leave whites unopened in the fridge because they need to stay cold.

Do I have to seat couples next to each other? No. In fact, it's better to break up couples at the dinner table so they not only don't chat just with each other, but also have a chance to make new friends.

What if I have a very shy guest? Encourage conversation by giving people points of reference—for example, "Sally, you rescue stray cats, and Tom here has a cat named Mr. Piddles who has six toes."

What about a drunken guest? Don't embarrass him by loudly proclaiming him soused. Rather, subtly pull him aside, give him a glass of water, suggest that he slow down, and ask him to leave his keys with you.

What wine goes with burgers? Any inexpensive cabernet will do.

Can I use an electric carving knife? No chef would be caught dead in a kitchen with an electric knife, and neither should you. Buy a good carving knife, such as the Wusthof Grand Prix II.

Is an e-mail thank-you note acceptable? It is not. Send a handwritten note after you've been to someone's home. Phoning is second best.

How do you greet a lady? "Never kiss on the first meeting," says the Finishing Academy's Diana Mather. "But after you've established a rapport with a woman, note

No, I am not an animal. But I grip a fork like a caveman, and I have serious deficiencies in other departments. There's no debating the fact that I cannot dance. And while I love my weekly hoops game, I am also not at heart a "sportsman." I'm a good guy, certainly good enough to find a girl to marry me, but I am not a gentleman in the most expansive sense of that word.

Mather and Penny Edge, another Finishing Academy managing director, realized there were many men like me. They had a hunch that we would come

her body language: Does she step in to greet you the next time you meet? Then it's probably time for a kiss. But remember, an air kiss is just that—air—and does not mean anything. The best kiss for a greeting is cheek to cheek. A lady should never feel your wet lips."

How can I escape an unpleasant conversation? Explain sheepishly that you need to use the bathroom, and politely excuse yourself. Or at a break in the action, note that you've enjoyed chatting, but there's someone over on the other side of the room with whom you must discuss something. Or bring someone else into your tête-à-tête—then take off once those two are talking.

How do I behave like an evolved man at the table? Never pick up a dinner roll and bite it. Break off one piece of the bread at a time. And no mopping up the red sauce with your roll. Bring the fork up to your mouth, not your mouth down to the plate. When the soup is almost gone, finish it up by tipping the bowl away from you. Don't ask for seconds—or hot sauce—ever. Sorry.

How can I dance without fear? First, relax. It's supposed to be fun. A tense dance partner is worse than a bad one. Second, know that you'll eventually get the hang of it. Basic dances like the foxtrot and the waltz require minimal practice. Until comfort clicks in, your best friends are your balance and your sense of control. And third, always lead, never follow. She'll thank you.

NUMBER OF SECONDS IT TAKES THE AVERAGE GUY TO DECIDE WHAT TO WEAR:

60

from all across the world and pay a pretty penny to unlearn bad habits and cultivate new skills. When I told my friends that I was going to a "gentlemen's school," most pictured me among a bunch of Bad Manners Bears, all of us struggling to walk with books on our heads and speak clearly with pebbles in our mouths. And that's part of it. But a man obsessed solely with cultivating these parts of the puzzle conjures up a quasi-guy who's hopelessly unmasculine. When you add the sporty skills into the mix (shooting, golf), along with a pinch of modern-life know-how and practi-cality, a higher-minded notion of what it means to be a gentleman emerges: to become a man in full, equipped to handle any situation that arises.

In that spirit, we release our bodies, minds, bad habits, and $1,500 into these women's hands. They have 3 days to make men of us.

STEP 1: MASTER THE ART OF THE FIRST IMPRESSION

The seven other "delegates" (as we are called) joining me hail from five coun-tries and span nearly 6 decades of unrefined living. The youngest guy is Diet-rich, a 24-year-old Aussie living in London, who has the wide eyes and unflappable energy of a Jack Russell terrier. The oldest are Ravinda, 57, from Bombay; and Michael, a computer geek living in the north of England whose wife gave him the course as a 50th-birthday present. To the untrained eye, we don't look like a disaster area needing to be roped off. The sorority of sophis-ticated ladies at the Finishing Academy, however, is not the untrained eye.

"If you don't look and act appropriately, you have to work that much harder to get what you want in life," says Mather, bubbling with energy like a fizzy bottle of champagne as she instructs us on the importance of image. She is talking about our outward appearance, but the lesson applies to most every-thing else we learn this weekend: Being a gentleman can help you in every part of life, from self-esteem to relationships to professional success. "We're teaching you to get rich and get lucky" is the not-so-subtle subtext.

Edge invites me into a hula hoop to demonstrate body language, which she says makes up 93 percent of first impressions. Stand 2 to 3 feet from the person you're talking to, she says. When you shake hands, lightly touch the person's arm with your other hand for 3 seconds and you have an 80 percent chance of making a good connection; touch it for more than 5 seconds and you come across as patronizing. When talking, look into the other person's eyes. And, she adds, don't talk to a woman's breasts.

Good to know.

STEP 2: APPLY THE RULES OF STYLE

PERCENTAGE OF THE AVERAGE GUY'S CLOTHING THAT NEVER MAKES IT OUT OF HIS CLOSET:
10

HOW MUCH THE AVERAGE GUY SPENDS ON CLOTHES EACH YEAR:
$713

Our days at the academy are peppered with maxims like "you don't get a second chance to make a first impression" and "the best suit is useless if you don't stand and walk in it correctly"—all variations on the same self-improvement-is-a-gift-to-yourself-and-the-world theme. Michaela Jedinak, a pretty fashion consultant suspected of being from Sweden, leads us in an impassioned dissection of what types of clothes are best for each body type.

Short guys: Wear one color to keep your body in one lengthening piece. Tall guys: Break up the body with distinct colors. Fat guys: No stripes. Darker-skinned guys: Wear dark clothes. All guys: Buy bespoke, or custom-made, suits whenever possible. We're told that among the eight of us, six are wearing their pants too long, which is not only sloppy but also makes shorter men appear shorter still.

During my one-on-one session with Jedinak, I grill her about wedding attire; she listens, and then, after 30 minutes of masterful instruction about how I need to go easy on the black, why off-whites will bring out my pretty

PERCENTAGE OF MEN WHO SAY THEY DON'T NEED A STYLE MAKEOVER:

87

blue eyes (aw, shucks), and the reason double-breasted suits are not my move, my muse finally says, "But I'd really just ask your fiancée."

STEP 3: SAVOR THE GUSTATORY ARTS

I may be living in a castle, eating rich and delicious Scottish delicacies, and surrounded by acre after acre of pristine land, but this is no gentleman's holiday. The days and nights are packed. Each and every event is an occasion for more instruction.

There's the simple act of serving wine, which many men yearn to master. It seems a little scary, but it's not so hard. Never fill a glass of wine more than halfway, our wine-appreciation instructor explains. (You need to allow the vino room to breathe.) Don't hold a white-wine glass by the bowl. (Your hand warms the wine; this applies to your water glass, too.) And no clinking during a toast! To clink is to risk chipping the fine glassware you're drinking from. And we can't have that.

Meals at the Finishing Academy fill us up with knowledge ("When seated between two women at a dinner party, talk to one woman during the first course and then the other woman during the next course"; "Place your silverware at 5:20 on your plate to indicate that you are finished with the dish"). We pepper our conversation with formal niceties ("You, sir, are too kind") that start off as a goof but become addictive. Turns out, it's as easy to be pleasant and polite as it is to be rushed and rude. Dietrich gets into a habit of beginning every conversation with "My good man," and I surprise myself by not wanting to smack him.

STEP 4: UNLEASH YOUR INNER FRED ASTAIRE

There's much common ground in what it takes to find success in dancing, golfing, and clay-pigeon shooting: poise, patience, concentration, coordination.

These are not my strengths. The sadists running this show have scheduled not one but two dance sessions. "Scottish Reeling for Fun and Fitness" is led by an insane little Scottish man named Major Mike, kilt and all, who has an endearing way of mocking us even as he teaches us to hop around like bush sprites. And with whom shall we have this dance? Eight local ladies, ages 15 to 65, have been dragged over the hill and into the castle. They're kind of a hoot, and, mercifully, patient and empathetic. I didn't really see the point in Scottish dancing—it's not useful or graceful—but I suppose part of being a Renaissance man is to embrace local customs. Regardless, it's all over in an hour and a half.

PERCENTAGE OF MEN WHO OWN A TUXEDO:

13

PERCENTAGE OF MEN WHO CAN TIE A BOW TIE:

17

Later, I fare better at the foxtrot and the waltz. My fiancée has spent many a wedding trying to quash my impulse to pogo during the swing dancing, and if there is one transformation she yearns for, it's in my skills on the dance floor. As Alan Milne, a thin man with a '70s 'stache straight out of a soft-porn flick, whirls his wife around the room and gives us instruction, I realize that despite being one of the worst dancers ever, I can learn the foxtrot and the waltz.

And I do! I do in no small part thanks to the patience of my partner, Nila, the only woman I have ever danced with who lives in a castle (just down the road). Sure, sure, to be human is to embrace a lifetime of learning . . . but when it actually occurs to me that with continued will, there is a way that I, Larry Smith, can become a decent dancer, it's a moment that sticks to my bones.

STEP 5: LEARN TO BE A GOOD SPORT

What does it take to be a better man? Big question, and one addressed all weekend with broad strokes and fine lines.

PERCENTAGE OF MEN WHO AREN'T SURE WHAT THEIR SPORT-COAT SIZE IS:

18

NUMBER OF MEN WHO CHECK THE REAR VIEW IN A THREE-WAY MIRROR WHEN TRYING ON NEW PANTS:

2 in 5

I think about this as I ponder the 9 iron that's been placed in my hand. I've always been against golf. It seems like a slow, expensive, sad excuse for men to hide from their wives. Then again, I've never actually swung a club. Which is why, then and there, on a beautiful Scottish golf course, I suspend my biases and take lessons. Two hours later, I'm told my stance is excellent, my swing has steadily gone from terrible to a trifle less terrible, and I have learned this about myself: I derive scant pleasure from whacking a little white ball.

The next afternoon, I find myself on a murky moor with a rifle in my hand, attempting to master the effete pastime of clay-pigeon shooting. Without getting all Dick Cheney here, it does feel great to be in the woods with pals, with a powerful, roaring weapon in my hand. It calls for concentration and a laser-sharp awareness of one's surroundings—parts of my personality I would like to improve. In fact, I'll surely visit the shooting range again. Elderly Republican lawyers, you're on notice.

STEP 6: PUT IT ALL TOGETHER

Everything we have learned leads to The Performance—a final exam in which we sell our new selves to the group in the form of a 5-minute speech. We've been specifically schooled in public speaking with all the various and sundry tips and tricks addressing a crowd demands, but our presentations are a chance to put to work the broader range of skills we've learned.

"You're not actors," says Mather, who was one herself back in the day, "but when you're giving a presentation or speech, you have to be able to entertain. And you! You've got a wedding coming!" she says, her piercing gaze upon me.

Even here, among men who are now mates, I feel the heat. While I wait my turn, I take long inhalations and exhalations, a relaxation technique Mather had suggested earlier that works as advertised. I go last, knowing that Ravinda's perfectly presented, informative presentation on wine, during which he referred to no notes and quoted Oscar Wilde, will be tough to beat. And make no mistake:

NUMBER OF PAIRS OF NONATHLETIC SHOES THE AVERAGE GUY OWNS:

between 5 and 10

Every well-balanced, book-on-head-walking, color-coordinated part of me wants to win.

"Good afternoon, gentlemen," I begin. "What I am about to tell you could profoundly change your lives. My remarks today are entitled, 'New York Women: Who They Are, Where to Find Them, and Why They Cannot Wait to Meet You.' "

I mean every word I say, finishing it off with a dramatic removal of my fiancée's photo from my wallet. "Gentlemen, I have taken my own advice, which is why this woman will be marrying me in 3 months' time. She is off the market, but there are 4.5 million women left. What are you waiting for?"

Ravinda makes his way over to me. "Yours was the best, my friend," he says, so graciously, so brimming with sincerity and class. Every competitive bone in my body shatters. "But Ravinda, my topic was quite silly. Your history of wine was fascinating, and so beautifully delivered."

"You see, this is what it is, precisely," he says in a manner unmistakably his. "We learn from each other. Alone we are nothing."

Can I continue to hold my fork properly in the months to come? Will I waltz with style at my wedding? I honestly don't know, and I'm not sure how much it matters.

What we learned, most of all, is that etiquette and manners are very different. Good etiquette requires learning specific rules that society deems appropriate. Good manners, however, mean carrying yourself with grace and style and doing everything within your power to make those around you feel comfortable.

Over those 3 days, I began to understand why—and how—these two notions work together. And at that moment, a man who could not be more different from me proved to be the pure embodiment of both. And showed me exactly what it means to be a perfect gentleman.

MAKE A TO-DON'T LIST

Here are 19 things a man should never do.

1. **CHECK YOUR BLACKBERRY IN BED.** To a woman, that's like having a threesome with your boss.

2. **ASK FOR A KISS.** Her eyes will say yes or no, and nothing kills the mood like asking for a translation.

3. **WEAR LOW-RISE JEANS.** So what if David Beckham flashes his hash in every other men's magazine? It's important to have some sack, not show it.

4. **MESS WITH ANOTHER MAN'S AUTOMOBILE.** We don't care if he stole your wife, your job, and your dog. It's blasphemy.

5. **SEND AN ANGRY E-MAIL.** Have the huevos to pick up the phone or, better yet, have a tête-à-tête. Fireworks aren't just for Independence Day.

6. **DISMISS A WOMAN WHO SHOWS ANY INTEREST IN WATCHING BASEBALL WITH YOU.** She wants you bad.

7. **SNOOP THROUGH HER E-MAIL, CLOSETS, OR MEDICINE CHEST.** There's probably nothing there you need to worry about. But rest assured, you'll find something you don't want to see.

8. KEEP A HOME-RUN BALL HIT BY THE OPPOSING TEAM. Or one hit by any player on the juice. We don't care if it's worth millions. Throw it back or you're a traitor.

9. FORGET AN UNDERSHIRT. Go ahead, let 'em see you sweat. Just don't let 'em see sweat creeping out from your underarms like dark, foreboding tunnels to your moistened soul.

10. FOUR WORDS: INNER-THIGH ADDUCTOR MACHINE. It might be a tough-to-reach muscle group, but there's never been a better way to strain your self-esteem.

11. TALK POLITICS OR RELIGION WITH NEW FRIENDS. And if you consider sports one of the two, leave that off the table, as well.

12. TALK SALARY. The more you make, the easier it is to cheapen your image.

13. HAVE THAT EXTRA DRINK. You know, the one that takes you from hilarious to hyena. Always respect your tippling point.

14. DIY PLUMBING. You think it looks easy. Then your house falls down. Water, like Hulk Hogan's wife, is not to be flirted with.

15. LEER. Sure, her buttons are quivering to rein in her pendulous bosoms. Sure, it looks "cold in here." And sure, each giggle causes her chest to sway suggestively. But "pervert" isn't a label you can just peel off.

16. ARGUE WITH A COP. You were caught. Own up. Accept defeat. The only thing you can win in that battle is a humid cell and a roommate nicknamed Stabby.

17. HANG ANYTHING—YOUR CELL PHONE, YOUR KEYS—ON YOUR BELT. You'll never get laid again. True story.

18. PLUCK YOUR BROWS. It's okay to groom. It's okay to like a woman who grooms. It's not okay to groom like a woman.

19. GO TANNING. Forget skin cancer. Being trapped between heating elements is for cheese.

LEARN WHAT WOMEN WISH YOU KNEW

Men's Health's ambassador to Guyville, Lisa Jones, demystifies the female mind. Listen up! These 24 pointers will make you a better man.

1. "You're beautiful" has the most impact when I'm not wearing makeup.
2. Anniversaries always call for champagne.
3. Raising your voice at me makes me physically incapable of remaining objective.
4. I want you to start undressing me in the doorway.
5. I am allowed to blame my outbursts on my hormones—you are not.
6. Know my cycle. Mark your calendar, if you have to.
7. When dining out, I get the seat facing the restaurant, not the wall.
8. If you tell me your buddy's cheating on his wife, you'd better follow with what an ass he is.
9. A big hug a day keeps the couples therapist away.
10. "I love you" does not substitute for "I'm sorry."
11. The tank top flatters no man.
12. When in doubt, go with the shirt that matches the color of your eyes.
13. Inscribing a gift triples its thoughtfulness.
14. Holding hands never stops being sexy.
15. You are required to give a toast at a dinner party with my family.
16. Laughter turns me on.
17. Other men look especially attractive when you're not paying attention to me.
18. It makes me happy when you call just to say hi.
19. Simply seeing that I have an e-mail from you makes me feel good.
20. Love and respect comes with spanking privileges.

NUMBER OF WOMEN WHO LIKE A MAN'S BASEBALL-CAP BILL TO BE WORN SLIGHTLY OFF CENTER:

1 in 12

21. Talking to my mother for 5 minutes on the phone shows me you care more than giving me flowers ever will.

22. No matter how expensive, ordering takeout will never equal cooking me a meal.

23. A pedicure in the summer shows me that you take care of every detail.

24. I remember every aspect of our first date. So should you.

KEEP YOUR COOL

Of course, you want to get noticed, but not for the sweat rings on your armpits or the blue veins popping out of your forehead.

Heart-pounding anxiety might be hardwired, but your body is full of natural short circuits. Want an example? Just look down. In a recent study, British researchers found that sex slashed anxiety and quelled blood-pressure spikes for people performing public speaking and taking math tests. Here are surefire stress busters for five big nerve-racking events.

EARLY-MORNING APPOINTMENTS

Skip the Starbucks. British researchers found that caffeine causes people, especially men, to feel less confident in their ability to finish stressful tasks.

>> Am I Normal?

I'm prone to tactile habits like chewing the skin on my lips, grinding my teeth, and kneading my elbows. Am I normal?

Yes, says Daniel G. Amen, MD, a psychiatrist and brain-imaging specialist, and the author of *Making a Good Brain Great.*

Anxiety takes many forms—you worry, invent doomsday scenarios, or exhibit so-called motor anxiety, such as picking your skin or biting your nails. The reason the stress slips out into the real world lies in an area deep in the brain, called the basal ganglia, which acts as the interface between motor movements and the stress-response system. The more often you repeat a behavior, the stronger the neural bridge becomes between it and the source of anxiety. If you find that you're already locked in a habit, you'll have to wean yourself: Every time you catch yourself, mark a tally on a Post-it note or sheet of paper. Focusing on reducing the number of times the behavior recurs every day can help you beat it for good.

Men who consumed 200 milligrams of caffeine were less relaxed during public speaking and less effective at group assignments.

THE SOLUTION: Drink peppermint tea. The scent helps you focus and boosts performance, according to researchers at Wheeling Jesuit University. In another study, they found that peppermint makes drivers more alert and less anxious. You'll even get your caffeine fix: It has about half as much as coffee.

PLAYING SPORTS

Practice won't help come game day. But wearing the right uniform can raise your game.

THE SOLUTION: Wear red. According to a study published in *Nature*, red will rev your confidence and intimidate opponents. It also increases your chances of victory. An analysis of an international soccer tournament found that the same players performed better and won more often when wearing red jerseys than when wearing blue or white.

GOING STAG TO A PARTY

Unfamiliar social situations can send even an extrovert into a corner. "The longer you stay in one position, the more shy you become," says Walter Anderson, author of *The Confidence Course*.

THE SOLUTION: Move and mingle. Anxiety breeds anxiety, says Nicholas DeMartinis, MD, an assistant professor of clinical psychiatry at the University of Connecticut. "Once you dive in and talk to people, you prevent your mind from wandering." And movement dispels nervous energy.

PRESENTATIONS AND MEETINGS

An audience can detect only about 11 percent of a speaker's anxiety, according to researchers at Texas Christian University. "People make judgments as to how nervous you are based on emotions they can see," says Ralph Behnke, PhD, lead author of the study and a professor of communication studies at TCU.

THE SOLUTION: Fake it. Wear your best clothes, stand tall, and pull your shoulders back. "The idea is that if you act confident on the outside, it will filter back to the inside," says Patrick Cohn, PhD, a sports psychologist and the owner of Peak Performance Sports in Orlando.

SPEECHES, BEST-MAN TOASTS

Here's the twist on that sex-and-stress study: Actual intercourse might dull the jitters, but other forms of sex won't, says Stuart Brody, PhD, study author. "People who had penile-vaginal intercourse did twice as well as people who only masturbated or had no sex at all," says Brody. No love for you? There's still hope.

THE SOLUTION: Practice and repeat. There are two jittery types. If you're anxious from the moment the assignment is made until the speech is over, stop thinking about your nerves and start planning your speech, pronto. "Your anxiety will drop way down," Behnke says. If you're calm until you reach the podium, run through the first minute of your speech over and over until you're in command. After those first 60 seconds, your anxiety will fade.

STEAL THEIR STYLE

The Donald and Melania; Kid Rock and Pam Anderson; David Arquette and Courteney Cox. How do oddball guys manage to lure models and starlets into their arms? Sometimes it's money, sure. But we asked relationship experts to explain what gets these guys noticed.

MESSIANIC CRUSADERS: TOM CRUISE, SEAN PENN, JESUS

WHY WOMEN LOVE THEM: "He's a knight in shining armor for her and for the whole world," says Bonnie Eaker Weil, PhD, author of *Make Up, Don't Break Up*. "And feeling protected is a turn-on."

THEY ATTRACT: Damsels in distress. "Look at Katie Holmes and Cruise," Weil says. See also: famous distaff disciple of Jesus, Mary Magdalene. And Tara Reid desperately needs rescuing.

STEAL THEIR STYLE: Be a hero. Volunteer with a fire company or disaster-relief agency. And take care of her without being asked. "Bring her chicken soup when she's sick," Weil says.

NERDY GOOFBALLS: BEN STILLER, JIM CARREY, DAVID ARQUETTE, WOODY ALLEN

WHY WOMEN LOVE THEM: "They poke fun at themselves to make women laugh. That's the ultimate aphrodisiac," says April Masini, author of *Date out of Your League*.

THEY ATTRACT: Handywomen, like Rachael Ray. "Neurotic men attract women who are not just good-looking, but also inclined to protect and take care of them," Masini says.

STEAL THEIR STYLE: Trot out your most embarrassingly funny story that reveals the good guy underneath. Self-deprecation is good. You'll come off as thoughtful, caring—and funny.

MOGULS: DONALD TRUMP, HUGH HEFNER, P. DIDDY

WHY WOMEN LOVE THEM: Differences equal attraction, says Barry McCarthy, PhD, coauthor of *Getting It Right the First Time.* His uniqueness makes her feel special. Plus the money.

THEY ATTRACT: Narcissists who "would like to be powerful and have money, and by becoming symbiotic with this type of man, they can," Weil says.

STEAL THEIR STYLE: "Lavish her," says Weil. If you're not living the high life, pretend you are. Wear a suit, wine and dine her, or whisk her away for a weekend. Sweat the credit-card details later.

SENSITIVE PRETTY BOYS: ORLANDO BLOOM, JAKE GYLLENHAAL, *THE O.C.* BOYS

WHY WOMEN LOVE THEM: "Women sense that these men are complex, giving, and very intense, especially in bed," says Masini. And that's definitely a good thing.

THEY ATTRACT: Martha types who think they'll be the first and only woman to reach him. "He's so complex," says Masini, "she alone can understand him."

STEAL THEIR STYLE: Let actions speak—try volunteering at a homeless shelter. You'll meet women who are attracted to do-gooders. Beard and Birkenstocks are optional.

EDGY, DANGEROUS CADS: TOMMY LEE, KID ROCK, COLIN FARRELL, TED KACZYNSKI

WHY WOMEN LOVE THEM: They're tough to tame. "Women think they're going to rescue them," McCarthy says. "But most of these guys aren't asking to be rescued."

THEY ATTRACT: "The woman who wants a fling, and the woman who's fairly cynical about men and relationships to begin with," McCarthy says. Web gem Pam Anderson, for example.

STEAL THEIR STYLE: "Can you tell me the last time you heard of a guy being ditched for being too exciting?" Masini says. Let your impulses guide you—but make it fun for her, too.

THE NATTY LADY-KILLERS: JAMES BOND, GEORGE CLOONEY, CLARK GABLE

WHY WOMEN LOVE THEM: They're confident, especially with women. "They like space and freedom more than connection," Weil says. For her, it's wanting what she can't have.

THEY ATTRACT: Big brains like Glenn Close who are up for a challenge, Weil says. "She thinks she'll settle him down." But the aggressive go-getter can turn cling-on in a heartbeat.

STEAL THEIR STYLE: James Bond took Dr. Holly Goodhead to the moon—literally first, then figuratively. Be exciting and active: Take her rock climbing or bowling instead of to the movies.

STOP BEING ANONYMOUS

Here's how to convert the crush and woo five women you've always wanted to meet.

THE SPANDEX QUEEN

She looks good in shorts, but bolts when the treadmill stops.

DO: Start slowly. Keep early conversation in the moment—the guy in the ridiculous shorts, the awful song playing, the monotony of ab work, says Teresa Strasser, a relationship expert and cohost of *How to Get the Guy*. Next: Ask for her opinion—about a gym class, a restaurant, a movie. She'll appreciate it without feeling threatened. Then ask about mundane stuff—the stuff that no one else asks her about. "Don't attack me from the beginning," says Amy, a 34-year-old program director who met a guy over a few weeks in yoga class. "It felt like he was getting to know me."

DON'T: Correct her form as an excuse to talk. Insecurity runs high at the gym. "The message is 'You don't know what you're doing,'" Strasser says. And don't approach her when she's sweating. She's exerting; intrusions are annoying.

ALSO GOES FOR: Fellow train commuters, running-club members, adult-ed classmates . . .

THE OFFICE SIREN

You see her every day. And if something goes wrong, you still will.

DO: Spread the love. Sharing credit for job tasks shows confidence, says Lisa Daily, a dating coach and the author of *Stop Getting Dumped!* A group is going out for drinks? Invite her. She won't let the fact that you work together stop her. "If a woman likes a guy, it might be awkward, but she'll still be excited about it," says Alison, a 32-year-old finance director.

DON'T: Enlist an office matchmaker. Gossip kills romance, and she wants to be taken seriously. For privacy, use e-mail, but keep the flirtation

IT-friendly. If she balks, back off quickly. This isn't the place for heavy pursuit.

ALSO GOES FOR: Physical therapists, business clients . . .

THE HOT WAITRESS

She's attentive and friendly, but is she just working for her tips?

DO: Stand out. Come in regularly, sit in her section, and be polite to every-one. In a business where she gets the brunt of bad behavior, "manners are an aphrodisiac," Strasser says. Refer to things she tells you—her favorite dish, the test she's studying for—in future conversations. Listening is your move.

DON'T: Overtip. She'll feel objectified; stick with 20 percent.

ALSO GOES FOR: Flight attendants, bartenders, hairstylists . . .

THE BARISTA

She's neck-deep in lattes; you can't get a word in edgewise.

DO: Empathize. Show up after the morning rush, when she's less frazzled, and ask if it's a tough day. You're into her, not just her iced mocha, says Debbie Magids, PhD, coauthor of *All the Good Ones Aren't Taken*. Build slowly. Then tell her those 5 minutes make a big difference in your day. And tell her you look forward to your daily chats with her. "If a guy would do that, it would register," says Alka, a 19-year-old college student who works behind a café bar.

DON'T: Call her by name at first, even if she's wearing a tag. It's intrusive and highlights the subservience, Strasser says. And don't talk her up when she's busy or with others. Respect her boundaries and the rhythms of her job.

ALSO GOES FOR: Bookstore clerks, doctors' receptionists, hotel clerks . . .

THE WOMAN WITH THE LEASH

She looks happy, until your dog starts humping her leg.

DO: If she appears passionate about her pooch, show interest: Ask about the breed, its habits, and where she regularly walks. When you're confident, sug-gest meeting up. She could be looking for playmates.

DON'T: Ignore your own pup. She'll watch how you treat it. And don't force your pit bull on her poodle.

"If our dogs can't coexist, we can't," says Elyse, a 40-year-old teacher and whippet owner.

ALSO GOES FOR: Neighborhood gardeners, nannies . . .

THE HONEST TRUTH ABOUT WOMEN
FROM OUR LOVELY NEIGHBOR

Is breaking the ice with a compliment a turn-off?

Not if the compliment is unique (think "striking cheekbones," not "beautiful eyes") and you sound 100 percent sincere. But what comes out of your mouth sometimes has a lot less impact than the way you look saying it. One study by Princeton psychologist Alex Todorov, PhD, found that people often decide whether someone is attractive and trustworthy one-tenth of a second after laying eyes on them. My point: If you fit a girl's preconceived notion of a cute, hot, cool, or interesting-looking guy, you could say just about anything and get a smile in response. Take a shot.

Is there a way to let a woman with a boyfriend know I'm sincerely interested in her without her thinking I'm a sleaze?

Have you considered that she might already know? I'm not questioning your discretion; it's just that if you've spent any length of time with this woman, you've probably sent out dozens of unintentional signals—a few extra seconds of eye contact, a goofy grin when she gives you a compliment—that women pick up on faster than a dog can catch the scent of bacon.

But let's presume she doesn't know. The best you can do and still retain your dignity is make a very lighthearted comment about what a lucky guy her boyfriend is and how you'd give your left testicle—that is, your right arm—to date someone like her. Say it with a smile and leave it at that. Trust me, it'll register.

My confidence with the ladies has been shaky ever since my last girlfriend dumped me. How can I give off a better vibe?

Start by upgrading your appearance. I guarantee your female acquaintances will notice your new look and compliment you. Hearing how good you look will give your ego a spit shine, and that will make approaching pretty strangers a little easier. Select one of these instant overhauls: (1) Take yourself someplace warm for a weekend. Come back with a healthy glow. You'll look better, plus you'll have an interesting travel story to tell. (2) Start dressing more formally. If you wear khakis, switch to dress pants and button-downs. If you wear dress pants and button-downs, switch to designer suits. (3) Get a cool new pair of specs. (4) Lose 5 to 10 pounds. Your features will become more pronounced, and you'll look and feel like a born-again stud.

I wasted 2 hours flirting. Is it okay to just ask a girl if she's single?

You can, but not right away. Wait a good 10 minutes or so into the conversation, then say something like, "There's no way you're single, right?" If she's interested, a woman will take the question in stride. If she gets offended, you probably didn't have a chance.

I'm head over heels for a bartender. How do I ask her out and not seem like every other jerk?

You're in luck, because one of my closest friends (a tall, blonde, long-legged Canadian) worked as a bartender for years—in Paris, no less. The one line that inspired her to say yes was, "Look, forgive me if this is the tenth time you've been asked out tonight, but I promise you: It's the first time I've ever done something like this." Don't offer to buy her a drink. Don't tell her she's gorgeous. Just be straightforward and self-effacing. (And sober—wait until the next night, if you have to.) My bud also loved when the man suggested a daytime date. "It showed a certain degree of sensitivity, because he realized my nights were busy," she says. Lastly, take her to the zoo, take her to an art gallery, take her anyplace where food and drink aren't being served.

SEND IN THE CLOWNS

If you can make a woman laugh, she'll be more likely to overlook your short-comings. In a study reported in the journal *Evolution and Human Behavior,* women were asked to choose between two pictures of equally attractive men with accompanying biographies. The women chose men with a good sense of humor over more earnest men, even though they found the funny guys less honest and less intelligent.

DON'T STINK UP THE PLACE

How you smell is as important as what you wear on a first date. Your scent will stick in her memory as much as anything you wear or say, according to a new Cornell study. Researchers asked 37 people who knew each other to wear the same T-shirts for 3 days straight, and then smell a selection of the used shirts to sniff out their own and those of their friends. Half of the testers correctly identified their own odor, and nearly 39 percent picked out their pals'. "Scent is as important as how you look or sound when it comes to how people remember you," says lead author Shannon Olsson, PhD. Wearing the same fragrance consistently with a new woman may make you seem more familiar and friendly, especially if she likes the scent.

THINK LONG AND HARD

Just in case the idea of taking a scalpel to your genitals wasn't discouragement enough, here comes a study from England that says more than 65 percent of men who undergo penile lengthening surgery are dissatisfied with the results. The average increase in length of a stretched, flaccid penis was 1.3 centimeters, or about half an inch. Erect length was in effect unchanged, notes urologist Nim Christopher, MD, the study author. Instead of surgery, he suggests psychiatric counseling to deal with any dissatisfaction.

PUT HER FIRST

Next time a woman tells you that men are slime, refute her claim by citing new research from the University of Chicago. Researchers found that men are more likely than women to put their partners' happiness ahead of their own. This unremarkable conclusion came after a survey of altruistic tendencies among 1,300 men and women. True, the study found that women are more altruistic and empathetic in virtually all other areas of life, but that's not the subject here. "Women are more empathetic toward abstract humanity—'strangers' or 'poor people,'" says study author Tom W. Smith, PhD, "while men's altruism is more focused on their intimate others." Another finding: People who put the welfare of significant others ahead of their own were 17 percent more likely to describe themselves as happy in their marriages.

CULTIVATE YOUR ARTSY SIDE

Next date, let slip your knack for banging out Petrarchan sonnets, or at least mention your Popsicle-stick mobiles. Artsy types get more sex, according to a study of 425 men and women. The journal *Proceedings of the Royal Society B* reports that professional artists and poets averaged 4 to 10 sex partners in their lifetime (mean age was 40), while the average for noncreative folks was 3.

"Any really rare talent is attractive," says lead researcher Daniel Nettle, PhD, a lecturer in psychology at the University of Newcastle upon Tyne. "If you have a talent, nurture it; you will be admired."

READ HER SIGNALS

Science has provided men with a reminder to slow down. A study published in *Psychology of Women Quarterly* found that when meeting a woman, a man tends to infer sexual interest before it's really there. That is, we interpret the slightest signs to mean she wants to jump our bones—way before it even occurs to her. In an experiment, men and women met and talked for 5 minutes. In subsequent interviews, the men rated their female partners in more sexual terms than the women rated the men. The men also rated themselves in more sexual terms than did the women. If the conversation went smoothly, men tended to find women sexier and perceive "chemistry"; women, not so much.

"Avoid assuming sexual interest on her part without a clear signal," says study author Maurice Levesque, PhD, of the University of Connecticut. Shy guys, note: Women found a guy more attractive if he was agreeable and extroverted.

PERCENTAGE OF MEN WHO SAY THEY WOULD MARRY THEIR CURRENT SPOUSES IF THEY HAD IT TO DO OVER AGAIN:
96

FACE FACTS

Women can tell a lot from your mug. In a study in the *Proceedings of the Royal Society B,* women rating photos were able to identify men who wanted children, and the women preferred those men as long-term mates. They could also spot guys with high testosterone levels, and favored them for a fling. How they do this (as with many female skills) is unclear. However, it seems that brow prominence can mean high testosterone, softer features can indicate lower T levels, and a broad jawline can signal masculinity.

A separate study at the University of Liverpool found that when a man's partner is at her most fertile, he is better at recognizing dominance in other men.

LEAD HER BY THE NOSE

Bathing in aftershave can act like Off! for women, but skipping cologne can put you at a dating disadvantage, too. In a poll conducted by market-research firm Zogby, 60 percent of the 1,700 single women surveyed found cologne sexy on men.

Bring a female friend to the men's fragrance counter to help choose a scent that suits you, says Rochelle Bloom, president of the Fragrance Foundation. "It's an impartial opinion, and the one that matters." Apply cologne before you get dressed; you want the scent on your skin, not your clothes, where it can linger for weeks. And don't overdo it; your sense of smell isn't as sharp in the morning as it is later in the day.

>> Am I Normal?

I can't help but glance at women's chests when I think they're not looking. Sometimes I can't even stop myself from staring when they are looking. Does every guy have this problem? Am I normal?

Of course you're normal, says Daniel Amen, MD, a psychiatrist and brain-imaging specialist, and the author of *Making a Good Brain Great*.

We all want to sneak a peek, but the prefrontal cortex, the part of our brains that handles judgment and impulse control, helps us stay socially appropriate. When that part of the brain is injured or diseased, it causes trouble. I once treated a CEO who was hit with a sexual harassment suit for staring at his secretary's cleavage. Turned out a brain scan showed very low activity in his prefrontal cortex.

I told him the same thing I'll tell you: You may want to try "response prevention," a fancy term for forcing yourself not to look. By wresting your attention away from her grand canyon, you prevent the built-in reward response you get from staring at her cleavage. The desire to look heightens at first but eventually calms down. Stifle that early urge and you should be better able to control your gawking.

GET MARRIED, BE HAPPY

Bachelorhood is appealing, but it won't bring bliss. Men in relationships are generally happier than single guys, and married men have the greatest sense of well-being, according to a new Cornell University study. "If you have more commitment, you have a greater sense of security; you can see a long-term horizon in your relationship," says study author Claire Kamp Dush, PhD.

"What on earth do women want?" Those six words echo throughout time, from generation to generation. Most likely they were first uttered when men began grunting at each other across a campfire.

When *Man's Guide* polled a bunch of women about what they want in men, they were eager to tell us their thoughts. Perhaps too eager. They were happy to tell us that three of their top 10 attributes in a man were "faithful to me," "laughter," and "patient/good listener."

In this part, we hope to advance your own understanding of the fairer—and certainly more mysterious—sex. Use our Keeper Test to determine when to hold her, and when to run. Discover how to push her orgasm over the edge. Find out about a woman's deepest fantasies and learn how to make them all come true. Then uncover her sexual personality; it'll give you insights to rock any woman's world.

THE KEEPER TEST

KNOW WHEN TO HOLD HER, AND WHEN TO RUN

BY EMMA TAYLOR AND LORELEI SHARKEY

Women are notoriously bad at recognizing "The One." We nurture dreams of marriage after one great date. We abide by draconian rules about who's our "type." And, most of all, we fall over and over again for men who are the human equivalent of dirty-water dogs.

Conversely, we're experts at knowing a good woman for you when we see her—it's embedded in the female genetic code. And, just as important, we can spot a bunny boiler in the making.

You're at a disadvantage, especially when smitten. Which is why you need our list of questions you must ask yourself about your gal before offering her a permanent position. Our grading scale: Three strikes is forgivable, otherwise neither of us would pass our own test. (Em is not terribly quick on the credit-card draw when out with her fiancé, and Lo's gym visits are rarer than an Amazon River dolphin.) Four strikes is a bit sketchy, though, and as for five or more—don't make us say, "We told you so."

ARE YOU THE CENTER OF HER UNIVERSE?

It might feel nice to be worshipped for a while, especially if you've just been dumped, but that'll get old fast—particularly when she calls four times during the season finale of *The Wire*.

SHE'S A KEEPER IF . . . she has at least one non-work-related hobby she's passionate about. It means she knows how to have fun without a man and that she won't need you constantly by her side. And if she continues to make time for her own friends (loyalty is good), she won't freak out when you plan a poker night.

HAS SHE INSISTED ON PAYING FOR SOME DATES, OR AT LEAST THE DRINKS?

We know an uptown sort of lady who boasts to her friends, female and male, "I have never had to pay for a drink in my life." According to her retro worldview, men pay for everything, and her boyfriends wait on her hand and foot while she watches *Desperate Housewives*.

SHE'S A KEEPER IF . . . she likes treating you sometimes. It means she'll approach relationships in a more egalitarian way—and when she says she'll take you for richer or poorer, she'll mean it.

MISSY'S RULES

What she looks for in a guy

Missy Peregrym, 23, plays a gymnast in *Stick It*. In life, she flips for men with certain qualities: "I like men who can bare it all. If you're insecure, great, be insecure. If you're confident, fine. Having a hard time? Cool. Let someone get close to you.

"Is he good with his mother and his sisters? How much does his family love each other? That stuff runs into new relationships, too.

"He should open doors—a small thing, but sweet."

HAS SHE ALWAYS EXERCISED?

If she still has her seventh-grade swimming trophy and a collection of 10-K T-shirts, chances are she'll work out for decades to come, which means the great butt and killer legs that first grabbed your attention are here to stay. But those who go on exercise binges (is that a Tae Bo tape?) or fad diets, only to lose interest quickly, are destined for saddlebags. And if, like the girlfriend of a certain friend of ours, she stays slim by eating a plain celery stalk for dinner every night, pack her a nice sandwich before you dump her.

SHE'S A KEEPER IF . . . you can set your watch to her 30-minute gym visit. An active lifestyle means way more than having shuffled through a half-marathon 6 years ago.

DOES SHE EVER SURPRISE YOU?

A just-because present, perhaps? We know it sounds hokey. But we're not talking about a throw pillow bearing a photo of the two of you and the inscription "2gether 4ever" (unless it's a gag gift, in which case she's hilarious and a total keeper). No, we mean the little things that say she's thoughtful and likes the idea of taking care of you.

SHE'S A KEEPER IF . . . she notices that you're out of shaving cream and buys some; you arrive for a date and she's cooking, with a good bottle of red already breathing; she initiates sex.

DOES SHE HATE HER JOB?

Our friend John dated a woman who always complained about work. "Turns out," he told us, "all that criticizing was just a cover for being hopeless at her job and her excuse for not getting off her butt to improve the situation." She wouldn't take responsibility for her own happiness, so she tried to find a sense of purpose in him—a burden nobody needs.

SHE'S A KEEPER IF . . . even if she's not in her dream job yet, she has a plan for getting there.

DOES SHE BUY CONDOMS? DOES SHE OWN A VIBRATOR?

If so, don't feel threatened. Taking an active role in her sexual health and sexual enjoyment bodes well for a long-term sex life. Women who use vibrators have higher sex drives, more orgasms, and better sex lives with their partners, according to a recent survey.

SHE'S A KEEPER IF . . . she knows how to harvest her own orgasms. Then she can show you how to, as well. (Ergo, no faking, and less pressure on you.) Stock up on double A's.

DOES SHE ALWAYS AGREE WITH YOU?

Yawn. You want a girl with an opinion. Not an annoyingly constant devil's advocate, but someone who will hear out your position and defend her own. A study found that couples who have heated spats but then make up have a better future in the sack than best-friend couples who never fight. Sparks are hot.

SHE'S A KEEPER IF . . . once in a while she plays Ann Coulter to your Al Franken. Or Maureen Dowd to your Rush Limbaugh.

ARE YOUR ZODIAC SIGNS COMPATIBLE?

Trick question. If she cares, worry.

DO YOU HAVE A SNEAKING SUSPICION THAT SHE MAY BE BRIGHTER THAN YOU?

That's a good thing. We've found in our own love lives that relationships are best when each thinks the other is a bit smarter. Life is richer with a woman who can teach you a thing or two. There's a difference between a woman who says or does impressive things and one who says or does cute things.

SHE'S A KEEPER IF . . . you're in bed and can't get something she said out of your head—and it wasn't when the two of you were talking dirty.

DID SHE DARE TO ASK YOU OUT OR SLEEP WITH YOU ON THE FIRST DATE?

We can't tell you how many male friends have told us that first-date sex—oral or otherwise—is a long-term deal breaker. It's time to upgrade your thinking, gentlemen. This unabashed passion probably informs her work, her play, her politics, her future kids, her future libido, and more. Our friends Melanie and Andrew, who got wasted and "went all the way" the first time they met, have been married for 5 years and have an adorable son. (And the sex is still very good. Hey, people tell sex-advice columnists everything.) Don't let a great girl get away because of your old-fashioned prejudices—keep her!

>>A MAN'S GUIDE POLL

Who does more talking in your relationship?

ME	HER
29%	71%

ADVENTURES IN THE FEMALE ORGASM

PUSH HER OVER THE EDGE WITH THESE 10 SIMPLE TIPS

BY DEBBY HERBENICK, PhD

I teach sex to college students. The course, Human Sexuality, covers everything from hormones to hairstyles—but my students usually want to skip straight to the final exam: the female orgasm. Women want to have them, men want to deliver them, and the gap between the two sexes is never more evident than on the first day of class, when 150 students pile into a lecture hall alive with sexual tension.

"I should be able to tell if a woman is faking it, right?" ask the timid guys.

"Why does it take me so long to orgasm?" ask the frustrated girls.

It's at this point that the men start looking confused and a little somber. "If women are flummoxed by their orgasms," they're thinking, "what hope do we have?"

Lots, it turns out. Sure, the female orgasm is among the most fickle of human behaviors. But by the end of a semester, most guys and girls have learned enough to study it in the wild. You can, too, because I've boiled down a semester's worth of learning into 10 simple starter tips. So sit down, listen up, and whip out your pencil. Class is in session.

TAKE HER OFF THE CLOCK

Just as you're concerned about lasting longer, many women are so self-conscious about taking too long that they end up faking orgasm or deciding to go without. The solution? Stop obsessing over orgasms—yours and hers. A recent brain-imaging study by Swedish researchers shows that relaxation is the single most important factor in bringing a woman to orgasm. So tell her she has all night. The better you convey not just tolerance for a lengthy buildup but also appreciation of her sexual pleasure—orgasm or not—the easier it will be for her to unwind and explode. Oh, and studies show that it takes 15 to 40 minutes for the average woman to reach orgasm. Going somewhere?

TURN HER ON WITH YOUR TALENT

The best sex starts long before the clothes come off. Talent—more than rugged good looks or a chiseled midsection—is a powerful aphrodisiac, according to research by my colleagues at the Kinsey Institute. (Less surprisingly, poor hygiene and a messy home are among women's biggest turn-offs.) So nail "Paradise City" during karaoke. Or make her die laughing at your self-deprecating display of atrocious dartsmanship. Yes, humor is a talent, too.

WHEN THE CLOTHES COME OFF, SPEAK UP

Women who worry about the way they look down there are less likely to orgasm easily during oral sex, according to my research. And a recent study published in the *Journal of Sex Research* suggests that women who feel embarrassed or ashamed about their bodies have less sexual experience and are less sexually assertive. Clearly, you have everything to gain with flattery. If you love the way she looks naked—and you do, right?—share the news.

ALWAYS BE TENDER UP TOP

During foreplay, gently brush the tops, bottoms, and sides of her breasts; these areas are actually more sensitive than an unaroused areola and nipple. Gradually move in toward her nipples, paying attention to how she responds. As things heat up, the nipples will become flushed with blood and the sensory receptors will become primed for direct stimulation. You'll kick-start the blood flow and lubrication down below, starting her slow buildup.

LEARN HER KEY STROKES

One thing many women love during manual stimulation: a slow buildup. Here's how to do it. Lie next to her, lightly bracing the heel of one hand just above her clitoris. Now run your ring and middle fingers along the length of her outer lips. Graze the skin at first, adding pressure as the tension builds. Cup the area around her clitoris with your palm to add indirect stimulation—most women are too sensitive to receive direct contact early on. As she becomes aroused, brace your hand on her mons—her pubic mound, the fleshy area that covers her pubic bone—and tease the clitoris with the middles and tips of your fingers as you move your entire hand.

BANG!

An orgasm isn't that different from an electrical capacitor, building up arousal until a firing threshold is reached. Stop and she'll return to her baseline—and you'll start from scratch. Here's how to create sparks every time.

Stage 1: She Becomes Aroused

Sexual triggers—grinding on the dance floor, George Clooney movies—unleash a cascade of physiological responses that begin to prepare her body for sex. Her body starts to lubricate the vaginal canal and inner labia. The brain orders the release of the chemical vasoactive intestinal peptide, which increases blood flow to the pelvic area, swelling the inner and outer labia and causing her to feel sexual tension.

Stage 2: Her Body Unwinds

The parts of her brain that process fear and anxiety start to relax, and the uterus tips upward, making the vagina longer. (The process is called "tenting.") The clitoris swells, as does the spongy tissue around the urethra, which is why some women feel as if they have to pee when aroused. Indirect touching of the clitoris will make her crave direct stimulation, adding fuel to her sexual-feedback loop.

Stage 3: Her Vital Signs Increase

As her heart rate and breathing speed up, pumping more blood to her extremities, the color of the labia deepens, and her clitoris—ultrasensitive at this point—extends, fully engorged, awaiting contact with your penis. Slow, steady stimulation that builds rhythmically will help coax her body toward the threshold to climax. The more anticipation she feels, the better she'll respond.

CHANGE YOUR ANGLE

Play Ponce de León and go exploring: Try out various types of penetration to figure out what turns her on most. Your first stop: her G-spot, located 1 to 2 inches up the front wall of her vagina. This spongy region swells during arousal. Try massaging the area slowly with your fingers. A lot of women find it mind-blowing. Not her thing? Just move on.

Stage 4: She Nears Her Threshold

The conscious part of her brain, drowning in neurotransmitters, enters a trancelike state. Just prior to orgasm, the subconscious part—which also handles things like breathing and heartbeat—signals a vaginal nerve to start muscular contractions. You may feel the outer third of her vagina "grabbing" at your penis, but her arousal may fade and she will still revert to stage 1 if stimulation ceases or changes.

Stage 5: She Reaches Orgasm

The orgasmic stage—with rhythmic or sporadic contractions in the vagina, uterus, and anus—typically lasts 10 to 60 seconds. At this point, some women prefer more intense stimulation that matches their orgasmic response. The chemical oxytocin is released in the brain, promoting a feeling of closeness, according to some research—which could explain why she wants to cuddle after sex.

Stage 6: Her Rest Period Begins

Unlike men, some women can have multiple orgasms without experiencing a refractory period after each one. Without stimulation, however, they will return to a baseline level of arousal. Contractions stop, the uterus lowers, and the clitoris goes back into its shell. Heart rate and breathing slow, and blood flow returns to normal. The clitoris will probably be too sensitive for direct stimulation, but other parts of her body will be yearning for attention.

USE MOVES THAT MULTITASK

To maximize her pleasure, increase the amount of contact you'll have with her most sensitive parts. Here's one move that will drive her wild. Ask her to lie on her back, with her legs stretched out. Now climb on top. Curl your arms around her shoulders, supporting yourself with your elbows and moving your chest up by her chin. The goal is to bring the base of your penis in contact with her clitoris. Thrust slowly, focusing on up-and-down movement instead of in-and-out penetration. Another great trick: Move your pubic mound in a circle or up and down against her clitoris. You'll get a break from high-intensity stimulation, and she'll receive focused attention where it often matters most.

LEARN TO SENSE HER ONCOMING ORGASM

Ease into oral sex—don't just attack. First kiss her inner thighs and her inner and outer lips, then work your way inside using firm, broad strokes with your tongue. Watch her hips for a clue to the rhythm she likes. Listen to her gasps and moans as you experiment with different techniques. And watch for signs she's close to climaxing, such as a subtle deepening in the color of her labia caused by increased blood flow. Or rest a hand on her stomach and feel for the muscular contractions that immediately precede her orgasm.

FOLLOW HER LEAD

Once you reach your point of no return, you'll climax even if you're interrupted by a tuba-playing, thong-clad Bea Arthur. But your lady could hit the "off" switch if you stop or change moves midway to orgasm. We love it when you try new things, and it's important to vary your technique, but once you've found a winner, stick with it until she crosses the finish line.

LET HER FINISH FIRST

Stalking the elusive tandem orgasm is an admirable goal, but many women—especially those with sensitive clitorises—respond better to a "ladies-first" strategy. If you rub the clitoris for a long time—during thrusting, for example—it can become too sore or desensitized to respond to manual or oral stimulation later. So satisfy her before intercourse. Bonus: A woman's orgasm threshold drops after her first one, so it's often easier to bring her to climax through penetration after she's already had one. How does that sound for an encore?

THE ULTIMATE GUIDE TO HER VAGINA

READ ON AND IT'S POSSIBLE
YOU'LL KNOW MORE ABOUT IT THAN SHE DOES

BY NICOLE BELAND

That's right, we're shining a spotlight on the almighty vajayjay. And it's about time. Given the ridiculous amount of maintenance it requires—gynecologist visits, bikini waxes, Monistat, and more—you'd think we'd know everything about this attention-getting organ's intricate design and how to keep it running smoother than a top-of-the-line Lexus. Yet even women who feel perfectly comfortable in their skin don't give much thought to the nooks and crannies of their nether regions. "Many women never connect with their sexual anatomy because of our society's 'keep away' attitude toward the vagina and vulva," says Elizabeth G. Stewart, MD, coauthor of *The V Book*.

The following guide to a healthy honeypot explains a few things you might still wonder about, like why discharge varies during her cycle and the secret to finding the nerve-packed hot spots that make intercourse feel as good as a clitoral rubdown.

THE VIP LOUNGE

Most people call the whole kit and caboodle between a woman's legs the "vagina." But the compendium of visible outer parts is technically the "vulva." Meant to keep dirt and bacteria out while providing a welcoming environment for worthy partygoers, the vulva is like a VIP lounge where the clitoris is the DJ. "The labia majora [outer lips] are a protective layer of fat covered by skin and hair," says Lillian Schapiro, MD, an Atlanta ob-gyn. Their job is to keep sex comfy even if your partner's pelvis is bonier than Iggy Pop's. Located inside the labia majora (though sometimes extending beyond them), the labia minora, or inner lips, act like a pair of swinging doors guarding the entrance to the vagina and the urethra, the tube that leads from the bladder. "The labia minora are much thinner than the labia majora and even more sensitive," Dr. Schapiro says. Plus, they contain erectile tissue, made up of clusters of tiny blood vessels, which means they become slightly stiffer (though not as stiff as the clitoris) during arousal. The anatomist who named the parts of the vulva must have found it loungelike, too, because the area between and including the inner folds of the labia minora is called the "vestibule."

THE SPRINKLER SYSTEM

Hiding just below the skin of the labia and clitoral hood (called the prepuce) are hundreds of small glands that secrete oil and sweat to protect these delicate areas from friction and overheating. That means it's normal if the crotch of her yoga pants is soaked by the end of a workout. The inside of the vagina also stays moist to maintain healthy tissue, but as you've no doubt noticed, it gets wetter when she's turned on. That's because the lining of the vagina fills with blood during arousal, causing the salt water in blood plasma to push through the vaginal wall. The Bartholin's glands—on either side of the vaginal opening—also pump out a few beads of slippery mucus. In missionary position, most of this fluid collects in the back of the vagina and fails to lubricate the opening, making sex uncomfortable. Unfortunately, in some women, lubrication occurs for only a few moments, then stops. In both cases, a water-based personal lubricant is key to ensuring a smooth entry.

PLEATS AND RUFFLES

Like an haute-couture handbag, the vulva and vagina feature a variety of textures. Most of the vulva is smooth, but some women's labia minora have a ruffled appearance. "Labia come in all shapes and sizes," Dr. Stewart says. "The tips of the nipples and labia are similar because they both contain small, bumpy-looking glands." Examine her labia minora closely and you may see the glands, which sometimes look like tiny pimples. Separate the labia minora and you may notice that the entrance to the vagina also has a ruffled border or just a few irregular bits of skin. Those are the remnants of the hymen, a

NUMBER OF NERVE ENDINGS ON THE VISIBLE TIP OF THE CLITORIS:

8,000

thin membrane that once partially covered the entrance but has been torn or pushed aside by sexual intercourse. As for the texture inside the vagina, it's full of bumpy ridges called rugae. Similar to pleats on a skirt, the rugae stretch and retract to accommodate objects ranging in size from super-slender tampons to roly-poly 8-pound babies.

FINDING THE WISHBONE

In a body full of hardworking organs, the clitoris is like a trust-fund baby who does nothing but party. It's the only part of the human body whose sole purpose is pleasure. The one thing the clitoris has that a trust-fund baby lacks? Depth. "The clitoris is larger than it seems," says Laura Berman, PhD, president and director of the Berman Center and author of *The Passion Prescription*. Beneath the visible pink button, called the glans, lies a wishbone-shaped structure comprising a shaft, which extends about an inch up toward the pubic bone, and two 3-inch arms called crura that reach down and back toward the pelvic bone in an inverted V shape. Though the shaft and crura send pleasure signals to the brain during sex, the glans is more sensitive. That's why it has a hood—without it, a pair of tight jeans would send her nervous system into overdrive.

Two bulbs of erectile tissue run alongside the crura. Many experts, including Berman and Helen O'Connell, MD, a urologist at Royal Melbourne Hospital in Australia and the first person to map the clitoris using magnetic resonance imaging, believe that this tissue is part of the clitoris, too. In studies, Dr. O'Connell found that the clitoris is also connected to erectile tissue surrounding the urethra and extending up to the front wall of the vagina—where the enigmatic G-spot has been known to pop up.

OVER THE HEDGE

Before she shaves or waxes it into a perfect triangle, landing strip, or lucky shamrock, the hair that covers the pubic mound and outer labia grows in a pattern called the escutcheon (based on the Latin term for an ornamental shield).

When allowed to grow wild, some escutcheons will wander up toward the navel and down toward the upper thighs, while others wouldn't breach the borders of a Brazilian bikini. The shape of hair shafts differs depending on ethnicity: In Asian women they're typically round, in women of African descent they're elliptical, and in Caucasians and Latinas they range between the two. "Elliptical shafts are more likely to become ingrown after shaving or waxing as the hair curls in, pierces the skin, and creates a bump," says Susan C. Taylor, MD, a Philadelphia dermatologist and author of *Brown Skin*. "A depilatory breaks the hair at the surface, which can make ingrowns less likely, but only if the chemicals don't irritate your skin." Whenever a woman tries a new depilatory, she should spot-test the product on her inner thigh before using it on the bikini area. Another way to create an aesthetically pleasing patch is with laser hair removal, but only by a trained professional who uses a laser like the Nd:YAG, which Dr. Taylor says won't create dark spots by damaging surrounding skin.

X MARKS THE SPOT

While the vagina is nowhere near as responsive to touch as the vulva, it does contain hundreds of nerve endings. If a woman were lying on her back with a clock placed upright inside the lower part of her vagina (don't ask how it got there), the most sensitive area would be at 12 o'clock, right behind the urethra. In a 1982 study of more than 400 women, Rutgers University sex researcher Beverly Whipple, PhD, and two colleagues found that when this area was stimulated after a woman was already sexually aroused, a dime-size bump of tissue appeared and could sometimes trigger an orgasm. She named the area the G-spot after Ernst Grafenberg, the German doctor who first documented it in 1950. Further examination of this spongy tissue found it identical to that of the male prostate gland, a well-established pleasure zone. Some doctors believe the G-spot should be renamed the female prostate. Supporting that belief is a study showing the similarity between the fluid expelled by a very small percentage of women through the urethra during a

G-spot orgasm (a.k.a. female ejaculation) and that produced by the male prostate.

Whipple says don't sweat it if you've never found her G-spot: "There are many sensitive areas inside the vagina that, when stimulated by a finger, vibrator, or penis, can contribute to sexual pleasure."

HONORABLE DISCHARGE

That strip of cotton in the crotch of every panty is there for a reason—even if it's not that time of the month, it will collect moisture. The vulva and vagina produce an average of 1 to 2 grams of vaginal discharge (or about ¼ to ½ teaspoon) every 8 hours. But even normal discharge doesn't make a pretty picture. "It may be clear, white, or yellow, and fluid, waxy, stringy, or clumpy," Dr. Stewart says. Some of it is a buildup of the oil that the glands in the vulva produce. Some is cervical mucus. Still more comes from normal vaginal secretions. Throw a sample under a microscope and you'll also find bacteria, skin cells, and yeast spores. Quantity and consistency change over the menstrual cycle. "During ovulation, secretions are thinner and more plentiful," Dr. Stewart says. "After ovulation, discharge becomes thicker. As you near menstruation, there's less."

TILT-A-WHIRL

As seen on the diagram in every Tampax box, the vagina tilts back 30 degrees from the opening. A side effect of this 30-degree angle is that in missionary position, the penis has little to no contact with the supersensitive front wall of the vagina. As far as orgasm goes, this is not good. Placing a pillow under her hips, wrapping her legs around your lower back, and rocking back and forth to create clitoral friction can help you get maximum bliss out of missionary, but other positions typically yield better results.

"The best positions for G-spot stimulation include woman-on-top and rear entry," Berman says. Woman-on-top lets you experiment with different angles to find the most feel-good sensations. "Leaning back targets the anterior wall," Berman says. Zero in on her G-spot in rear entry by having her lie flat on her stomach and tucking a pillow under her hips. Or try reverse cowgirl, where she faces your feet—and with that view, you'll be one very happy cowboy.

THE BIG SQUEEZE

You've heard of sex-enhancing Kegel exercises: A woman squeezes the muscle she'd use to stop urine midflow (except while actually peeing, since that can cause bladder infections), holds it for as long as she can, releases, and repeats. But perhaps you haven't seen Berman's vaginal barbells. Neither had we. For beginners, there's the Isis, which looks like a slim, clear plastic bow tie with smooth, rounded edges. And for women with power vaginas (Asia Argento? Shakira? Condi Rice?), there's the Juno, a plastic rod containing four spherical, 0.3- to 1.5-ounce weights in a row from smallest to largest. (You'll find both for sale at www.mypleasure.com.) She'll start by inserting the bigger end in her vagina, tightening the pelvic floor muscles around it, and holding it in place with her hand. She knows her muscles are getting stronger when she can hold the smaller end in her vagina with no hand support. "Just like other muscles, strengthening pelvic floor muscles is more effective when you add resistance," Berman says. "Over time, using the Isis or Juno leads to improved vaginal tone and enhanced arousal and orgasm ability." But even without resistance, Kegels make a real difference; according to Dr. Stewart, if a woman squeezes out 10 to 20 daily, she'll sense stronger orgasms in about 3 months.

VAGUS, BABY

Many lucky-as-hell women report experiencing three different kinds of orgasms (four, if you include the faux-gasm): one that radiates from the clitoris and feels a little bit superficial, a more satisfying one that happens deeper inside the vagina, and an even bigger bang that's a divine blend of the two. Makes sense, considering that women's brains receive pleasure signals through as many as four sensory fields. According to *The Science of Orgasm,* a new book coauthored by Whipple; Barry R. Komisaruk, PhD; and Carlos Beyer-Flores, PhD, clitoral stimulation sends tingles up the pudendal nerve; sensations inside the vagina travel up the pelvic nerve; and pleasurable contact with the cervix activates the pelvic, hypogastric, and vagus nerves.

That last link—between the cervix and the vagus nerve, which controls activities as seemingly unrelated as swallowing and sweating—is a new one that Whipple's team discovered during a clinical study of women with spinal cord injuries. "We don't yet know if it's a supplemental tract that the genitals normally use to send messages to the spinal cord or if it's activated only if the spinal cord is cut off by injury," Dr. Stewart says. But one thing the involvement of the vagus nerve makes clear is that female orgasm is just as mysterious on the inside as it can seem from out here.

HER DEEPEST FANTASIES

A WOMAN'S SEXUAL WISH LIST IS SURPRISING, LUSTFUL, AND DRIVEN BY CAN'T-WAIT URGENCY. JUST ASK TO MAKE HER DREAMS COME TRUE

BY NICOLE BELAND

Most women aren't very good at asking for what they want, especially in the beginning of a relationship. And by "beginning," I mean anywhere from the first night to the first 2 years. For one thing, we're hopelessly romantic. We imagine that the right guy will instinctively grant us every sexual favor we've ever fantasized about, without our having to say anything. Ridiculous, sure, but a girl can dream.

Also—trust me here—we dread being perceived as high maintenance. We see how put out you guys are by the idea of phoning us once a day or escorting us to a cousin's wedding. So asking for 45 uninterrupted minutes of cunnilingus seems outrageous.

The good news is that we are fantasizing about sex. (Wow—you, too?) And we will get around to requesting our favors just as soon as we feel comfortable and confident enough. If your partner isn't there yet, let me give you an idea of what those favors might be—then maybe you can coax them out of her. Speaking on behalf of my gender, I wish you'd . . .

SHOWER BEFORE BED. Seeing you emerge from a steamy bathroom with droplets of water clinging to your biceps makes me want to dry you off with my tongue. That includes all those soft, warm, sensitive places—but only when they're Zestfully clean.

TALK DIRTIER. Much dirtier. Trot out a variety of nasty words one night, and if I grunt and moan in agreement, kick it up a notch. When I respond with total silence, dial it back down.

MOW THE LAWN IN JEANS AND NO SHIRT. I can play Desperate Housewife from the window. Then come inside smelling of freshly cut grass, sweat, and

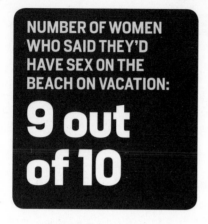

NUMBER OF WOMEN WHO SAID THEY'D HAVE SEX ON THE BEACH ON VACATION:

9 out of 10

pheromones, and make love to me on the dining-room table.

ASK ME TO PERFORM YOGA POSES NAKED. I've been preparing for it every week while bent over and staring through my legs at the mirror on the yoga-studio wall. This is not a performance I'll volunteer for. I need a little encouragement, goading even, but I will give in. And you'll especially appreciate the views when I'm in Camel pose and Standing Bow.

SLIDE YOUR HAND UP MY SKIRT when you're following me upstairs.

CONFESS YOUR LATEST SEXUAL FANTASY. But say that you did this with/to me in a dream. That'll allow me to maintain the illusion that it isn't something you used to do with an ex-hookup, or an idea you picked up from porn. I might not agree to reenact it, but hearing about it will make me feel like your naughty little confidante, which is very hot. Bonus: It'll give me the courage to tell you mine.

READ UP ON SEX. There are books on boinking that are worth the embarrassment of buying them. Like Ian Kerner's *She Comes First,* for example. It's a guide to giving oral sex so well that your partner will insist on cooking you blueberry pancakes the next morning. Yes, you're an amazing lover already, but Kerner has a PhD for a reason.

AMBUSH ME IN THE SHOWER and direct a strong stream of warm water precisely at my clitoris. Adjust your aim even as I giggle and squirm around the tub. I've done this by myself, plenty of times, but having you do it to me is way sexier and a hundred times more fun.

MAKE YOUR MOVE THE SECOND WE WALK IN THE DOOR. Or while we're still in the hallway. I don't know what, if anything, happened between Benicio Del Toro and Scarlett Johansson in that elevator, but if Del Toro acted as if having sex with her right then and there was the only reason he was put on this planet, I could certainly understand if she obliged. When a guy lusts after me so urgently that he can't even wait the 90 seconds it takes to get to the bed, it makes me feel like a movie star.

ASK TO TAKE BLACK-AND-WHITE PHOTOS OF ME NAKED. I want you to, but I'm not so cocky as to suggest that my body could qualify as a work of art. That's why I need you to do it for me. Bring it up after we've had sex. Tell me that the curve of my hips needs to be immortalized. Then, one rainy Saturday night, produce a bottle of wine and a camera.

NUMBER OF WOMEN WHO SAID THEY'D SUNBATHE TOPLESS ON VACATION:

8 out of 10

TREAT SEX LIKE A BUFFET. Take breaks during intercourse to go back for appetizers. Too often, making out, manual stimulation, and breast caressing get cast aside when the more serious stuff starts. But without generous amounts of all three from start to finish, the female orgasm is infinitely harder to achieve.

SIT BACK ON YOUR HEELS from the missionary position and caress my legs slowly, from ankle to thigh. When you take the time to stroke my body thoughtfully during sex, it lets me know that you're savoring the experience as something meaningful to you.

BUY MORE OF THOSE SNUG, GRAY BOXERS with the buttons on the crotch. I want to work them open with my teeth.

KISS ME IN FRONT OF FRIENDS or co-workers and slip me the tiniest bit of tongue. They'll think we have a smokin' sex life. Other women will wish they had a guy like you. That will make me feel very lucky, and very horny.

GET ME DRUNK ON CHAMPAGNE, prop me up on the hood of your car, and eat me like an apple.

REWARD ME FOR FOLDING YOUR T-SHIRTS and cleaning the drain by making one long night of sex all about me. Light a candle. Rub massage oil on my body, back and front, shoulders to toes. Next, bring me close to orgasm using just your hands. Then your tongue. Then pull me on top so I can orchestrate the finale myself.

WATCH ME SHAVE MY LEGS. Offer to help me shave other places.

MANEUVER ME INTO 69 at least once a month. Sometimes with me on top, sometimes you. Sometimes on our sides. And, at least once in our lives—when you've been lifting and I'm at my lightest weight—standing up with my thighs on top of your shoulders.

WHY WOMEN CRY

HERE'S THE SCOOP ON WHAT GETS A GIRL'S TEARS FLOWING. CONSIDER THIS ONE MYSTERY OF WOMEN SOLVED

BY SANDY HINGSTON

The editor who asked me to write this story did so because he knows I'm a crier. He's seen me cry at appropriate times (on 9/11), at inappropriate times (in editorial meetings), and at just plain weird times (when my pen runs out of ink). Like most men, he's scared when I cry. I can see it in his eyes as he edges back from my desk: What's the matter with her? Is she coming unhinged? How can she get so upset over a lousy pen?

Tom, you moron, it's got nothing to do with the pen. Any woman could tell you that.

But what it does have to do with is something I never really gave any thought to. I cry because . . . well, because. Because I feel bad. Because it feels good. Because I have unresolved attachment issues and am regressing to a preverbal state to reforge a symbolic internal connection to my mother.

Or maybe it's because I'm getting my freaking period, okay?

CRY, BABY

I first cried on the day I was born. Like most babies, I cried at a pitch between C and C-sharp. Yet my mom could pick me out by the sound. I cried because it was all I could do, the only tool I had to summon food and comfort. I cried more and more for the first 6 weeks of my life, then at a steady rate—mostly in the evening—until I was 12 weeks old, when I began to cry less. That was also when I started to cry tears you could see.

Tears—made up of mucus, water, and oil—had already been moving across my eyes every time I blinked. These constant, involuntarily produced "basal tears"—from 5 to 10 ounces a day—drain through small holes in the corners of the eyelids into the nasal cavity, which is why your nose runs when you cry.

Just at the point when I was beginning to smile and make eye contact and coo responsively, though, I was also learning to use my crying more cleverly, experimenting with pitch and duration and tone. And my tears overwhelmed my body's drainage system, spilling over my eyelids. Puling gets old. But who can resist a baby's tears?

Not even a baby, it seems. Whenever my mother set me beside a crying playmate, I would start up. Mom laughed, but NYU psychology professor emeritus Martin Hoffman, PhD, thinks I was demonstrating that empathy is one of the first emotions humans experience. Babies don't usually cry when they hear recordings of their own crying—but they do when they hear that of others.

64 CRIES PER YEAR

Randy Cornelius, PhD, a psychology professor at Vassar College, is one of only a few dozen scientists in the world who study tears. The dearth of researchers may be due to the thorniness of even the simplest questions about crying. For instance: Why do women cry more than men?

"We're not sure," says Dr. Cornelius, who despite his sorrowful specialty is quite cheery. "There's been speculation it has to do with the way male and female brains are put together. But that hasn't panned out yet." He points out that up until children start school, boys and girls cry at equal rates, which suggests a societal root: Parents let girls sniffle, but crack down on crybaby boys as they grow. The discrepancy could be an evolutionary adaptation, though. Crying, Dr. Cornelius says, is how we signal to other humans that we're vulnerable and in need. Women are good at vulnerability; we share our emotions as a sign of trust, and that trust helps us survive. But a male *Survivor* contestant who bursts into tears might as well tattoo "Vote Me Off" on his chest.

One substance being studied in connection with crying is the hormone prolactin, levels of which increase in women during puberty, menstruation, pregnancy, and breastfeeding, as well as when we're under stress. We average up to 60 percent more prolactin in our bodies than men. William H. Frey, PhD, biochemist and author of *Crying: The Mystery of Tears,* theorizes that prolactin lowers women's emotional bar by stimulating the endocrine system, which makes us more prone to tears.

And we do cry more—on average, 64 times a year, compared with 17 times for men. We cry when we're sad or frustrated or angry, whereas men cry at major losses, like death; when they get frustrated, they just get mad. Ask a man the last time he cried in front of someone else and chances are he'll have a hard time remembering. A woman won't.

But a funny thing happens as we reach midlife. Women cry less and get angry more—just as our levels of female hormones drop off, leaving a higher concentration of the male hormone testosterone. In men, a decline in testosterone makes for increased impact from their female hormones. And guess what? As guys get older, they get angry less—and cry more.

TWO SOURCES FOR TEARS

As physical creatures, we're accustomed to straightforward cause and effect: You scrape your knee and you bleed. So we're mystified by the link between our physical nature and our emotions. Just how do we get from hurt feelings to tears?

Crying, explains Darlene Dartt, PhD, a cellular physiologist at Harvard's Schepens Eye Research Institute, started out as a protective response mechanism. There are sensory nerves in the cornea, just like the pain nerves in your skin. When you walk into a strong wind or slice into an onion, the nerves in the eye send impulses to the brain stem, which regulates involuntary processes like heartbeat, swallowing, and breathing. The brain stem releases hormones that travel to the glands along the eyelids and tell them to produce tears, which wash away the irritant. These are "reflex tears."

But the nerves in the cornea also reach higher in the brain, into the cerebrum, and that's where "emotional tears"—the kind women shed watching *Titanic*—get their start. When Jack Dawson dies, we feel sad. Our sorrow is registered in the cerebrum, which signals the endocrine system to release hormones that travel to the eyelid glands and generate tears. It's no coincidence, it seems, that the cerebrum is also the part of the brain that controls speech. Crying is a form of communication, likely the earliest form, and certainly the one we use first.

Why do we cry when we're sad rather than when we're, say, curious? One of the first crying researchers, Paul D. MacLean, MD, PhD, an NIH neuroscientist emeritus, linked it to an ancient ritual, speculating that as early humans cremated dead loved ones, the reflex tears produced by the smoky pyres combined with the emotional devastation our ancestors felt. The result: an inexorable connection between death and tears, sadness and sobbing.

A TEARY TIME OF THE MONTH?

I try to control my crying. But once a month, I lose the battle. Two days before my period begins, I fall into a bottomless emotional pit in which I sob for, well, no good reason at all.

Which is why I was unpleasantly surprised by the results of research done by Ad Vingerhoets, PhD, a psychology professor at the Tilburg University in the Netherlands. Dr. Vingerhoets's studies show that while in Western cultures women link crying to their menstrual cycles, in non-Western cultures, they don't. What's more, when we keep diaries of when we cry, there's no correlation whatsoever between weeping and menstruation, regardless of where we live.

It could be that women connect crying to menstruation because we like to think of tears as part of our deeper, uncontrollable animal nature; that gives us permission to indulge in those cry-till-you-gag jags. Yet how can tears be animalistic when we're the only animals that cry? It's more likely that we weep because we're so highly evolved—because our minds tease out endless ribbons of regret and conjecture and what if. Tears, says Tom Lutz, author of *Crying: The Natural and Cultural History of Tears,* distract us from all that inner anxiety by sending us off to find a Kleenex and blow our noses. They relieve our turmoil by refocusing our attention from the mental to the physical.

In that sense, tears are about buying time until we heal. An English scientist who set out to determine what sort of music makes us cry found we tear up when a grace note delays the return to the tonic—the base note in a scale. We know what we expect from a melody. When our expectations are thwarted, we weep.

If there's any constant to crying, it may be that our bodies and minds seek a return to balance, an equilibrium. When a baby sobs for its mother, or a teenager weeps at a friend's betrayal, or a woman mourns her dead husband, the common thread is a longing for happiness once had but lost. Tears are our response to life's unfairness. We cry to try to make things right.

UNCOVER HER SEXUAL PERSONALITY

It's easy to draw quick conclusions about a woman's sexual personality. Easy, but the results are often inaccurate. Rush to judgment and you could miss your chance to be her most memorable lover. Here are the insights you need to rock any woman's world.

THE SEXPERT

Her extensive sexual résumé and range of bedroom appetites make yours seem virginal.

WHAT YOU MIGHT THINK: "She's already done the double-jointed McTwist with her ex—on a plane. How could I top that?"

WHY YOU'RE WRONG: "Women like this don't notch their bedposts, and they're often more vocal about what they want," says Patti Britton, PhD, sex therapist and president of the American Association of Sex Educators, Counselors, and Therapists. "All you have to do is listen. Even a new twist on an old trick will stoke her fires."

THE NOVICE

She's reluctant to try new things. It's all missionary, all the time.

WHAT YOU MIGHT THINK: "Is it me she doesn't like, or just sex in general?"

WHY YOU'RE WRONG: Her inner freak will emerge. "Her body might just be undiscovered country," says Debby Herbenick, PhD, the *Men's Health* "Bedroom Confidential" columnist. Help her learn to tap into her pleasure centers. "Once that arousal system is switched on, women are more primal," says Gloria G. Brame, PhD, author of *Come Hither: A Commonsense Guide to Kinky Sex*. No lectures, just positive feedback.

THE DIVA

She's the puppet master, you're the puppet. Sex, for her, is a one-way street.

WHAT YOU MIGHT THINK: "If I do what she wants, she'll reward me by returning the favor."

WHY YOU'RE WRONG: You're not her sex slave. Don't reinforce the behavior. Step 1: Take away her control. Playfully pin her hands down and give her a deep, hard kiss when she gets bossy. "You have to reestablish the emotional connection," says Britton. Step 2: Maneuver her into a position that allows you both to receive pleasure. If she lets up, so do you. She'll catch on.

>>A MAN'S GUIDE POLL

Pubic debate

The younger a woman is, the more likely she's following the well-shaved path of porn stars and post-'97 Playmates, a survey says.

PERCENTAGE OF ALL WOMEN	AGES 18–34	AGES 35–44	AGES 45–54
23% of women think most men prefer a manicured pubic area on a woman	41%	34%	14%
25% of women say they closely trim their pubic hair with scissors or clippers	35%	36%	21%
23% shave part of their pubic hair	36%	31%	19%
9% shave off all of their pubic hair	22%	8%	5%
23% don't trim their pubic hair at all	8%	14%	31%

THE HIBERNATOR

The sex is great, when she's in the mood for it.

WHAT YOU MIGHT THINK: "She has some serious hang-ups. Is she frigid?"

WHY YOU'RE WRONG: She could have stage fright. So take away the expectation of sex. Launch a make-out session, then let up. "She'll crave what she can't have," says Candida Royalle, author of *How to Tell a Naked Man What to Do.* "The more she's put in the role of the aggressor, the more she'll want to make use of that passion."

SEXUALITY SHIFT

Are women becoming more open to same-sex flings? Or just more willing to admit to them? According to a new study, bisexuality among American women has nearly tripled in the past decade, reports the Centers for Disease Control and Prevention's National Center for Health Statistics. In-person surveys of 7,000 women showed that 11 percent reported having had at least one sexual experience with another woman in their lifetime, up from 4 percent 10 years earlier. Among men, 6 percent said they'd had a sexual experience with a man, up from 5 percent.

THE QUESTION: "What's your sexual orientation?"

WOMEN (AGES 18 TO 44)
Heterosexual 90%

"Something else" 4%

Bisexual 3%

No answer 2%

Homosexual 1%

MEN (AGES 18 TO 44)
Heterosexual 90%

"Something else" 4%

Bisexual 2%

No answer 2%

Homosexual 2%

GIVE HER THE GIRLFRIEND GAUNTLET

She likes football, hates John Mayer, and looks great in a pair of jeans. Nice trifecta. But if you're thinking of keeping her around for a while, you need a real measure of her mettle. We call this the gauntlet. You call it long-term relationship insurance.

THE TRAIT: RESPONSIBILITY

THE TEST: Play the blame game. Next time she rear-ends someone during rush hour or spills coffee on her lap, listen to her postgame analysis. "Successful couples focus on positives," says Scott Haltzman, MD, a psychiatrist and the author of *The Secrets of Happily Married Men*. "Is she the eternal victim? Or does she accept responsibility?"

THE TRAIT: PATIENCE

THE TEST: Talk about work. The story of the time she made an intern cry may have made you laugh, but all that attitude won't stay cooped up in cubicle land. "If she tears a co-worker a new one for no reason, watch out. Her attitude at work will show what she's like under pressure," says John Van Epp, PhD, author of *How to Avoid Marrying a Jerk*.

THE TRAIT: EMPATHY

THE TEST: Take her shopping. Malls are buffets of human interaction—peeved customers, airhead clerks, moms with kids, all of them begging for vitriolic color commentary. "You want to see empathy for the stressed and clueless. If she thinks most situations and solutions are clear-cut, expect the same absolutism with you," says Dr. Haltzman.

THE TRAIT: ADAPTABILITY

THE TEST: Make last-minute plans. Sure, you were planning to see a chick flick, but now the only film not sold out is *Scary Movie 19*. Relationships change constantly, so see if she can roll with it. Another time, show up 15 minutes late. If things like that set her off, "she will have no problem finding ways you disappoint her," Dr. Haltzman says.

THE TRAIT: FLEXIBILITY

THE TEST: Cook dinner at her place. If she's a control freak who can't cede dominion over her kitchen, she'll have a hard time letting you take the reins elsewhere in life. Even if she's a gourmet, she should still willingly accept your different, yet still effective, way of chopping carrots, says Pat Love, EdD, author of *The Truth About Love.*

THE TRAIT: CONFIDENCE

THE TEST: Deprive her of the spotlight. Take her to a friend's party, then watch her mingle. Does she seek constant male attention? Could be needy. Dodges women? Not good: Women "deliver necessary honesty" to other women, says Love. Also, she knows that your female friends will offer a more realistic review of her. Talking with them shows brass.

IMPRESS HER FRIENDS

A woman's friends are her velvet rope. Make a good impression, and you'll be whisked inside the club; flub your approach, and you'll be kicked to the curb. "If you charm a woman's friends, it's that much easier to impress her," says Susan Rabin, a dating coach and the author of *Lucky in Love*. First make them happy—and then make her yours.

READ THE DEFENSE

Scan the room like Ben Roethlisberger. "Huddling behavior means they're closed to outsiders," says Dennie Hughes, a relationship expert and the author of *Dateworthy*. Your best bet is an outward-facing group or a line of women doing their own scanning. Aim for groups of three women or more, so no one ends up alone. "It doesn't matter how much a woman likes you," says Hughes, "if leaving with you means stranding her friend, you'll lose."

MAKE THE APPROACH

The handshake and easy intro ("Hi, my name is . . .") works one-on-one, but you'll look like a politician if you greet an entire group that way. So make use of your surroundings. If the ladies are gathered near the pool table, visit the nearby jukebox. Take song requests or rack up at the table. Watch what they watch, and comment: "Nice mullet, eh?" or "Hey, I saw you checking out SportsCenter—you a Cubs fan?" Introductions will naturally follow.

FOLLOW THE LEADER

The woman guiding the conversation is your "logical starting point," says Hughes. (If you begin with the shy woman on the periphery, her protective friends may close ranks.) Topics? Use the 30-day rule, from Phyllis Davis, author of *E2: Using the Power of Ethics and Etiquette in American Business*. Keep the conversation current: Bring up only events that have happened in the past month or will happen in the next. "It will make you more fascinating; it's alive, it's interesting, and it's personal," says Davis.

CONTROL THE FLOW

Indicate interest with body positioning, not come-ons. Subtly mirror her gestures: If she nods, you nod; if she laughs, you laugh. When you turn your head toward whoever is speaking, keep your shoulders square with hers. "This is subtle but effective," says Davis. Note which topics capture her attention, and guide the group toward anything she finds interesting. She likes Spanish cooking? Talk tapas.

SPLIT SUBTLY

The finale is quiet, a tête-à-tête. Ask her to help you grab some drinks or pick songs at the jukebox. "That's when you make her blush," says April Masini, author of *Date Out of Your League*. "If she likes you, she'll love that you spent time with her friends but ultimately chose her. You'll feel more confident, and she'll feel less pressure."

GET HER TO SHOW SOME SKIN

Coaxing her out of her clothes is easier once you've supplied the right sweet nothings for her to wear underneath. Drool your way through the Victoria's Secret catalog and you might learn what makes Heidi Klum feel sexy, but the key to unleashing your woman's inner vixen is doing some serious background research.

"Buying lingerie requires precision and finesse," says Lash Fary, author of *Fabulous Gifts*. "If you find something that fits her personality, she'll feel sexy and beautiful, and she'll act that way when she's wearing it. But if you buy her something that doesn't complement her sexuality, she'll feel self-conscious, and her passion will be stifled."

Start by carefully scouting out her size. "It's okay to peek into her drawers this once," says Fary. "Size is one thing you just can't get wrong." Then match the tone of the lingerie to the occasion. "If it's a spontaneous, sexy purchase, something skimpy might be okay. But if it's a romantic anniversary, go with something more reserved," he says.

The final step for choosing lingerie she'll love to show off: finding the right fabric and style to match her exact body type and tastes. That's not such a simple task—which is why we've created a three-step guide to finding the perfect fit for any woman.

STEP 1: WHAT STYLE?

YOUR CLUE: Her body shape.

PEAR: Bigger on the bottom than on top. "Two pieces will counterbalance her bottom half," says Fary. One-piece items may fit her wide hips but not her narrow torso. Go with a sexy camisole and boy shorts.

APPLE: Large breasts and waist, slender hips and legs. A bustier will accentuate her assets, says Fary. Pair it with a thong (if you know she likes them) to play up her underappreciated bottom half. Hanky Panky makes a one-size-fits-all thong (www.hankypanky.com).

LEAN ATHLETE: Lack of curves is not a problem. "You can go a little bit sexier with this body type," says Fary. "They do best with one-piece items." Examples: a short chemise or negligee. (Buy a matching robe.)

HOURGLASS: Big breasts, thin waist, voluptuous hips. "This is a more versatile shape to shop for," says Fary. "The possibilities are endless." Highlight her bust and butt with a pushup bra and boy shorts.

STEP 2: HOW RAUNCHY?

YOUR CLUE: Her jeans.

CLASSIC LEVI'S 501S: Stick with traditional, conservative pieces.

BOOT-CUT: Pick something whimsical," says Lori Ann Robinson, a Los Angeles fashion consultant. Look for embroidery, rhinestones, or other embellishments. Try La Perla (www.laperla.com).

STRAIGHT-LEGGED: "Keep frills to a minimum," says Robinson. Buy European-made lingerie, like Cosabella (www.cosabella.com).

LINGERIE LINGO

Here's a primer for what those teeny pieces of clothing are called.

Boy shorts: a sexier take on conventional boxers or briefs

Bustier (pronounced "boos-tee-YAY")**:** Madonna, sans cones; like a bra that extends to the hips

Camisole (pronounced "CAM-i-sole")**:** a glorified tank top, typically worn as an undershirt

Chemise (pronounced "sha-MEEZ")**:** a sexy nightgown that looks like a dress

G-string: trace amounts of fabric held together by strings on the sides and the derriere

Pushup bra (pronounced "more cleavage")**:** a bra that provides padding and lifts the breasts

String bikini: fabric in the front and back, with thin string sides

Thong: fabric in front, room for junk in the trunk

SUPER-LOW-RISE: "Something daring, dramatic, and racy works," says Robinson. Check out Frederick's of Hollywood (www.fredericks.com).

DESTROYED: She just seems low maintenance. To tease her wild side, shop Agent Provocateur (www.agentprovocateur.com).

STEP 3: WHAT FABRIC?

YOUR CLUE: Her sheets.

FLORAL: Think girly, says Sarah Petitt, coordinator of fabric styling at the Fashion Institute of Technology. "Anything lace, silk, or satin."

ANIMAL PRINTS: Grrrr. Go risqué—choose anything sheer or lacy, suggests Petitt. (Or even leather.)

SOLID COLORS: "Stay minimalist," Petitt says. If you see a satin bedspread or velvet drapes, consider those fabrics.

STRIPES AND OTHER PATTERNS: Mix and match. Try a silky fabric with lace trim, advises Petitt.

READ HER SIGNS

My wife, Kathy, and I are very much alike, except for one thing: She loves to talk. Me, I have conversations in my head. And sometimes I think I've told her something when it never left my lips. That occasionally causes a rift between us.

Marriage counselor Gary Chapman, PhD, says not only am I not talking, but when I do I'm probably not speaking Kathy's "love language."

"Couples often speak different emotional love languages . . . as different as Chinese is from English," says Chapman. "And no matter how hard you try to express love in English, if your spouse understands only Chinese, you will never understand how to love each other."

Chapman went through 12 years of notes from his counseling sessions and identified five types of emotional languages: Quality Time, Words of Affirmation, Receiving Gifts, Acts of Service, and Physical Touch. They formed the basis for his book *The Five Love Languages,* which has sold 3.4 million copies. If you can figure out what type of expression of love makes your partner feel most loved, says Chapman, you can dramatically improve your relationship.

"One reason couples argue so much is that they don't feel loved," he says. "And that makes their differences seem so much bigger."

After Kathy and I completed Chapman's quiz, it was obvious that her love language was Quality Time—talking and togetherness. Chapman suggested three tips to help me learn to speak it:

1. **I SHOULD SET ASIDE 10 MINUTES EVERY NIGHT TO GIVE KATHY MY FULL ATTENTION, TO TALK, TO LISTEN, OR JUST TO SIT AND BE TOGETHER.**

2. **WHEN I TALK TO HER BY PHONE AT WORK, I NEED TO TURN AWAY FROM MY E-MAIL.** "A lot of men pride themselves on multitasking," he says. (Guilty as charged.) "But women see right through that. You're not paying attention."

3. IN CONVERSATION, I SHOULD REPEAT BACK TO HER THE POINTS SHE'S MAKING SO THAT SHE CAN REALIZE I'M LISTENING AND MAKE SURE I'M COMPREHENDING WHAT SHE'S SAYING.

The results, Chapman promises, will be dramatic. "I had a guy say to me, 'My wife's language is Acts of Service,'" he says. "'If I had known that taking out the garbage before she asked me to was sexy to her, I'd have communicated that love to her long ago.'"

And think of how much he might have saved on jewelry.

KEEPING SCORE IN THE BATTLE OF THE SEXES

When couples move in together, the man tends to improve his eating habits, British researchers say. Men start eating more vegetables and less fatty meat, and drinking less alcohol. But women are apt to gain weight, thanks partly to the use of food to cope with stress.

ADVANTAGE: Men

Men tend to nurture their anger, while women seek to dissipate it. In an experiment, researchers irritated test subjects, then told them they would get a chance to vent on the jerk running the test. While waiting, men chose to read negative news. Women read more positive articles.

ADVANTAGE: None

A German study found that men are more likely than women to choose performance-based pay over fixed wages. Researchers theorize that men are more self-confident and tend to enjoy risk more.

ADVANTAGE: Men

ASK THE GIRL NEXT DOOR

How can I tell whether a girl is straight or a lesbian?

You can't. And unless you want to be beaten up by a woman in public, I don't recommend asking.

If a woman asks if I have a girlfriend, does that mean she's interested?

Maybe. There are two reasons a woman asks that, so listen closely to her tone. If she's bold ("So, are you single?"), she probably wants to fix you up with a friend or find out if you're gay. (Relax—maybe your hair is styled too well.) If she's shy and indirect ("Hey, you're going to this party, right? Are you bringing anyone?"), she has a crush on you. We're pretty skittish when it comes to our own emotions. If the interest is mutual, be sure to shoot the question right back at her, and smile when she says she's single—it could be the start of something big.

The girl I'm seeing has suddenly gotten moody and difficult for no real reason. What's up?

I know exactly what you're talking about, and it drives me nuts, too—even when I do it myself. You'll be happy to know that it's just a test. She wants to see if you'll be able not just to put up with her, but to actually love her when she's at her worst. And she's probably not even conscious she's doing it. It's definitely an immature, self-defeating maneuver. But if you know why she's doing it, maybe it'll be easier for you to tune out the tantrums the next time around.

PERCENTAGE OF WOMEN WHO SAY THEY'D PREFER A LONG-TERM PARTNER WHO'S A CREATIVE BUT POOR BUSINESSMAN TO A RICH BUT UNCREATIVE BUSINESSMAN:

66

I see these girls at nightclubs dancing together and kissing. Are they asking to be taken home together?

Let me put myself in these girls' shoes. So I'm wasted and grinding/making out with a hot girl on a crowded dance floor. I could be a lesbian, but statistically, it's much more likely that I'm a straight chick having a wild night out.

My comely partner and I may not be "asking to be taken home together," but based on the fact that we've gone this far, I can assure you that it's within the realm of possibility. More than a few of the women I know have had at least one threesome, and most of the time it involved a female friend and a confident guy who wasn't afraid to hit on two girls at once. The next time you see a pair of babes playing naughty, bring them each a champagne cocktail and ask them to dance. The odds aren't great, but you might get lucky.

The girl I'm hooking up with invites friends along every time we go out. What's up with that?

So you guys party together in a group, then she takes you home to get it on? Sounds like fun. What it doesn't sound like is a relationship of any significance. Girls who are head-over-heels crave one-on-one time with their man. She must be looking for a bed buddy, not a boyfriend. But don't be discouraged; many a friend with benefits has turned into a significant other.

Is it true that some women can orgasm through nipple stimulation alone? If so, where can I find them? (Just kidding. Kind of.)

Chances are, they're not advertising on Craigslist. Treat your next partner to a session of breast exploration to learn what kinds of licking, touching, and light grazing of her nipples or other parts she likes best. Every woman is different, but one study shows that the upper portion of the breast, from 10 o'clock to 2 o'clock, is ultrasensitive, so start there, working your way in toward the areola. Remember: Breasts can be tender—you have to warm up the rest of her body before you stimulate them directly.

ADD IT UP

Oral sex? Missionary position? Doggie-style? How about all of the above? According to the *Journal of Sex Research*, investigators asked 19,307 Australian men and women about their most recent erotic encounter and found that the more sexual practices women engaged in during a single session, the more likely they were to climax. Just half the women who only had intercourse got off, compared with 70 percent who were helped along by manual or oral stimulation. And those who went for the whole shebang—intercourse plus manual and oral sex—had an 86 percent chance of orgasm. (The number of sexual practices did not influence men's likelihood of orgasm. No shocker there.) What works best for a man is not necessarily what feels best for a woman, says study author Juliet Richters, PhD.

SCORE ONE FOR OPEN-MINDEDNESS

Enthusiasm about sex is hot in a woman. So is her open mind. Now a study in *Psychological Science* puts it all together: Straight women with high sex drives are 27 times more likely to be attracted to both sexes than are straight men with high sex drives, according to a survey of more than 3,500 people.

"Women tend to come in more shades of gray, while men are more polarized—more either/or—in their sexual orientation," says author Richard Lippa, PhD, a psychologist at California State University at Fullerton. But, he warns, just because she finds women attractive doesn't mean she wants a threesome.

LET HER TAKE CONTROL

Tell that easy hookup that you know what she likes. Women who endorse casual sex are more likely to fantasize about dominating a man, reports a study in the *Journal of Sex Research*. Study participants completed a survey on sexual attitudes, then wrote out two fantasies. Researchers then checked the stories for themes of power. "Examples of dominance fantasies included pinning men to the bed, ordering them to perform a specific sex act, and initiating a younger man into sex," says study coauthor Megan Yost, PhD. But don't break out the handcuffs just yet; you still have to read her signals and talk, Yost advises. If a woman takes over the conversation and is willing to share her sexual fantasies with you, chances are you can safely broach the subject, she says.

If she whispers something shocking in your ear, ask her if she'd like to take control—at least part of the time. Just sit back and enjoy the show.

ORDER HER A DOUBLE LATTE

Invite her up for coffee; maybe she'll stick around. Scientists found that female rats on a caffeine buzz come back for more sex much more readily than their caffeine-free friends. *Pharmacology, Biochemistry, and Behavior* reports that female rats injected with caffeine before mating came back to the male faster and stayed with him until sexually stimulated.

CONSIDER THIS FAIR WARNING

Women who watch professional wrestling are more likely to pick fights with their partners. When researchers at Wake Forest studied high-school teenagers who watched wrestling six times over 2 weeks, they found that the females were twice as likely to be perpetrators of dating violence than the men were. Researchers say males may be less affected because they're exposed to more media violence.

PART 3
DATE GREAT

Robert Palmer wasn't joking when he sang "Addicted to Love." There's hard science behind that dizzying, euphoric feeling of being newly in love. Scientists studied 10 women and 7 men who had recently become infatuated with someone. Functional MRIs showed that when the volunteers looked at photos of their new loves, the area of their brains that became active was the same region that fires up when we satisfy a craving, whether it be for food, drink, or drug.

This part of the book aims to help you continue to satisfy that craving. You'll learn how to plan your hottest dates ever. Then take it to the next level with unforgettable romantic getaways for two, perhaps in one of America's best boutique hotels. If yours is one of the millions of long-distance loves, you'll discover how to survive those long absences. You'll also learn how to keep the flame burning, in both those fragile early dating stages and as your relationship grows. Here's to building a love that lasts!

YOUR HOTTEST DATES EVER

SEIZE THESE 5 FORGOTTEN HOLIDAYS TO KEEP HER PASSION BURNING BRIGHT, ALL YEAR LONG

It's hard to stand out on Valentine's Day. And of course you already know what to do on her birthday, and certainly you remembered the anniversary of the day you met. Here are five other holidays to give you a reason to celebrate.

FEBRUARY 28: INTERNATIONAL PANCAKE DAY

Sharing simple chow is just as meaningful to her as a $400 dinner. "It reaffirms intimacy in a way that's even more powerful than sex," says Jay Mechling, PhD, a professor of American studies at the University of California at Davis.

YOUR CELEBRATION: Re-create the first low-key meal you shared at home, but add fine champagne.

JUNE 6: ANNIVERSARY OF THE FIRST DRIVE-IN MOVIE

In the pre-multiplex era, drive-in movies sparked a pop-culture craze and a hookup hot spot. Although a thousand of them still remain across the United States, they're fading fast. Find one near you at www.driveinmovie.com.

YOUR CELEBRATION: Bring a picnic dinner to a double feature. Swap buttery popcorn for sexier dark chocolate.

JUNE 21: SUMMER SOLSTICE

Today, you have 15 hours of sunlight to soak up. Use the sun's sluggish course as an excuse to savor summer's finer points.

YOUR CELEBRATION: Chart a meandering hike, stake out a scenic spot, and break out a cache of goodies (berries, a blanket, massage oil). "Simple rituals can give you a brief respite from routine," says Mechling.

AUGUST 18: BAD POETRY DAY

Most greeting cards are sappy yet safe, and quickly forgotten. Earn points by turning your own inside jokes and funny memories into verse.

YOUR CELEBRATION: "Write her a really rotten poem—if it's done with a twinkle in your eye, she'll love it," says Tom Roy, founder of nearly 100 US holidays. It may not be John Donne, but it will be a card she'll actually keep.

3 HOLIDAY TRADITIONS TO SKIP THIS YEAR

You're an original, so why give in to these unoriginal traditions? Make new ones, instead.

Giving roses on Valentine's Day. Sidestep the convention and back up one demure bud—a lily or orchid—with a thoughtful mix tape or framed photo. Classy.

Drinking green beer on St. Patrick's Day. Your ancestors didn't emigrate from the Emerald Isle in 1643 so you could turn their beloved brew into shamrock swill.

Making out with strangers on New Year's Eve. The average openmouthed smooch swaps 5 million bacteria, and the DNA of the six other dudes she's kissed.

>>A MAN'S GUIDE POLL
Which Valentine's Day gift leads to the best sex?

Chocolate	16%
Lingerie	23%
Jewelry	47%
Flowers	14%

SEPTEMBER 16: INTERNATIONAL APPLE DAY

The apple is ripe for picking now, and orchards—with their secluded glades—offer many opportunities for mischief.

YOUR CELEBRATION: Find an orchard (www.applejournal.com/trail.htm) and handpick your dessert. Make her warm apple compote served over vanilla ice cream.

ROMANTIC GETAWAYS

RUN AWAY TOGETHER WITH THESE 6 STRATEGIES
FOR AN UNFORGETTABLE TRIP FOR TWO

BY CHRIS CONNOLLY

For a new couple, there's no better test of compatibility than that fateful first trip. There's much to be learned from seeing your sweetiemunchkins removed from her network of coping mechanisms and creature comforts. You may uncover negatives, like her packing 11 pairs of shoes for a weekend upstate. You may also discover a charming quality, like how cuddly she gets after one umbrella drink.

"When you travel, your companion is in your space all the time," says Patti Britton, PhD, president of the American Association of Sex Educators, Counselors, and Therapists and author of *The Art of Sex Coaching.* "This kind of proximity magnifies everything: the sore spots and the sweet spots, the good, the bad, and the ugly."

US couples go on 155 million romantic getaways every year. While some of these couples will end up necking in the lost-luggage office, others will find themselves at the precipice of an enchanting waterfall, arguing about who should carry the binoculars. Your journey should start with our step-by-step guide to travel for twosomes.

STEP 1: START SMALL

Don't be too ambitious too soon. "Early in a relationship, a shorter trip is more prudent," says Linda DeVillers, PhD, author of *Love Skills: A Fun, Upbeat Guide to Sex-cessful Relationships.* Long trips raise expectations, cost more, and represent a commitment. Unless you have a very good feel for her, put a 3-day cap on your maiden voyage.

DO: Spend a weekend in Vegas.

DON'T: Go on a 2-week elk hunt.

YOUR BEST BET: Pick a spot that's no more than 4 hours away—half a day of livid silence on the way home is not fun. And opt for a place with plenty of activities to choose from. This way, if she's not a golfer, she can hit the spa while you hit some balls.

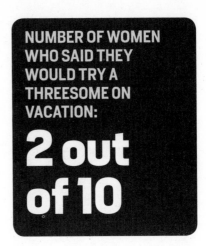

NUMBER OF WOMEN WHO SAID THEY WOULD TRY A THREESOME ON VACATION:

2 out of 10

STEP 2: DISCUSS GREAT EXPECTATIONS

No, not the Dickens classic (although it's quite good). Talk about what you both want from the trip before you pack a bag. "This conversation doesn't have to be some big emotional thing," says Susan Moynihan, editor-in-chief of *Destination Weddings & Honeymoons* magazine. "It can merely be a discussion of your dream vacation. She can say, 'I want to lie on the beach all day, then go have cocktails.' Then he can say, 'That would drive me crazy. I want to go kiteboarding all day, then go have cocktails.' Don't make an issue out of it. It's okay to have different interests. Other than cocktails, obviously, which are nonnegotiable."

DO: Have a lighthearted, enjoyable chat about your vision of the ideal trip.

DON'T: Make it a tense summit meeting.

YOUR BEST BET: Meet someplace fun but quiet and keep the conversation casual. Concentrate on your expectations. Do you want to see the sights or spend the day on the beach? Must you spend every minute together, or can you split up for a few hours? How much time are you going to spend in the room (hint, hint)? What about shopping?

Oh, and one final do: Make sure you establish what the trip means. If you think you're going skiing and she thinks you're going to propose, things might turn ugly.

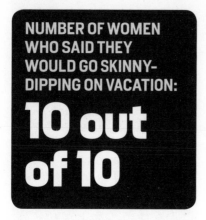

NUMBER OF WOMEN WHO SAID THEY WOULD GO SKINNY-DIPPING ON VACATION:

10 out of 10

STEP 3: DON'T FOLLOW THE LEADER

Many relationships have a natural leader who winds up making most of the decisions. If you just thought, "Yeah, that's me," you're the one. If you just thought, "Yeah, that's her," she's the one. Take this into account when planning, so neither of you winds up being dragged along on the other's dream vacation.

DO: Embrace democracy!

DON'T: Expect her to understand when you skip the butterfly gardens because you want to get a good spot at the swim-up bar.

YOUR BEST BET: Identify the leader in your relationship. As a man, there's a strong possibility you are the leader. If this is the case, make absolutely sure your shy gal chooses her fair share of activities. Give her all the time she needs and encourage her to express her likes and dislikes. If she's reluctant to do this or gives you the ol' "Let's just do what you want to do," use your leadership abilities to coerce her into expressing herself. In other words, order her to give you orders!

STEP 4: DON'T MESS AROUND WITH MONEY

Joy Davidson, PhD, the author of *Fearless Sex*, once went to Venice with a companion on a meals-included package. When she suggested exploring Venice's restaurants, "he couldn't stand the idea of wasting that money. I knew we had different outlooks on money before, but this really highlighted it. We ended up having a huge fight and spending most of our time apart."

Be frank about finances and split costs as equally as possible without allowing them to dominate the experience.

DO: Work out a system ahead of time.

DON'T: Insist on being "The Man" and paying for everything.

YOUR BEST BET: "The best way to deal with it is to divide the payment by days," says Davidson. "For example, he pays for everything on Monday, she pays for everything on Tuesday, and so on. You'll end up spending roughly the same amount, but you won't have money overshadowing the good times every time you're presented with a bill."

NUMBER OF WOMEN WHO SAID THEY WOULD HAVE SEX IN AN ELEVATOR ON VACATION:

5 out of 10

STEP 5: GO SOLO FOR AN HOUR

You love your lover, but you also love it when she goes away for a while, right? "It's important to create some alone time in a way that's sensitive to your partner," Britton says.

DO: Go for an hour's jog on the beach.

DON'T: Blow the day playing blackjack.

YOUR BEST BET: Take the pressure off. Split up, then reconnect to compare notes. Individual enthusiasms can be arousing. Or relax together with a room-service meal. Not every moment has to be life-changing.

STEP 6: STEAM UP THE HOTEL ROOM

Hotel sex is one of the not-so-secret pleasures of travel. "There's a lack of responsibility in a hotel room," says Britton. Be irresponsible.

DO: It.

DON'T: Not do it.

YOUR BEST BET: Pack something surprising in your suitcase—a toy, a DVD, or lingerie. DeVillers says: "It creates anticipation."

THE SUITE LIFE

PLAN A HOT ESCAPE TO ONE OF AMERICA'S BEST BOUTIQUE HOTELS

BY ANTHONY BOURDAIN

There's nothing quite like arriving dirty and fatigued after a long time on the road—sleeping in hard beds between scratchy chain-hotel linens, enduring weak, unreliable plumbing—and then finally allowing yourself to succumb to the warm embrace of a world-class establishment. That first hot, high-pressure shower bakes the pain out of jet-lagged muscle tissue. You slide gratefully into soft, maximum-thread-count sheets and pull a thick duvet over your head knowing that anything you need is a button-push away. And when you wake up, you don't have to rush to the window in hopes of discerning an identifiable landmark to tell you which city you're in—you know where you are. The perfectly maintained Victorian plumbing tells you you're back in London, inside the three adjacent townhouses that make up Hazlitt's. The 1940s-vintage kitchenette heaped with empty Champagne bottles and half-eaten orders of orecchiette pasta, overflowing ashtrays, and the punk band who've apparently fallen asleep on your floor tell you you're at the Chateau Marmont in LA.

I travel a lot and stay in a lot of hotels. And my favorite hotels in the world fall into two categories: the grand, fabulous "luxury" hotels, where a man can't help but feel like a prince; and the quirky, wonderful boutique hotels with no-other-place-like-it qualities. It's easy to book a fine time in a world-class luxury hotel. More challenging and even more rewarding is finding a quirky gem to steal away to when the mood arises.

The problem is that "boutique hotel" has lost its meaning as corporations, like Starwood with its W hotel chain, have gotten into a business that is about being singular. It takes more than U2 piped into the lobby and a staff dressed like Agent Smith from *The Matrix* to make a place special.

To me, L'Hôtel (www.l-hotel.com) is a real boutique. A brass ram's head hangs over a narrow doorway on a charming side street in Paris' Saint-Germain-des-Prés neighborhood. At the tiny bar, photos of Johnny Depp and Sean Penn confirm that you are definitely not at the Marriott. Each of the intimate rooms around a graceful oval stairwell has its own character. The room to stay in is #16, the notorious "Oscar Wilde Suite," where the libertine had the good taste to die. But perhaps the most naughty feature of a hotel that seems designed to meet the desires of one's mistress is the small thermal bath and "relaxation area" tucked away in the cavernlike cellar. Guests can reserve it for their personal use—without fear of interruption.

Travel used to be about going to new places and experiencing something of the local culture. At some hotels, it still is. At the Chateau Marmont, the service is what you'd expect from Los Angeles: dodgy but diligently tolerant of the unusual needs of the hotel's wildly eclectic clientele. Feel free to call room service and order up a case of fine wine and an assortment of power tools for the Hells Angels who'll be joining you in your suite later. Sadly, the Chateau and L'Hôtel are rapidly becoming the exceptions in an ever-chaining world, so maybe what true sybaritic travelers need is a new definition—a "unique" hotel or a "bespoke" hotel—for a special setting where the staff seem to actually care about you, where they look after your every need and never flinch, no matter how unique those needs might be.

To that end, we scoured the country for properties that remain true to the idea of boutique. Here are our selections for the Best Boutique Hotels for Grown-Ups. (Prices listed are the base price per night.)

MAISON 140, LOS ANGELES: Brad Korzen and Kelly Wearstler, whose credits include the Avalon, Viceroy, and Chamberlain hotels, scoured European antique markets to create a pocket of 1920s Paris a few blocks from Rodeo Drive. The hotel's romantic, candlelit Bar Noir features a mix of red French slipper chairs, Asian antiques, and Lucite stools. ($259/www.maison140beverlyhills.com)

XV BEACON, BOSTON: The Beacon occupies the site of 18th-century business tycoon Edward Bromfield's Beacon Hill mansion. This Beaux Arts building is now a posh 60-room hotel that cleverly juxtaposes original details and decadent amenities, such as gas fireplaces, stocked bars, and entertainment systems. ($295/www.xvbeacon.com)

THE MERCER, NEW YORK CITY: The hotel that set the boutique gold standard owes its success to hotelier André Balazs; interior designer Christian Liaigre; and restaurateur Jean-Georges Vongerichten, whose Mercer Kitchen offers tasty items like aged sirloin with gingered shiitake mushrooms. High ceilings and huge windows lend a loft feel to each of the 75 rooms. The first-floor lobby (for guests only) is homey, with a floor-to-ceiling library. But unlike your living room, this space has 24-hour food and drink service. ($440/www.mercerhotel.com)

HOTEL TEATRO, DENVER: With spectacular views of the Rockies, a prime downtown location, and in-room touches like cavernous marble tubs, it's not surprising that this is where celebrities like Bono and Kate Hudson stay in the Mile High City. Built in 1911 as the Denver Tramway Building, the hotel houses two of the city's top restaurants, Prima and Restaurant Kevin Taylor. ($200/www.hotelteatro.com)

HOTEL LUCIA, PORTLAND, OREGON: The lobby is full of buttery-soft dark leather couches and 680 original prints by Pulitzer Prize–winning photographer David Hume Kennerly, on display exclusively at the hotel. Rooms feature king-size mattresses with pillow tops, and phones with "get it now!" buttons that provide access to a VIP concierge service. ($185/www.hotellucia.com)

WATERMARK HOTEL, SAN ANTONIO: This stately brick hotel with giant arched windows overlooks San Antonio's Riverwalk. The property has a 17,000-square-foot spa with 19 private rooms featuring muscle-relaxing Vichy massage showers and hydrotherapy tubs. The hotel's alfresco restaurant, Pesca on the River, cooks up wild fish flown in daily from around the world. ($329/www.watermarkhotel.com)

HOTEL BURNHAM, CHICAGO: Named after Daniel Burnham, who designed New York City's Flatiron Building, this hotel is the result of a $27.5 million renovation of the architect's 111-year-old Reliance Building. Architects often call it the predecessor to the modern skyscraper. Its glass-and-terra-cotta exterior has been completely refurbished, and interior designer Susan

Caruso has transformed the offices into romantic guest rooms. ($200/www.burnhamhotel.com)

THE GLENN HOTEL, ATLANTA: The new buzz in the Old South is a downtown business hotel with a vibe that's more après hours than antebellum. Rooms are furnished with plasma TVs, Aeron desk chairs, and Wi-Fi. Upstairs is Atlanta's only rooftop bar, which has sprawling views of the downtown skyline. ($150/www.glennhotel.com)

HOTEL DEREK, HOUSTON: With wingback chairs, goose-down duvets, and cowhide throw rugs, the Derek is a mix of European and Texan styles. Business lofts feature work alcoves with oversize desks, flat-screen desktop computers, printers, and FedEx supplies. For client dinners, there's Bistro Moderne, the hotel's carnivore-friendly restaurant that serves up foie gras and Texas hanger steaks. ($245/www.hotelderek.com)

HOTEL ANDRA, SEATTLE: This hotel's Scandinavian-inspired design is a blond-wood refuge from a notoriously gray city. Located in the trendy Belltown neighborhood teeming with galleries, restaurants, and boutiques, rooms here are fitted with Tivoli radios, alpaca-fur headboards, and goose-down duvets. The hotel's restaurant, Lola, specializes in Northwest Mediterranean fusion, with dishes like wild king salmon kebab. ($209/www.hotelandra.com)

THE JEFFERSON, WASHINGTON, DC: This 100-room DC institution, built in 1923 as a luxury apartment building, opened as a hotel in 1955. Defense attorney and power broker Edward Bennett Williams bought the hotel in the 1970s. His collection of antiquarian books and rare Thomas Jefferson manuscripts is on display in the cozy, antiques-filled lobby. The hotel caters to Capitol Hill lawyers with amenities such as in-room snack baskets for all-night work sessions and a "law concierge" with information on law libraries and courts. The spacious suites feature galley kitchens and original artwork. ($250/www.thejeffersonwashingtondc.com)

THE INN AT IRVING PLACE, NEW YORK CITY: Smack in the middle of the bustling city exists a sleepy oasis overlooking Gramercy Park. The 12 cozy rooms in this 1834 brownstone feature marble fireplaces and Edith Wharton–era antiques, complemented by modern amenities such as high-speed Internet and access to the neighborhood New York Sports Club. ($325/www.innatirving.com)

CLIFT, SAN FRANCISCO: Philippe Starck channeled Alfred Hitchcock to design this Union Square fun house. A quick spin through the first floor—from the massive oversize French chair in the lobby to the soaring hallways filled with glass-and-metal furniture—just might give you a case of vertigo. The avant-garde design is also a dead giveaway that this is the work of Ian Schrager, the godfather of boutique hoteliers. The ground-floor surrealism is completely abandoned upstairs, where tranquil rooms are finished in soft ivories, grays, and a touch of lavender silk. ($300/www.clifthotel.com)

GRAVES 601, MINNEAPOLIS: Rooms at this ultramodern hotel tower come with 42-inch plasma TVs, etched-glass headboards, and "power showers" with five separate body jets. The Cosmos, on the first floor—Minnesota's only AAA Four Diamond restaurant—serves up gems like seared cinnamon-smoked squab and confit of sea bass with cauliflower risotto. In winter months, you'll appreciate that the hotel is connected to downtown by the Skyway, a 7-mile track of second-floor, glass-enclosed walkways. ($209/www.graves601hotel.com)

LONG-DISTANCE LOVE

SURVIVE YOUR LONG-DISTANCE RELATIONSHIP WITH THESE 11 TRICKS

BY CRISTINA GOYANES

When my boyfriend and I were "just friends" in college, I saw him at least once a day. But the urge to spend every waking moment with Mikel didn't hit me until 5 years later, when, as luck would have it, we spent every waking moment 200 miles apart. I was working in New York; he was in grad school in Maryland. Suddenly we were one of the four million American couples dating long distance. Married people do it, too—three million people live far from their spouses, according to Greg Guldner, MD, founder of the Center for the Study of Long Distance Relationships, an organization that tracks data on this phenomenon.

There were benefits: I hung with the girls, trained for a triathlon, and worked long after the building's central AC switched off for the night. Okay, so that sucked, but it scored me a promotion. Still, as nice as the copious me-time was, I wished Mikel and I lived in the same town—no one does the long-distance thing because it's fun. Military couples don't have a choice. Neither do those at the mercy of the job market. "In this tight economy, people take jobs farther away or accept transfers," Dr. Guldner says. And now that men and women are equally focused on their careers, both may be reluctant to quit their good gigs and relocate for a relationship, says Judith S. Wallerstein, PhD, coauthor of *The Good Marriage*.

Luckily, loving across state lines is easier than ever, thanks to tech candy like Treos, webcams, and videophones. But communication is just one relationship hurdle for the geographically challenged. (Hello! We're talking nooky deprivation here.) Help your

MILES BETWEEN LONG-DISTANCE PARTNERS, ON AVERAGE:

125

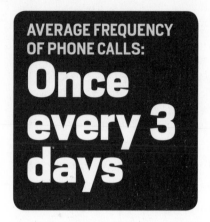

AVERAGE FREQUENCY OF PHONE CALLS:

Once every 3 days

relationship go the distance with these 11 love-saving strategies.

LONG-DISTANCE HURDLE: YOU'RE AN INSTA-COUPLE

You've been on only a few dates, but since you live so far apart, you're already sharing a toothbrush and spending whole weekends in bed.

PACE YOURSELF. It looks and feels like a relationship, but something's missing: intimacy. And not the kind you find between the sheets. "Bonding happens over time and creates deeper feelings," says Jackie Black, PhD, a couples coach in California. Rush in and you'll end up disillusioned. Keep first visits short and consider staying in a hotel. Once on the other's turf, go on dates just as if you lived close by.

AVOID ASSUMPTIONS. Don't presume anything about the relationship unless you've discussed it in depth—for example, that you are both monogamous and can lose the condom. "Remember, you're both putting your best foot forward," Wallerstein says. You don't really know each other yet.

LONG-DISTANCE HURDLE: WARMUP WOES

You hug him and think: "Who the hell is this guy?"

TAKE THE PRESSURE OFF. "You have to build closeness," Black says. The reentry phase can take an evening or a whole day. Watch *Lost,* cook dinner, or read the paper. These separate-but-together, everyday activities help reestablish your comfort level. If you've just started dating, the opposite applies. Go out to dinner when you arrive and reconnect at the table.

TAKE A SOLO BREAK. If you have a hard time transitioning to 24-hour togetherness, go for a run or take a shower—by yourself. "Solitude can be a nice break from the intensity of a reunion," Dr. Guldner says.

LONG-DISTANCE HURDLE: LONGING ISN'T LOVE

She's not there, and you want her like crazy. That means you're in love, right? Wrong.

KNOW THE DIFFERENCE. "When you don't see your partner every day, she becomes a reward to you," says Ian Kerner, PhD, a sex and relationships counselor in New York City. So how do you tell the difference

LENGTH OF AVERAGE CALL:

30 minutes

between loving her and just missing her? Pinpoint exactly what you miss most. If it's having someone to ride bikes or share dinner with, then it's coupledom you crave. But if you can name what makes her rare and lovable, then she's worth the cell phone bills.

LONG-DISTANCE HURDLE: IT'S ALL TALK, ALL THE TIME

When the bulk of your relationship consists of phone calls or e-mails, you eventually run out of things to say.

TELL HER WHAT YOU ATE FOR DINNER. "Sometimes couples feel the need for intense 'I love you' conversations," says Katheryn Maguire, PhD, assistant professor at Cleveland State University. But simple chitchat is the glue in a relationship. You learn more about her by asking what she had for breakfast than by only exchanging sweet nothings.

CALL AT ODD TIMES. Next time you're in the middle of dinner with friends, give her a ring. That way she's involved in your daily life, says Helen Fisher, PhD, author of *Why We Love*.

LONG-DISTANCE HURDLE: MISCOMMUNICATION

You're dealing with a major technology pitfall: Sometimes what you hear on the phone or read in an e-mail isn't what the other person means.

READ BETWEEN THE LINES. If you keep misunderstanding each other, hang up or log off for a while. You might need 20 minutes or the whole night to clear

AVERAGE TOTAL AMOUNT LONG-DISTANCE COUPLES SPEND A MONTH TO KEEP LOVE ALIVE:

$278

your head. When you return to the conversation, ask simple, unbiased questions, says Elayne Savage, PhD, a California relationships coach and author of *Breathing Room*. Her suggestion: "I heard you say [this]. Did you mean [this]?" Give her 5 minutes to make her case. Then take another 5 to express your points using sentences starting with "I," not "you."

INVEST IN TECH. Leave less to the imagination with a webcam, such as Live! Cam Voice with built-in microphone ($100/www.creative.com).

LONG-DISTANCE HURDLE: YOU NEED SEX!

Your sex life feels like the weather in India: drought, flood, then drought again. Which makes the secretary down the hall look better and better.

THINK ABOUT THE FUTURE. Most people in long-distance relationships see each other twice a month. But more important is knowing the ultimate goal. Assuming you both want to live in the same city, plan for it. Create a realistic timeline and you'll feel more secure in the relationship—and better able to resist temptation.

SHORTEN THE GAPS. Researchers at LaSalle University found that people in long-distance relationships who had some face-to-face contact within a 6-month period were more satisfied than those who had none. You have to be together—at least some of the time—to stay together.

DATING UP

SHE HIRED HIM. SHE COULD FIRE HIM. BUT WHY LET SUCH MINOR DETAILS GET IN THE WAY OF LOVE? LEARN FROM ONE GUY'S ADVENTURES DATING THE BOSS

PERCENTAGE OF US COMPANIES THAT HAVE A POLICY ON CO-WORKING COUPLES:

12

BY DAN BOVA

When it comes to women, I've never done anything remotely ballsy in my life. That is, until 6 years ago, when I flew in the face of everything that Michael Douglas and Demi Moore taught us in the movie *Disclosure:* I put the moves on my boss.

It all started when I was at the job interview. Maybe because she was cute, maybe because she was funny—or maybe because I was seriously light-headed from inhaling exhaust fumes at the bus station—but somewhere between discussing health benefits and 401(k) plans, I found myself falling for her. I know, I know; it was crazy. What was I thinking? Well for one thing, I was thinking that she was pretty damn good-looking. When the interview ended, a friend of mine who already worked there walked with me out of the building. I turned to her and said, "So, what's the deal with Lisa*?" My friend looked me dead in the eye and said, "Bova, don't even think about it. She is totally out of your league."

I took that advice—for the first few months, anyway. Then I got to know my boss better and realized she was a really sweet, funny person. And after a short time working together, I started to think that maybe we could be more than co-workers. We laughed at the same stuff in meetings, talked about the same stupid TV shows in the mornings. Why the hell not? I mean, yes, she was way out of my league. She was smarter, more successful, and, I assumed, didn't live in a crappy apartment with a gassy roommate and a cardboard box

---

*No names have been changed. There are no innocents to protect in this story.

PERCENTAGE OF WOMEN WHO'VE DATED THEIR BOSS:

15

PERCENTAGE OF MEN WHO'VE DONE IT:

10

that served as a dinner table like I did. But what did all of that matter? Wasn't romance about more than what kind of car you drove (or, in my case, what subway line you rode)? I decided to go for it, and the hard-core flirting commenced posthaste.

Whenever the office went out for a night of boozing, I'd find myself tap dancing, performing magic tricks, basically making an ass of myself to get the boss lady's attention. Sometimes she smiled. Sometimes (and this is a direct quote) she told me I was "annoying." But eventually it paid off.

About a year after we started working together, I finally made some serious headway. She had just bought an apart-

>> A MAN'S GUIDE POLL

So, Where'd You Meet?

Fantasy and reality don't always jibe when it comes to finding our one true love. A new poll asked men and women what they consider the best ways to meet a mate. Then the poll asked couples how they actually met. The answers mostly coincide, especially in the top spot: meeting through friends. But the reality of other meeting places, notably work, isn't so romantic. Here are the top five "best places" to meet, as ranked in the poll, followed by the real-world percentages.

WHAT WE THINK	REALITY SAYS
#1 Through friends	34%
#2. By chance	17%
#3. At a party, bar, or club	15%
#4. Online	3%
#5. At work	19%

ment, so I asked her if she could share some advice on navigating New York City's treacherous real estate waters. She wrote me an e-mail saying, "Sure. Want to talk about it at lunch? Or drinks?" "Holy Jesus," I thought, "my cute boss wants to get drinks with me!"

So we went out. And it was fun. It was a blast. . . . Okay, it was incredibly awkward. Should I pay for the drinks even though I make one-tenth of her salary? Would she fire me if I bored her to death? It was a little bit stressful—especially at the end of the night. I walked her to her apartment, and she asked me if I wanted to come up for coffee. We had never clearly established what exactly was going on that night. Was this about real

PERCENTAGE OF CANOODLING COUPLES WHO'VE TRYSTED ON THE JOB:
23

NUMBER OF WORKPLACE ROMANCES THAT RESULT IN MARRIAGE:
1 in 5

estate . . . or something more? I panicked. What should I say? "I need to get home to Brooklyn" surely wasn't what I should have said, but unfortunately that's what came out of my mouth. (Now do you believe the part about me not being a player?)

Clearly I had blown it—or so I thought. A few playful (read: desperate) e-mails later the next day, we had a second real estate seminar planned. We went out for drinks and in the middle of it, Lisa looked at me and said, "I know this is going to sound weird, but is this a date?" I managed to squeak out a "Yes?" and away our secret office romance went.

Sure, it was risky for both of us—Lisa could have fired me, I could have claimed sexual harassment. If we got busted, she could have lost her professional credibility. But that's also part of what made it exciting. And though I'd never had a "thing" for authority figures, I have to admit it added to the thrill.

Company policy didn't officially forbid filling a co-worker's toner after hours, but common sense said it was a bad idea. We worried that our co-workers wouldn't be able to deal if they found out. The thing was that we

PERCENTAGE OF MEN WHO HAVE HAD AN OFFICE ROMANCE:

42

had no problem compartmentalizing our dual lives. At work what she said went; after work I had equal authority in deciding between Chinese and Thai. And the more we dated, the more the potential consequences seemed worth it. The thrill and danger that made our relationship initially exciting was replaced by love. We successfully kept things hush-hush for about 8 months, until one day I walked into the office and every head spun in my direction. An intern had spotted us holding hands on the way to brunch over the weekend and blabbed. Damn you unpaid, college-credit-receiving laborers!

People were cool about it once they knew, but I could tell that some wondered if any of their confidential lunchtime bitching had made it to Lisa's ears. Now that everyone knew about us, she felt self-conscious every time she needed to talk to me about work stuff. By that point our relationship was way more important to both of us than our jobs. So rather than risk any weirdness in the office messing things up outside the office, I found a new job.

Any regrets? Today, as we sit in our living room (oh yeah, we've been married for 4 years now) playing with our 2-year-old son, Henry (oh yeah, we procreated), I have just one: A $1 million settlement for sexual harassment would have come in handy when Henry heads to college.

FAN THE FLAMES

A new romance can fizzle fast if it's not carefully tended. Here's how to make sure the spark lasts past that first passion-packed week.

FORGET THE RULES

Don't let a lost weekend together be followed by a week of radio silence. "There's a momentum to the courtship process, and it will take off at a pretty high velocity," says Ian Kerner, PhD, a sex and relationships counselor in New York City. "Even if you don't see each other often at first, stay on her radar." Instead of swamping her with daily phone calls, strike up e-mail banter or check in with text messages—and let her set the pace. "Doubling up on unreturned calls or e-mails just seems desperate," says Kerner.

PACK UP YOUR PAST

There's only one way to sum up past loves: quickly. Have a 2-second summary of your former relationship at the ready—"We had fun, but it just didn't work" will suffice—in case she probes. Anything more and you're inviting overanalysis. "Bemoaning a relationship that soured shows you're still fixated on that failure," says Lisa Clampitt, founder of the Matchmaking Institute. "And boasting about a great past relationship can seem like an attempt to pump up your own self-image."

TAKE IT SLOW

Unhealthy codependencies are established early on. "A relationship is about extending our personal boundaries, but it should be a gradual process," Kerner says. So let her keep a toothbrush at your house if she wants to. But encourage her to make her own plans and keep her own friends—and do the same yourself. "It's easy to get sucked in at the beginning, with the rush of a fresh start. But the sooner you depend on each other for everything, the faster the relationship can burn out," says Clampitt.

>> He Said/She Said

DATING IQ

What's your favorite type of restaurant for a first date?

HE SAID		SHE SAID
30%	Hole-in-the-wall	32%
36%	Midlevel Italian	28%
26%	Familiar chain	22%
8%	Expensive bistro	8%

What signals do you give off if you're interested?

82%	Making eye contact	69%
53%	Leaning in close	65%
66%	Asking questions	56%
21%	Sharing my food	20%

What's the worst dinner-date turn-off?

11%	Chewing loudly	20%
40%	Checking cell phone	18%
15%	Looking around	16%
6%	Bragging	15%
9%	Talking about the ex	17%

If a woman spends a lot of time in the restroom, she . . .

37%	Wants to escape	43%
15%	Has a small bladder	29%
48%	Wants to impress	28%

SIZE UP THE COMPETITION

You have a great gal. So great, in fact, that she attracts packs of men who try to capture her attention or, worse, coax her out of her clothes. They could be platonic friends. Or they could be interlopers, scourges bent on emasculating and circumventing you. What to do?

"Everything starts with having ground rules, open communication, and strategies for how to proceed," says Janice R. Levine, PhD, a psychologist in Lexington, Massachusetts. Either blowing your lid or turning a blind eye could create more problems than addressing the situation head-on.

The following tips will help you suss out a suspect and stand your ground without devolving into a raging, soon-to-be-single maniac. Read on: Your love life could depend on it.

THE OVERLY INTERESTED BOSS

WORRY WHEN . . . she's focused on pleasing him, not doing her job.

NOT WHEN . . . he's a kindhearted mentor. His motives could be sincere, and if she's happy at work, she'll be happy at home, says Jeffrey Bernstein, PhD, a psychologist and the author of *Why Can't You Read My Mind?*

YOUR MOVE: Lead with concern for her, not your issues. If she thinks you have an agenda, she'll become defensive and fail to see any negatives, just to prove you wrong. Say, "It seems your boss is really helping you. How's that going?"

THE EX SHE'S STILL FRIENDS WITH

WORRY WHEN . . . they talk frequently and secretly. Regular contact sends up flares. Covertness fires a cannon.

NOT WHEN . . . she has a once-a-year, 15-minute phone call. There's a lot of history—some good.

YOUR MOVE: Calmly say, "I have a problem with the relationship because I don't understand it. Can you tell me what it does for you?" suggests Jackie

Jaye Brandt, MFT, a psychotherapist in Universal City, California. You're not being invasive, you're just gathering information. An ultimatum, however, leads to resentment—or abandonment. Be ready to walk out the door if she picks him.

THE EX SHE STILL PINES FOR

WORRY WHEN . . . she drops his name in subtle or obvious comparisons to you. If he initiated the breakup, there's a big chance she's holding on to the fantasy.

NOT WHEN . . . it might be just fond memories, so the threat could be all in your head.

YOUR MOVE: Say, "I just need some reassurance here." She should respond

>> He Said/She Said

WHAT DO YOU THINK ABOUT PLATONIC FRIENDSHIPS?

Do you think platonic friendships really exist?

HE SAID		SHE SAID
57%	Yes	71%
13%	No	11%
30%	Sure, if they're hot	18%

Have you thought about sex with platonic friends?

46%	Yes, all of them	11%
47%	Yes, but only a few	55%
7%	None	34%

Is your partner's best friend sexually attractive?

60%	Yes	24%
40%	No	76%

Who is more likely to cross the friendship boundary?

70%	Me	25%
30%	My partner	75%

definitively that you're her man, Levine says. If she pauses, follow up with, "I'm not trying to control you. I just want to be with someone who knows what she wants." She needs to think it's something to fix. If she doesn't, walk.

THE HANDS-ON PERSONAL TRAINER

WORRY WHEN . . . she spills intimate details about his life. Chances are, the sharing goes both ways. "The relationship should be friendly, not familiar," says Rita DeMaria, PhD, a marriage and family therapist in the Philadelphia area.

NOT WHEN . . . he's just pumping her up. It's his job to give her encouragement and attention.

YOUR MOVE: Once again, share your discomfort and watch her response. If she's open and says, "I didn't realize that," she's not drinking in the man's attention, and she respects your feelings. If she's defensive, she might be guzzling it, so back off for a few weeks and see how she deals with it. It's up to you how far you push.

THE SMITTEN SUITOR

WORRY WHEN . . . she's ignoring the situation because she hates conflict. That's bad for your relationship, because this issue will recur.

NOT WHEN . . . she's simply working at her own pace to let her admirer down easy.

YOUR MOVE: If you've given her pace a chance, let her know you're uncomfortable. Offer to help. If she allows you, meet the guy: Put your arm around her and introduce yourself as her boyfriend. That should be enough. If it's not, say, "I think it would be best if you limited contact with her," Levine says. Use restrained strength, not tough-guy tactics.

ENJOY THE HEAT, WITHOUT GETTING BURNED

Summers are made for the sort of passionate yet casual romance that burns bright and fizzles out just before things get too serious. "The season has a natural beginning and end to it," says April Masini, author of *Date Out of Your League,* "and the heat conjures up all kinds of steamy possibilities." Here's how to make the most of the hottest season.

GO WITH THE FLOW

"Flings let both of you retain your independence more than in a normal relationship," says Nancy Pina, author of *The Right Relationship Can Happen.* "If she really thinks it's short-term, she won't call you every day, won't talk about the future as much, and will make plans without you." You, of course, should do the same.

SET SMART BOUNDARIES

If you harp on the expiration date—"Just so you know, this isn't anything serious"—your message will backfire. "No woman wants to be reminded that you're not in it to win it," says Logan Levkoff, PhD, a sex educator in New York City. Give her subtle signals that you're flying solo: Go stag to a wedding or invite a buddy when your parents come for dinner.

MAKE THE MOST OF IT

"You have to harness the heat if you want something memorable," says Levkoff. So seduce her on your rooftop. Or have sex in the woods. "She'll feel safe because you're not just a one-night stand, and she won't feel as if she's ruining a long-term relationship by being kinky."

GO OUT WITH A BANG

She's leaving for another city or you're moving on? Instead of letting the relationship fizzle or pulling away from her emotionally, charge through right to the end. "It gives you both a sense of closure and makes it easier to move on," Pina says.

TEST YOURSELF

Who can predict whether a relationship will flourish? Scientists, that's who. Those who study couples know that lasting qualities are not always the same elements that first caught your attention. Is she a one-date wonder or your dream woman? Find out:

1. HOW SIMILAR IS SHE TO YOU?

    A. Not at all: We're polar opposites of each other.

    B. Somewhat: Our differences aren't deal breakers.

    C. Are you kidding me? We're like clones.

Dating your female clone wears thin, a new study from the University of Geneva found. Men who date women with "ideal" qualities are more likely to stay with them than those who date people similar to themselves, says lead author Marcel Zentner, PhD. The lesson? Approach women who embody your ideal characteristics—physically, emotionally, and mentally. The payoff could outweigh the potential rejection.

2. YOUR TYPICAL PHONE CONVERSATION RESEMBLES . . .

    A. An interrogation: She fires off questions, I just try to keep up.

    B. A soliloquy: She pontificates, I yawn.

    C. A tennis match: We can volley all night.

"Telling you every detail about her life or grilling you about yours won't necessarily bring you closer," says John Badalament, EdM, a relationship coach. "The relationship can become old quickly," agrees Terrence Real, author of *The New Rules of Marriage*. E-mail can help you figure out a match: If she can convey opinions and feelings in writing, she's open and comfortable with you. The more insightful her questions, the better the potential.

3. ON YOUR LAST DATE, YOU . . .

    A. Went to a gallery opening and a tapas joint.

    B. Watched a movie and ate takeout.

C. Woke up the next morning with a splitting headache and no recollection of the night before.

Couples who party hard tend to hit it off early but have a short shelf life, says Real. Quiet nights can curb conversation and become a rut. Seek out challenges by dragging her to a work function to meet your colleagues or asking her to take rock-climbing lessons. How well do you ad-lib as a team without a script?

4. WHEN SHE'S ANGRY, SHE . . .

A. Screams: She blows up, we fight, it's over.

B. Sulks: She gives me the silent treatment or goes passive-aggressive until I blow my top.

C. Lets it slide: She goes out with her girlfriends.

Women who fight it out tend to make better partners than those who don't, says Ian Kerner, PhD, a sex and relationships counselor in New York City. New studies confirm that avoiding arguments results in "out-of-control" emotions and long-term anger, especially in women. Call her out; it's better than her keeping it bottled up.

SCORECARD

1. A = 3, B = 2, C = 1

2. A = 2, B = 1, C = 3

3. A = 3, B = 2, C = 1

4. A = 3, B = 1, C = 2

4–6 POINTS: She's oil, you're water; at some point, you'll probably separate.

7–9 POINTS: She's great, but better not get her name tattooed on your arm just yet.

10–12 POINTS: Marry her, or someone else will.

DO SOME RESTAURANT RECON

Tune in to the right signals during a dinner date and you'll satisfy more than just your palate. "Romantic meals allow for powerful courtship exchanges," says Heather Trexler Remoff, PhD, author of *Sexual Choice*. "Women drop vital clues during a meal—read them right and dessert could be at her place." Your guide:

SHE GIVES YOU HER UNDIVIDED ATTENTION

If she snags the seat facing the wall, odds are she's there to focus on you. So give her something to look at. "Women are far more skilled at interpreting body language," says David Givens, PhD, a nonverbal-communication expert in Spokane, Washington, and author of *Love Signals*. Display confidence and masculinity with open palms or steepled fingers, a "showcase of mastery and thoughtfulness," says Givens. If she chooses to face the room instead, watch her eyes: Is she easily distracted?

SHE DRIES YOU OFF

If you spill a drink, loudly drop a fork, or fumble the bread, watch her reaction. "If she turns away, embarrassed, or does nothing at all, she's suppressing her maternal instincts for a reason: She has no connection to you," says Givens. But if she lends a helping hand, there could be chemistry. Letting her help will strengthen feelings of attachment.

SHE TASTES YOUR TENDERLOIN

Offer her a bite of your entrée. If she takes the fork from you and brushes the food onto her plate, hit the brakes, Casanova. "When you offer her a bite, look her in the eyes and move the fork slowly toward her mouth," says Sandor Gardos, PhD, a sex therapist and the founder of www.mypleasure.com. That way she can refuse gracefully if she's not ready to be fed. "In my research, I've never known a woman to sleep with a man who didn't first feed her," says Remoff. Bonus points: She offers a bite back.

SHE USES COMPLIMENTS AS CONVERSATION STARTERS

Women yearn for kudos, but on a first date, keep compliments confined to her jewelry or clothes. "She spent plenty of time making those choices, so she'll appreciate your attention to detail," says Givens. If she starts telling a story about the earrings or, even better, returns the compliment, it shows she values your opinion. A halfhearted "thank you" may be a brush-off.

SHE GRILLS YOU

Throw out a random question—about Maoist rebels or her high-school prom—and see where it leads. "If she finds a way to work it back to you, that's a great sign," says Gardos. Women approach dates as fact-finding missions, so thoughtfully answer any personal questions beyond the obligatory, and reciprocate with inquiries of your own.

SHE GUSHES OVER THE CHOCOLATE VOLCANO

Does she snack stoically on her dessert, or does she close her eyes and moan softly, savoring the velvety texture? "This means she appreciates the sensual, hedonistic side of life," says Gardos. "She's just had an orgasm on her tongue," agrees Laura Corn, author of *101 Nights of Grrreat Sex*. "Piggyback off that."

THE HONEST TRUTH ABOUT WOMEN FROM OUR LOVELY NEIGHBOR

Is Sunday brunch a good first-date idea?

Here's what my friends would assume about a guy who invited them out for pancakes: (1) You must be looking for love, since a hookup is pretty hard to pull off that early in the day. (2) You're over your wild phase and into cuddling on the couch. (3) You're mature enough to face an awkward social situation completely sober. All are appealing qualities to someone who's ready to settle down. But to a woman who likes the thrill of meeting after dark and tasting vodka on a new acquaintance's tongue, a brunch date might seem a little boring. And maybe even insulting—as in, "What, I'm not hot enough to merit dinner?"

My girlfriend and I have friends of the opposite sex, and we both get jealous. How do we keep the peace?

The only thing that's worked for me regarding jealousy is to sit down as a couple and acknowledge what trips your wires. Maybe neither of you minds if the other sees a hot friend for coffee, but you both get on edge if the meeting involves late-night drinks. Once you know what invokes the green-eyed monster, you simply make a pact not to go there. It takes a lot of sacrifice (what's more fun than getting wasted and flirting with a friend of the opposite sex?), but it beats having a vase hurled at your head.

My girlfriend's friend is hitting on me. Should I say something?

God, no. In keeping with her duplicitous personality, she'll probably swear that it was you who hit on her. (Rent the movie *Vanilla Sky* if you need to be reminded just how vindictive a scorned woman can be.) Your safest option is to scramble. When she slithers into a room, walk to the other side. And, if you get trapped talking to her, make sure the only words that pass from your lips to her ears are, "I'm not interested." Without your attention, it shouldn't be long before she grows bored and starts working someone else's man.

My girlfriend insists on knowing where I am 24–7, but is secretive about her own plans. What's up?

Probably one of two things: Either she's been two-timed by an ex and is now plagued by cheating paranoia, or she's up to no good. If it's the former, reassure her that you have nothing to hide. Step up the frequency of your calls and e-mails, say "I love you" every time, and introduce her to your friends as your "one and only." But the fact that your girlfriend keeps you in the dark about her own whereabouts makes me worry that she's scamming you. Until you're sure you can trust her, I suggest you continue using condoms.

How do I convince my girlfriend to dress sexier?

Give her more opportunities to get all dolled up. Take her out to the occasional swanky restaurant, velvet-rope club—any event where stilettos are the norm. Being surrounded by glam women will bring out her competitive edge (we all have one, no matter how deeply it's buried under a turtleneck) and motivate her to fill her closet with tiny evening dresses and low-cut tops. Manipulative? A little. But it'll work.

READ HER WARDROBE

Some women can't help looking hot. In a new study, researchers found that women unconsciously dress more attractively as they reach ovulation. UCLA researchers took photos of women at low fertility and high fertility, and judges deemed the photo at ovulation more attractive 60 percent of the time. The women tended to wear more fashionable clothes and show more skin at ovulation time, says lead researcher Martie Haselton, MD. "Fertility is not as concealed as we thought," she says. "Women are unconsciously considering their mating options." Got birth control?

TIME IT RIGHT

News from the sexual test kitchen: It may not be true that when it comes to arousal, men are microwaves and women are slow-cookers. A new study published in the *Journal of Sexual Medicine* suggests that physically, women reach peak arousal just as fast as men do. Scientists at McGill University had 58 people watch movie clips ranging from *The Best Bits of Mr. Bean* to pornography. Researchers focused a thermal-imaging camera on participants' genitals to measure body heat during the flicks. Increased blood flow to the genitals boosted the temperature at the same rate for both sexes, says Tuuli Kukkonen, a PhD candidate and coauthor of the study. Next time you start fooling around, remember: It takes about 10 minutes for her (and you) to reach peak arousal, says the study.

KISS TO MAKE IT BETTER

Spend a little time in the sack to help clear your sinuses. Kissing may reduce allergic reactions and help fight infection. In a recent Japanese study, researchers measured blood levels of immunoglobulin E (IgE), an antibody that can start an allergic reaction. They checked people with pollen, dust-mite, and latex allergies before and after the participants kissed someone for 30 minutes. At the end of the make-out session, the study subjects' levels of IgE had dropped 40 percent. Researchers think that kissing reduces the allergic response by increasing the production of Th1 cytokines, white blood cells that have been shown to halt IgE production. To make the most of a lip-lock, turn on soft music; the participants were serenaded throughout the study, which has previously been shown to improve immune function.

Bonus tip: Not just any form of affection will have a positive effect on allergies. Couples who hugged experienced none of the immune-boosting benefits that their kissing counterparts did.

SMOOCH YOUR BLUES GOODBYE

Smooching with your love in public may help you lick stress and mood disorders. In a survey of 3,004 people, couples who kissed frequently in nonsexual situations were eight times more likely to be stress- and depression-free than those who never kissed outside of the bedroom. Researchers at the Berman Center, a sexual-function clinic in Chicago that conducted the poll, say frequent contact reinforces the bond between partners, which, in turn, may help people deal with stress and avoid depression.

SAVE A FORTUNE ON THERAPY

Is great sex enough? Maybe. A study of 387 married couples at the University of Tennessee found that satisfying sex can compensate for the negative effects of poor communication. Great communication, however, results in marital bliss regardless of whether the sex is good or not.

PART 4

ENHANCE SEX

Eighty percent of men want to take her to the peak every time. Yet only 50 percent of women will climax through intercourse alone. This, of course, presents a challenge we know you're up for. We talked with dozens of experts to put together this section of tricks and techniques to make your sex life hotter than ever.

First you'll learn 15 things you probably don't know about your penis. Then a nationally known sex therapist reveals how to have your top five sexual fantasies fulfilled. You'll discover a woman's secrets to avoiding common bedroom mistakes made by men. And you'll learn how to make the most of the sex toy at the end of your arm. That will hopefully lead you to making good use of our sex position playbook. With any luck, this will all culminate in the best sex of your life!

AN OWNER'S MANUAL

15 THINGS YOU DON'T KNOW ABOUT YOUR PENIS

BY MIKE ZIMMERMAN

1. **SMOKING CAN SHORTEN YOUR PENIS BY AS MUCH AS A CENTIMETER.**
   Erections are all about good blood flow, and lighting up calcifies blood
   vessels, stifling erectile circulation. So even if you don't care all that
   much about your lungs or dying young, spare the li'l guy.

2. **DOCTORS CAN NOW GROW SKIN FOR BURN VICTIMS USING THE FORESKINS
   OF CIRCUMCISED INFANTS.** One foreskin can produce 23,000 square
   meters, which would be enough to tarp every Major League infield with
   human flesh.

3. **AN ENLARGED PROSTATE GLAND CAN CAUSE BOTH ERECTILE
   DYSFUNCTION AND PREMATURE EJACULATION.** If you have an
   unexplained case of either, your doctor's looking forward to checking
   your prostate. Even if you're not.

4. **THE AVERAGE MALE ORGASM LASTS 6 SECONDS.** Women get 23 seconds.
   Which means if women were really interested in equality, they'd make
   sure we have four orgasms for every one of theirs.

5. **THE OLDEST KNOWN SPECIES WITH A PENIS IS A HARD-SHELLED SEA CREATURE CALLED *COLYMBOSATHON ECPLECTICOS.*** That's Greek for "amazing swimmer with large penis." Which officially supplants Buck Naked as the best porn name, ever.

6. **CIRCUMCISED FORESKIN CAN BE RECONSTRUCTED.** Movable skin on the shaft of the penis is pulled toward the tip and set in place with tape. Later, doctors apply plastic rings, caps, and weights. Years can pass until complete coverage is attained. . . . Okay, we'll shut up now.

7. **ONLY ONE MAN IN 400 IS FLEXIBLE ENOUGH TO GIVE HIMSELF ORAL PLEASURE.** It's estimated, however, that all 400 have given it their best shot at some point.

8. **THERE ARE TWO TYPES OF PENISES.** One kind expands and lengthens when becoming erect (a grower). The other appears big most of the time, but doesn't get much bigger after achieving erection (a show-er).

9. **AN INTERNATIONAL *MEN'S HEALTH* SURVEY REPORTS THAT 79 PERCENT OF MEN HAVE GROWERS, 21 PERCENT HAVE SHOW-ERS.**

10. **GERMAN RESEARCHERS SAY THE AVERAGE INTERCOURSE LASTS 2 MINUTES, 50 SECONDS, YET WOMEN PERCEIVE IT AS LASTING 5 MINUTES, 30 SECONDS.** Are we that good or that bad?

11. **TURNS OUT SIZE DOES MATTER: THE LONGER YOUR PENIS, THE BETTER "SEMEN DISPLACEMENT" YOU'LL ACHIEVE WHEN HAVING SEX WITH A WOMAN FLUSH WITH COMPETING SPERM.** That's according to researchers at the State University of New York, who used artificial phalluses (ahem) to test the "scooping" mechanism of the penis's coronal ridge. Next up: curing cancer.

12. **THE PENIS THAT'S BEEN ENJOYED BY THE MOST WOMEN COULD BE THAT OF KING FATEFEHI OF TONGA, WHO SUPPOSEDLY DEFLOWERED 37,800 WOMEN BETWEEN THE YEARS 1770 AND 1784—THAT'S ABOUT SEVEN VIRGINS A DAY.** Go ahead, say it: It's good to be king.

13. **BETTER-LOOKING MEN MAY HAVE STRONGER SPERM.** Spanish researchers showed women photos of guys who had good, average, and lousy sperm—and told them to pick the handsomest men. The women chose the best sperm producers most often.

14. **NO BRAIN IS NECESSARY FOR EJACULATION.** That order comes from the spinal cord. Finding a living vessel for said ejaculation, however, takes hours of careful thought and, often, considerable amounts of alcohol.

15. **THE MOST COMMON CAUSE OF PENILE RUPTURE: VIGOROUS MASTURBATION.** Some risks are just worth taking.

YOUR TOP 5 FANTASIES, FULFILLED

JUST ASK. THE SEX OF YOUR DREAMS IS JUST A QUESTION AWAY

BY IAN KERNER, PhD

What's the best sex you've ever had?

There's a question that gets people thinking. (I'll pause here while you ponder it.) It's a line I use often in my work as a sex therapist and writer.

Since I became an author, I can't walk down the street without being stopped by someone: the UPS man, my building super, my upstairs neighbor—heck, I may know more about what turns on the guy behind the counter at my deli than his wife does. I've listened carefully to every man who would talk to me about sex—hundreds of them around the country.

It was all research for my book *He Comes Next* (the natural sequel to *She Comes First*, which was a bit more fun to research, since it involved talking to lots of women about what gives them pleasure). My best-sex-ever question unlocks doors to memories, to taboos, to the contours of a man's sexual landscape—what turns him on. More important, it often reveals what's missing from his sex life now.

Not only do I hear about the best sex guys ever had, I hear about the best sex they never had—experiences they've always fantasized about, or maybe experienced just one glorious time, and can't get out of their heads. Though they're happy to tell me, a virtual stranger, they're often afraid to ask their partners for fear of offending or seeming weird. Public sex, threesomes, videotaping, domination—I get all the details, while the women in their lives hear nothing.

But it's easier to open up than you may think. It starts with a "lovemap," a term coined in 1980 by John Money, PhD, of Johns Hopkins University, to describe "the sexual template expressed in every individual's erotic fantasies and practices." This lovemap informs your likes, dislikes, fantasies, and fears.

Great sex is about exploration and discovery, using each other's map. It's like finding buried treasure. Savvy?

The trick is in the asking. So I went back to a bunch of the women I interviewed for *She Comes First* and asked them what a man should say, or do, to get the sex he wants. Here's the resulting list of general principles and specific lessons. With these, the best sex you've ever had is still in your future.

START IN THE SHALLOW END

You have to ease your way into a fantasy. Acclimate her first. Here's something from my files from a 28-year-old woman named Jenny: "My boyfriend really wanted to have sex outdoors—like on the beach. I was reluctant, but he didn't pressure me. In fact, he did the opposite: He got me turned on about being a little exhibitionistic. First he would whisper sexy things in my ear when we were out at dinner with friends, or caress my leg under the table. Next it was my idea to go to a club without wearing any panties and fool around in a dark hallway, then continue the action on the cab ride home. Now I have my own fantasy: a quickie in an elevator. Beats sand in the crotch."

THE LESSON: A fantasy starts as an idea. Plant it in her mind, then let it take root. Not only did Jenny's boyfriend not pressure her, he let her make the fantasy her own. If you're nervous, tell her you had a wild dream about her, then play coy: Make her pry it out of you. You may find that she's extremely interested (and has had her own fantasies). Presenting your fantasy as a dream avoids making her feel like she isn't satisfying you. She can't blame you for having a sexy dream about her.

TALK BEFORE TAPING

Before we get to the exciting stuff, a quick lesson in sexual science. There are two common categories of sexual arousal: reflex-based and psychogenic. The former is stimulation through physical touch: Rub here to activate. Psychogenic refers to mental stimulation and other sensory stimuli—from thinking sexy thoughts to seeing a miniskirt to smelling that perfume. Most

NUMBER OF WOMEN WHO SAID THIS MIDDLE-OF-THE-DAY E-MAIL TURNED THEM ON: "I JUST REALIZED HOW MUCH I LOVE YOU. HAD TO TELL YOU":

9 out of 10

relationships start out in a psychogenic mode (everything is new!) and gradually become reflex-based. And, too often, boring.

Scheduled sex can be a good thing for busy couples, but it can also represent the worst of reflex-based sex, a kind of forced sexuality. The key is to add psychogenic stimuli. This is where a fantasy again can help. First, enjoy talking about it.

"My boyfriend really wanted to make a sex tape," one woman told me. "At first I thought no way, but then he told me about the scenarios he wanted to film, and it was really sexy stuff. He had this whole kidnapper/abductee thing, and we got so turned on just talking about it, we didn't need the costumes or camera—although we did make use of some of his old neckties."

THE LESSON: Arouse her mind, and her body will follow. After years as a sex therapist, I've found that people don't get excited over making sex tapes because they want to sit down later and watch themselves in all their sweaty, hairy glory. They like it because exhibitionism and voyeurism are two of the most popular types of fantasy on both men's and women's lists. In my research, I've concluded that there's a little bit of both in us all, and it doesn't take much to turn us on.

One guy said the key to convincing his girlfriend to make a sex tape was "giving her control over the wardrobe. I handed her my Amex card and told her to buy an outfit that made her feel sexy and comfortable, starting with the lingerie." That's an inspired move, and she gets to keep the clothes.

BONUS TIP: Offer to tape without hitting the "record" button—the camera's mere presence can be exciting. Flip the camera's LCD screen around for an occasional glimpse, or plug it into the TV so you're on-screen. That way you're on display but not being recorded. The thrill of this audition could lead to recording later.

MAKE THAT THREESOME HAPPEN

This fantasy has become a pop-culture cliché, one that's more often talked about than actually acted upon. But threesomes do happen, and I have the notes to prove it.

Said Angela, 32, "This guy kept talking about how hot it would be to have sex with two women, and I felt like, "What's wrong with me, am I not good enough on my own?" It really pissed me off. It was all about him, and the fantasy seemed totally selfish. Then I started seeing this really nice guy, and he told me he had a threesome fantasy. I thought, "Oh no, here we go again." But when I asked him why, he told me how beautiful I was and how sexy it would be to see me so turned on by another woman, and how much he loved the idea of two sets of hands on my body at once. Well, when he put it that way, I liked the idea, too. He made it all about me; not just in words, but also in action. And it was a great experience."

THE LESSON: Make sure she's the star of your fantasy, especially if it involves a supporting cast member. This is a sensitive issue with some women, so make sure everything is clear beforehand. As one 28-year-old man told me, "My girlfriend said she was willing to have a three-way, but I didn't want her to do it for me. I wanted her to do it with me. I told her she could back out and that I loved her no matter what, and she really appreciated that. Then she gave it the thumbs-up. Man, did she ever."

INCLUDE HER

Sounds simple, right? But it doesn't come naturally for guys who, let's face it, are used to doing certain things on their own: choosing porn, buying her lingerie, going to a strip club. Make her part of the process. It makes her think, which is half the battle.

> NUMBER OF WOMEN WHO SAID THIS MIDDLE-OF-THE-DAY E-MAIL TURNED THEM ON: "WHAT'S YOUR RECORD FOR ORGASMS? I WANT TO BREAK IT":
>
> # 3 out of 10

"It used to drive me crazy that guys are so into porn," said Heather, 26. "I always felt like I was in competition with porn stars and their bodies. But my current boyfriend said it would just be something fun to do together, and we went to the video store.

"In all honesty, I was kind of curious. I can't remember the movie we picked, *Hannah Does Her Sisters* or something like that. I do remember we laughed at it, but then tried some of the moves and positions. Now Friday night is our sexy-movie night, and it's really kept our relationship hot."

THE LESSON: Give her a chance to change her mind about porn. She literally may not know what she's missing. Mention this bit of science, if you think it'll help: A study at the Washington University school of medicine in St. Louis measured brain-wave activity of 264 women as they viewed erotic imagery. The conclusion: Women have responses as strong as those seen in men. My own research supports this—many women tell me privately that they enjoy porn, at least if it's well made. But I find that women have to feel comfortable in order to overcome societal taboos that keep them from admitting they might enjoy it. If she's still resistant, suggest watching a sex-education video together. The couples shown are not as intimidating as those in porn. And continuing education can be a wonderful thing; the take-home tests are really fun—no grading as long as you complete the assignment.

LET HER TAKE OVER

If you think you have a creative mind, wait till you hear what women are thinking about. "Act out my fantasy? It would be impossible," one woman told me. "I'd need a time machine and a guy with a 12-inch tongue." But it's fun to give her the opportunity to take the lead, especially when her fantasies involve things like tying you up and teasing you into exquisite oblivion.

I was surprised to find that nearly all the men I spoke with for *He Comes Next* had a fantasy of being dominated. I don't mean whips and chains—but simply letting a woman take charge. She's probably watched *Sex and the City;* give her a chance to turn some of that attitude into action.

"Exploring a fantasy is all about making a woman feel that she's not a freaky pervert for having them," Doug, 31, told me. "My wife is really into Paris and French culture, so I took her out for an amazing French dinner and then pulled out a book of erotica by Anaïs Nin later, when we were in bed. Let's just say Paris was burning."

THE LESSON: You're not the only one with fantasies. So encourage her to share hers. A study by the University of Vermont shows that nearly 25 percent of people feel guilty about their fantasies. No wonder it's so hard for us to talk about them.

NUMBER OF WOMEN WHO SAID THIS MIDDLE-OF-THE-DAY E-MAIL TURNED THEM ON: "CAN'T WORK. KEEP THINKING OF HOW GREAT YOU LOOK WHEN YOU LAUGH":

9 out of 10

I can also tell you, based on my clinical experience, that women need to be completely relaxed to enjoy sex. Brain scans of women during sexual arousal have shown that the areas of the brain that process fear, anxiety, and emotion nearly shut down. She needs to let go of anxiety to reach orgasm.

So do as the man above did—introduce a fantasy while she's deep in her comfort zone. You could have the best sex of your life.

THE DOS AND DON'TS

BE HER DO-RIGHT MAN BY FOLLOWING ONE WOMAN'S GUIDE
TO COMMON BEDROOM MISTAKES MADE BY MEN
WITH, OF COURSE, GENTLE CORRECTIONS

BY SARAH MILLER

You know how public pools post lists of unacceptable behavior? (Don't run, don't dive, don't vomit a New York strip steak and a bottle of cabernet franc into our brand-new filtration system.) Be assured that this is the last time I will ever liken my vagina to a public pool, but I've always thought how great it would be to post something similar in my own bedroom.

Look, we love that you love having sex with us, and we love having sex with you, too. But sometimes you do things that we don't like. Weird things. Things that you think are going to make us groan with gratitude and pleasure but really make us want to roll over and turn on the TV.

Luckily, these mistakes generally result not from lack of skill but from wrong information. You can easily unlearn them. Remember: I probably know what I like better than you do.

And if I had a bedroom sign, this is how it might read.

DO NOT ASK, "WHAT DO YOU LIKE?" the first time we have sex. It's our third date. Okay, so maybe it's only the second, or maybe we just met in an elevator. At any rate, we're making out. Pants are coming off, eyes are smoldering. You ask this question and,

> NUMBER OF WOMEN WHO SAID THE THIRD-DATE CONVERSATIONAL TACTIC OF A MAN ASKING HOW HER CAREER IS GOING MADE THEM THINK "WE'RE REALLY CLICKING":
>
> # 8 out of 10

bam . . . the magic is gone. First, I am embarrassed. I may have been ready to have sex, but not so up for talking about it! Second, I feel pressured to provide a provocative answer, something involving toys or systematic humiliation, but the only thing I can think of to say is, "Well, Steve, I suppose I like manual and oral stimulation followed by intercourse resulting in my eventual orgasm." Finally, I am annoyed. Are you trying to sound sexy, wild, open to anything? Because if you are, won't I eventually discover that?

DO ASK QUESTIONS LATER. Questions help an ongoing sexual relationship move forward. They slow a new one down.

DO NOT STICK YOUR TONGUE IN MY EAR. The innocent, unfortunate ear (a) is a semidiscreet spot, (b) is a hole, and (c) has folds. For these reasons, it has been mistakenly identified as a major erogenous zone. This is one of the great misperceptions in the history of Western civilization. Too many men work according to the metaphor that her ear is the fragrant soil of the French forest, and you are a truffle hound. Put yourself on a short leash.

DO TREAD LIGHTLY. I'm not saying never go for the ear. Just not every time. When you do, the ear is to be kissed gently, maybe licked on the edges, or nibbled with restraint. Then you can leave it alone. It's an ear.

DO NOT TRY TO STUFF YOUR SEMIHARD PENIS INTO MY VAGINA. I understand: You're hoping it will get harder once it's in. Or you're thinking that if you act like everything's fine, then everything will be fine. Or maybe you're treating your penis like a stubborn teenager—you're going to show him who's boss and send him to his room. The only thing more humiliating than stuffing a flaccid penis inside someone is being stuffed by a flaccid penis. In this one wretched act, we can feel all of your fear, desperation, and insecurity, concentrated in

> NUMBER OF WOMEN WHO SAID THE THIRD-DATE CONVERSATIONAL TACTIC OF A MAN ANALYZING THE UPCOMING CONGRESSIONAL ELECTIONS MADE THEM THINK "WE'RE REALLY CLICKING":
>
> ## 4 out of 10

NUMBER OF WOMEN WHO SAID THE THIRD-DATE CONVERSATIONAL TACTIC OF A MAN ASKING ABOUT HER RECENT VACATION MADE THEM THINK "WE'RE REALLY CLICKING":

8 out of 10

the precise place where you want us to feel something else. Add to this the odd sensation that we are getting a gynecological exam from a teddy bear.

DO ANYTHING BUT THE ABOVE. Kiss. Watch *The O.C.* Order a pizza. Unless it's a recurring problem requiring medical or psychiatric attention, it's not a big deal. Really.

DO NOT REACH FOR MY CLITORIS if you are in a position that is unsuitable for such a connection. Like when I'm clearly enjoying whatever we're doing. Or, say, if you're in the den watching TV and I'm in the kitchen making brisket. Such persistence is not admirable; it's annoying. It's good that you know clitoral stimulation is important. Now you need to know that if it's not done right—the right angle and pressure, the right motion—then it doesn't feel good, and it may even hurt.

DO ASK. It might help to take her hand and say, "Show me what you like here." Then you can follow the motion of her hand, or she can guide yours until you've figured it out. In certain positions, a woman just doesn't want stimulation there, or prefers to do it herself.

DO NOT SHAVE YOUR BALLS. Having sex with a guy who shaves his balls is like riding a horse with a saddle made of broken glass. If you are going to shave, you're going to have to do it regularly. Say, every half hour.

DO EMBRACE YOUR HAIRINESS. Unless you come up with a dignified solution—and they are expensive—try to accept your body hair. You're a guy. Your great-great-etc.-grandfather was a gorilla. No one blames you.

DO NOT HAVE A NERVOUS BREAKDOWN about ejaculating too fast, losing your erection, or not being able to get one. An occasionally temperamental penis is no cause for alarm, but a guy who freaks out about it is. (If you make a big deal about it, we'll start to think maybe it really is a big deal—one we'll have to worry about.) Conversely, it's also not a good idea to act as if nothing happened, because, well, that is just bull, and that never flies.

DO ACKNOWLEDGE IT, then laugh it off. The guy who says, "Wow, I usually only last for 5 seconds, so that was a record," or, "Gee, I guess those amazing anti-erection pills I got online are working"—that's the kind of guy who makes us want to try again. Later. After a movie. And possibly a chicken sandwich.

DIME-STORE SEX TOYS

FIND FUN AT THE PHARMACY

Depending on where you shop, these days you can find vibrators and edible body paint right on your pharmacy's shelves. And, man, we're all for that. But between the hair dryers and the duct tape, there's also a stealth trove of nooky-friendly items that work just as well. Isn't it even more erotic to use otherwise-innocent objects to make each other squirm and squeal? Plus, you won't have to explain to your kid why the pink rubber rabbit in Mommy's dresser isn't a toy.

VIBRATING TOOTHBRUSH

Unlike many other buzzing brushes, this one doesn't have any painful-looking rotating bristles. Place the smooth side of the head anywhere she wants good vibes, including that one spot where it'll really register (Oral-B Pulsar, $6.50).

FEATHER DUSTER

The label on this household staple reads, "Great for delicate dusting jobs." We couldn't have said it better. Use the whole brush, or pull out a feather or two.

MADE TO PLEASE

Find these little charmers right next to the condoms and the KY.

Handheld vibrator: Looks like the Starship Enterprise, feels just as cosmic, with three speeds and a flexible tip that flutters (Durex Little Gem, $60).

Ring vibe: You wear it; you both get the buzz (Elexa Vibrating Ring, $10 for one ring and one condom).

Edible body paint: Slather it on, lick it off (LifeStyles 4Play Taste, $9 for two paints and three condoms).

Sweep the creases of the body where the skin is thinner and more sensitive—at the knees and elbows, and especially where the shoulder meets the neck (Butler, $2).

SLEEP MASK

A game of blindfolded "guess what I'm going to do next" prolongs foreplay. And if she usually avoids lights-on sex, strap the blindfold on yourself. She can grind away with no worries about what may be bouncing around (Flents Siesta Mask, $3.50).

FISHNET STOCKINGS

Have her slip into these suckers when she's feeling frisky. They aren't $100 Wolfords, so you can go ahead and rip them if the urge should strike (No-Nonsense, $5).

HANDHELD SHOWERHEAD

Okay, so it's going to take a little advance planning to install this baby. But it'll be worth it. Aim at her clitoris and play with the settings until you hit shower nirvana (Pollenex, $22).

ONE-TOUCH AROUSAL

AMONG HER FAVORITE SEX TOYS IS THE ONE AT THE END OF YOUR ARM. USE IT WISELY

BY NICOLE BELAND

Last weekend my boyfriend and I were hanging out, working our way through a six-pack of lager, when he started to clean the inside of a vintage amplifier. As I watched him polish the delicate glass tubes, tighten minuscule screws, and run his fingertips among a network of wires, I felt a familiar weakness between my legs.

Those hands. The mere sight of them working touched off deep memories: in backseats, on blankets, in dark hallways, the first thrilling times with a guy. Ever since I was old enough to grope and be groped, a man's hands have been an exhilarating turn-on.

Lots of women feel the same. The sad thing is, we don't get this nostalgic (and reliable) treatment nearly as often as we'd like. Men over the age of 18 tend to dip their fingers for two reasons: (1) as a brief transition between dry humping and intercourse, and (2) to find out if our juices are flowing.

We want more. We want you to explore like an awestruck teenager again, to rub, tickle, circle, and probe in dozens of ways, under a variety of circumstances. Allow me to, um, take you by the hand. . . .

THE CAR

STRATEGY: A 30-mile tease, then 360s

WHY IT WORKS: It's slow and semipublic.

SPECIAL EQUIPMENT: Automatic transmission

A road trip is worth the price of gas if I can lie back and soak up the attentions of the driver's right hand. You should focus on the road.

We have nothing but time, so take things slowly—this is what we love. For the length of an average song (perhaps "Slow Hand" by the Pointer Sisters?), glide your hand languidly up and down her thigh, coming closer to her crotch with every upstroke. Then slide your hand up and let your palm rest on her pubic mound. Keep it there. Take in the scenery. Look at that barn. Mm-hmm. Nice.

True, you have no leverage. This limits you to gentle touching. We love gentle touching. A featherlight stroke over our pants or panties makes our nerves stand on end. Resist the urge to delve deeper.

Instead, alternate between lightly stroking her entire crotch and circling her clitoral area with a fingertip. (Okay, it's about time for her pants to come off. And maybe, uh, park—over there, now.) Once she's naked from the waist down, lightly slide a wet finger around her clitoris, then stroke just above it (her clitoral shaft runs under there) with a side-to-side motion. If it seems like she might climax, just keep it up. You'll get your turn.

A DARK LOUNGE

STRATEGY: A digital lap dance

WHY IT WORKS: The music, the beer, the risk.

SPECIAL EQUIPMENT: A skirt

A shadowy corner of a swank lounge is the grown-up version of a basement during high school. Here's one place where making out in public is condoned, if not encouraged. Kiss her neck, nibble her ear, and engage in deep, wet kisses while stroking her lower back and sliding your hands through her hair.

Invite her to sit on your lap sideways with her legs crossed. Slide your hand under her butt and between her thighs. It's a tight fit, but apply slow, pulsing pressure to her clitoris or just above to get the blood flowing. Achieving orgasm is a long shot, but being touched intimately in a crowded bar, with music blasting, a cold beer in hand, and your warm breath on the back of her neck is a thrill that lasts—and will continue at home.

NUMBER OF WOMEN WHO WOULD LIKE MORE HAND HOLDING:

9 out of 10

THE SHOWER

STRATEGY: All-body slipperiness

WHY IT WORKS: She sets the pace.

SPECIAL EQUIPMENT: Shampoo, soap

The pillars of female orgasm are rhythm and pressure, which is why we love to climb on top and sort of take over. One of the best ways to replicate that is only possible in the shower, with you providing a sudsy forearm as a hobbyhorse for her to ride on.

But hold on, cowboy. Just because you're both already hot and wet doesn't mean she doesn't need foreplay. I'm sure I'm not the first woman to tell you how sexy it feels to have our hair washed by a man. Massaging shampoo into her scalp will release tension and allow her to focus on her body instead of her to-do list. After rinsing out her tresses, suds her up from head to toe. A hypoallergenic soap like Dove won't irritate her sensitive nooks and crannies. Spend ample time on her shoulders, breasts, bottom, and thighs.

Rub her pubic mound in a circular motion with one hand and massage her bottom with the other. When her head tilts with pleasure, reach between her legs and slide your forearm back and forth over her entire vulva. Encourage her to move against your arm. Ultimately, she'll take over, setting the pace and pressure she needs to reach her peak.

AN UNCROWDED PLANE

STRATEGY: The stealth reach-around

WHY IT WORKS: It's how she does it.

SPECIAL EQUIPMENT: A blanket

Please forget the mile-high club. A jet's bathroom is dirty, cramped, and smelly. Much sexier—and easier to talk her into—is the high-altitude hand job, assuming you have a row to yourself. Raise the armrest and drape the blanket over the two of you. Wait for the lights to go down and the movie to start.

Have her lean back into the crook of your shoulder. She'll "read a magazine" as you slip your arm around her waist, under the blanket and between her legs. An over-the-clothes rub is a vintage sensation that's worked since she became aware of boys.

Rest your fingertips on top of her pubic mound. Exert medium pressure with all four fingers, alternately rubbing up and down over her clitoris and massaging with slow, circular motions. Many women masturbate in exactly this fashion, so there's a good chance she'll achieve maximum altitude.

NUMBER OF WOMEN WHO WOULD LIKE TO RECEIVE A HANDWRITTEN VALENTINE:

9 out of 10

THE COUCH

STRATEGY: Precision petting and probing

WHY IT WORKS: Nothing feels better.

SPECIAL EQUIPMENT: Your tongue

As you watch TV, give her a foot rub that gradually becomes a calf rub and then a thigh massage. By the time your hand is between her legs, the television should be off and your lips should be on hers. Raise her shirt and kiss her stomach, then head south while working her jeans off her hips. Softly kiss her pubic mound until your tongue reaches her clitoris. That's right, your hands get help here. Don't argue: A recent Australian study found that an oral-manual combination is the surest path to her orgasm. Slip a pillow under her butt and ease her thighs to either side.

Many women prefer to be stimulated on one side of—or just above—the clitoris. Rub gently in different spots, asking what she likes best. Insert the index finger of your other hand just inside her vagina and leave it there as you continue to attend to her clitoris. Alternate between oral sex and this two-handed technique until you find out which move makes her crazier than any other.

YOUR SEX POSITION PLAYBOOK

SWITCH IT UP TO HEAT HER UP

Sex shouldn't resemble Naked Twister. Too much twisting and contorting can leave a woman feeling like a sexless member of Cirque du Soleil. "Unlike men, women can lose an orgasm almost in the midst of having one," says Ian Kerner, PhD, a sex and relationships counselor in New York City. The solution? This simple series of positions, designed to help you flow naturally from move to move without ending up like a flesh pretzel. Move logically between positions to increase her arousal.

MISSIONARY

It's tame, but it's a natural starter because of strong eye contact, says Kerner. "But men often ejaculate faster because of the friction." To last longer and keep her happy, switch to a move that maintains clitoral pressure without so much thrusting.

SPIDER

Sit back and pull her toward you while you both lift your knees. "Physically, it allows her to feel a deeper, more intense, more intimate stimulation than missionary, with less friction," says Candida Royalle, author of *How to Tell a Naked Man What to Do.*

REVERSE COWGIRL

Encourage her to turn around and face away from you. This creates G-spot stimulation for her, and the change will help you hold out longer. If she seems uncomfortable on top, resume the spider.

DOGGIE STYLE

"It's the most arousing position for men, because it's the most primal," says Linda Banner, PhD, author of *Advanced Sexual Techniques.* The angle also allows for deeper penetration, which ups your chances of stimulating her G-spot.

BELLY FLOP

Grab a pillow and enjoy a little downtime. This position is similar to doggy-style in that you enter her from behind. But you're both lying on your stomachs instead of up on your knees. "Lay the woman on her stomach with the pillow under her hips so her pelvis is angled and you have a better chance of hitting her G-spot," says Banner. Extend your arms to keep your weight off her.

LAZY MAN

Here's another move that maintains intimacy. Simply sit down, lean back, and gently pull her on top. "This can help women feel in control," says Sarah Janosik, a sex therapist and cofounder and clinical director of the Austin Center for Sexual Medicine.

MAN CHAIR

Once past the basics, positions become "more about psychological novelty," says Kerner. Doggie style is about your dominance, but from there you can naturally transition into this rear-entry position that puts her in the driver's seat. Sit on the edge of the bed and gently pull her on top.

JUST PRESS FOREPLAY

Chill with the Marvin Gaye already. The seductive crooner had a good run, but researchers across the country are studying the art of using music to put a woman in the mood, and the science is screaming for men to dig deeper. What's more, studies show music's precise effects, from lowering her blood pressure to raising her libido. We've laid out the scenarios and selections. Grab a few CDs and start burning.

FIRST-TIME SEX

THE SCENARIO: This is really happening!

PLAY: Your first-date soundtrack

THE REASON: Familiarity is relaxing. In a study from the Long Island Conservatory, participants who listened to familiar music that they enjoyed had lower anxiety levels and blood pressure than those who listened to music they didn't like. "The emotional response triggers a profound physiological response," says George Stefano, the lead author of the study. "It's a feel-good system that allows us to relax."

QUICKIE SEX

THE SCENARIO: She's purring, and *Lost* is coming to a commercial break.

PLAY: Up-tempo indie rock like the Killers, the Black Keys, the New Pornographers

THE REASON: Press play to speed up her body's physiological response. Italian researchers found that subjects' ventilation, heart rate, and arousal levels increased when they were exposed to music with a quick tempo and simple rhythmic structure. Bonus: You burn 35 calories in 20 minutes of sex.

EXPERIMENTAL SEX

THE SCENARIO: There's a gleam in her eye—and cuffs on her nightstand.

PLAY: Punk or hard rock like Green Day, Jawbreaker, Tool

THE REASON: In a study of college students, those looking for physical stimulation and an adrenaline high listened to more punk and hard metal. "People who are sexually promiscuous are more likely to engage in sensation seeking," says Rob Weisskirch, PhD, an associate professor of human development at California State University at Monterey Bay.

CASUAL SEX

THE SCENARIO: You've known her for two beers and a cab ride.

PLAY: Suggestive hip-hop and pop like Common, Ne-Yo, Liz Phair

THE REASON: In one study, women who listened to sexually provocative lyrics placed a greater emphasis on the sex appeal of potential partners. "They had been 'primed' to think about sexuality and were more likely to view everything from that perspective," says Silvia Knobloch-Westerwick, PhD, the lead researcher.

JUMP HER HURDLES

What's your next move? Here's how to traverse four sexual thresholds.

IS SEX ON HER MIND?

THE TEST: Converse first. When a woman's willing, she'll give you the signal long before the foreplay begins. "If she's interested in sex, then she'll avoid personal stories that are not sexy," say Em and Lo, sex-advice columnists and authors of *Rec Sex*. "And she might be open to talking about some of her more intimate encounters."

IS IT NAKED TIME?

THE TEST: Turn the tables. "In the middle of making out, whisper, 'Will you take my shirt off?'" say Em and Lo. "If she demurs, chances are she doesn't want you taking hers off yet, either." Green light? Spend at least 10 minutes focused on her upper half before grazing the button of her jeans (or the zipper

≫ He Said/She Said

HOW LONG SHOULD SEX LAST?

In bed, she wants it all—the warmup, the cooldown, and a decent workout in between. "The warmup ensures she has a bigger, better orgasm," says Ava Cadell, PhD, sex therapist and author of *The Pocket Idiot's Guide to Oral Sex*. Time equals emotional involvement. "If a man can make love to a woman for 1 hour once a week, she'll be more likely to green-light the occasional quickie."

HE SAID		SHE SAID
5 minutes	Kissing	10 minutes
15 minutes	Foreplay	20 minutes
20 minutes	Sex	44 minutes
60 minutes	Cuddling	60 minutes

of her skirt). Give her the opportunity to move your hand, and even if she accelerates the undressing, keep things even in terms of how much skin is exposed. It should be "I'll show you mine if you show me yours" until you're both down to your Skivvies.

CAN YOU HEAD SOUTH?

THE TEST: Take it step-by-step. "For many women, oral sex is more intimate than penetration," says Patti Britton, PhD, a sex therapist and president of the American Association of Sex Educators, Counselors, and Therapists. "Go down her body gently and in increments, first with your hands, pausing to see how she responds." If she's enjoying herself, there will be no ambiguity when your mouth starts its downward trend.

WILL SHE EXPERIMENT?

THE TEST: Ask indirectly, "treating the talk like a game of cards in which you mutually up the ante," says Erin Bradley, sex-advice columnist for www.nerve. com. "Start in the safety of the third person, discussing your friends' sex lives." If she seems intrigued, raise the stakes.

CHANGE YOUR VENUE

Sex outside of the bedroom should mean more than his 'n' hers loofahs. "There are plenty of other things around the house that can really spice up your love life," says Laura Berman, PhD, president and director of the Berman Center and author of *The Passion Prescription*. You already have the tool; use these tips to pull off an *Extreme Makeover: Home Edition* of your own.

KITCHEN COUNTER

THE UPGRADE: Place her on the edge of the surface (the kitchen table or sink will work just as well) and stand facing her with her feet resting on your hips or behind your butt.

THE PAYOFF: "The solid surface will make even slow, small thrusts intense," says Isadora Alman, author of *Doing It: Real People Having Really Good Sex*.

PILLOWS

THE UPGRADE: Place one or two fluffy pillows under her butt during missionary-style sex. Slide your hands under her shoulders, moving forward until your chest is aligned with her face. Rock back and forth, using the base of your penis to put pressure on her clitoris.

THE PAYOFF: Orgasm hinges on clitoral stimulation for 65 percent of women, according to *The Hite Report*. This move also reaches different parts of her vagina, and "the angle may intensify your pleasure, too," says Joy Davidson, PhD, author of *Fearless Sex*.

WASHING MACHINE

THE UPGRADE: During the spin cycle (fastest vibrations), seat your partner on the edge of the machine with her legs bent and feet on your shoulders. As the machine pulsates, bend or kneel and provide oral stimulation.

THE PAYOFF: "The pulsations will bring blood to the pelvic area and enhance sensation," says Davidson. Bonus: no chin-in-the-mattress neck stiffness.

HAIRBRUSH

THE UPGRADE: Keeping your wrist loose, give her a sharp thwap on the caboose with a harmless hairbrush, wooden spoon, or spatula. Be careful not to overdo it.

THE PAYOFF: "Light spanking hyperstimulates the nerves, intensifying sensation in the stimulated areas," says Richard Emerson, author of *The Best Sex You'll Ever Have.*

MIRRORS

THE UPGRADE: Ask her to hold on to the sink and look into the mirror while you enter her from behind.

THE PAYOFF: More eye contact during the G-spot–targeting rear-entry position. "It's instant intimacy," says Emerson.

THE STAIRS

THE UPGRADE: Sit on the stairs, facing the railing, with one leg braced a stair or two down and the other leg slightly bent. Ask her to lower herself onto you, facing the rail and holding it for support.

THE PAYOFF: "This helps women who don't have enough leg strength to do the reverse cowgirl," says Davidson. "Plus, it's great when you can't quite make it to the bedroom."

SOFA

THE UPGRADE: Ask her to straddle the arm of the couch, facedown, as you enter her from behind. Bonus: Place a silk scarf over the sofa's arm. "Her breasts and clitoris will rub against the fabric," says Davidson.

THE PAYOFF: Multiple stimulation, minimal effort. "Sometimes the bed is too soft, too low, or too boring to achieve the position you want," says Suzi Godson, author of *Sexploration.* This will allow her soft spots to grind on the cushy arm of the sofa.

LET HER SET THE PACE

When it comes to sex, most men think faster means hotter. Women? Not so much. "Evolution built in a system that keeps the sexual brakes on longer for us," says Emily Nagoski, PhD, a sexuality instructor at Indiana University. Not to worry. Here are five tricks for building a slow burn that builds to a raging bonfire.

THE STANDING EIGHT COUNT

THE INSTINCT: You're ravenous; you want to carry her over your shoulder to the bedroom.

THE BETTER MOVE: Pin her against a wall and tell her how hot she makes you feel. "Women love the feeling of sexual anticipation," says sex therapist Ava Cadell, PhD. A slow, passionate make-out session in the hall sets the tone and helps jump-start her sexual excitation system (the ol' SES)—a combination of visual, tactile, and olfactory stimuli that, Nagoski says, convinces a woman's body to interpret things as white-hot erotic.

➤➤ He Said/She Said

WHY DO YOU TURN DOWN SEX?

HE SAID		SHE SAID
54%	I never turn it down	29%
19%	I'm not in the mood	26%
13%	I'm too stressed-out	12%
4%	Not enough foreplay	16%
2%	No emotional bond	8%
4%	The sex isn't worth it	3%
1%	He/she wants too much	3%

THE STRIPTEASE

THE INSTINCT: It's showtime; you want to tear off her clothes with your teeth.

THE BETTER MOVE: Coax her clothes off. "Some women feel uneasy if they're naked too soon," says Sandor Gardos, PhD, a sex therapist and founder of www.mypleasure.com. So pace yourself. Undo only her first two shirt buttons. Go beneath her clothes without removing them. Unzip her jeans. Run your fingers under her bra straps. You're trying to hint at what's going to follow once the clothes do come off. Aim for 4 minutes; any more and "she may think you don't want to see her naked," Gardos warns.

THE SMOOTH MOVE

THE INSTINCT: Her breasts are heaving; you want to be squeezing.

THE BETTER MOVE: Lighten your touch—your job is to please her, not satisfy yourself with a fact-finding grope. Remember: Breasts aren't Play-Doh. "A guy's 'average' touch is 20 percent more forceful than a woman's," Nagoski says. Concentrate on areas of her upper body that don't get a lot of play, like her collarbone, the inside of her arms, and the sides of her stomach. "This will stimulate her ventral spinothalamic tract, which is responsible for carrying sexual sensations through her body," says Nagoski. If she wants more, resist for 2 more minutes, then give her what she wants.

THE BAIT AND SWITCH

THE INSTINCT: She's begging; you're willing; it's on.

THE BETTER MOVE: Wait to penetrate—lead off with an oral exam. "Withholding intercourse will create a challenge for her," says Victoria Zdrok, PhD, a former *Playboy* playmate and the author of *Anatomy of Pleasure*. "Winning this challenge will become more emotionally and psychologically meaningful when the time does come." When you're going down, relax your tongue and apply light pressure, throwing in the occasional flicker of increased stimulation. From there, stay off the offensive. The more she wants, the more she'll chase you. Follow the movement of her hips for a cue to the rhythm that turns her on most.

THE REVERSE THRUSTER

THE INSTINCT: She's going wild and speaking in tongues, so you want to go faster, deeper, and harder.

THE BETTER MOVE: Try slow, shallow thrusts instead. "At the beginning, going slow and shallow will help the vaginal wall relax and expand, allowing for deeper penetration," says Gardos. Don't think of intercourse as a race to the top; it's a measured, gradual climb, so increase your intensity slowly, and only when her breathing and her body tell you she's ready. When you finally hit the summit together, it will feel like Everest up there.

TAKE IT SLOW

The clitoris is not a bull's-eye, power switch, or launch button. "You can't just go for the gold," says Rebecca Chalker, author of *The Clitoral Truth*. "You might short-circuit her body's elaborate arousal process." Here's your step-by-step guide to treating her right by taking it slow.

EASE INTO IT

The nerve-packed tip of the clitoris is sensitive at first, says Chalker. But just above the clitoral tip lies a short shaft—a genetic cousin to your penis—that can help her warm up.

TRY THIS: After some foreplay, stimulate this inner shaft. Push down on her lower abdomen with your outstretched fingers, massaging the skin on either side of her vagina in a scissors motion, causing the skin of her inner labia to caress the shaft.

MOVE TO THE MIDDLE

Gradually tease inward with your fingers, occasionally brushing against and lubricating the clitoral hood and the length of her inner lips in a light up-and-down motion.

TRY THIS: Position yourself between her legs and use your palm to cover her vulva, keeping your fingers stretched over her pubic mound (as if you were palming a basketball). Use her lips to gently tease the clitoris.

BE DIRECT

On the brink of orgasm, a symphony of muscles and ligaments pulls the clitoral tip back under its hood. "It's a good sign," says Debby Herbenick, PhD, the *Men's Health* "Bedroom Confidential" columnist.

TRY THIS: If she's comfortable with direct stimulation, replace your palm with two fingers on the tip of her clitoris. "Once she's fully aroused, she's just as eager and hungry as you are," says Susie Bright, editor of the *Best American*

>> He Said/She Said

DO YOU WANT TO HAVE SEX MORE OFTEN?

HE SAID		SHE SAID
76%	1st year of relationship	60%
70%	4th year of relationship	46%
66%	9th year of relationship	30%
60%	16th year of relationship	25%

Erotica series. Start light and increase pressure until you find her sweet spot.

DO AN INSIDE JOB

If direct touch is too much, stimulate the inner labia.

TRY THIS: Use your fingers or a toy to stimulate the buried "legs" of her clitoris, which run up into her vaginal wall like a wishbone at 10 o'clock and 2 o'clock. "Just before orgasm, look for contractions around her vagina and lower abdomen," says Herbenick.

PUT IT ALL TOGETHER

A woman's blood flows freely through her tissues after orgasm, making repeat performances easier.

TRY THIS: From behind, angle your penis down at the vaginal wall. In the missionary position, keep pressure on her most sensitive spot with your lower abdomen by tipping your hips forward.

ASK THE GIRL NEXT DOOR

THE HONEST TRUTH ABOUT WOMEN FROM OUR LOVELY NEIGHBOR

Why do women always interrupt foreplay to go to the bathroom?

Ah, we have to pee. There's not enough room in our bodies for a penis and a full bladder.

I've had girlfriends on the pill who've suggested we stop using condoms before I was ready. How do I politely decline?

Heads-up: What may seem like a hedonistic request for skin-on-skin contact is really a commitment test in disguise. By offering to go bare, she's telling you that she trusts you enough to put her sexual health in your hands. Do you feel the same about her? If the answer is no, keep your response short and sweet: "I'm not ready," followed by "There will be plenty of time for that later, so let's not rush things." Yes, she'll feel rejected. But she'll respect you for taking your health seriously, and maybe even fall for you harder.

When I'm at her place, should I flush a used condom or trash it?

If there's a plastic bag in the garbage can, tie the condom in a knot, wrap it in tissue or toilet paper, and throw it away. Even if the only receptacle is a dainty wicker basket, wrap the rubber and deposit it. Don't flush it, or you'll be courting a plumbing disaster. And please don't leave it for her to peel off the floor the next morning; you guys really need to knock that off.

My girlfriend says I'm the best she's ever had in bed. How do I know it's true?

Look, my boyfriend tells me I'm the most beautiful girl in the world. I seriously doubt that. But of all the faces on the planet, he prefers mine, because I'm the one who regularly listens to his problems and makes him plates of nachos with two layers of chips and cheese. The reward center in his brain lights up more for me than when he's watching Evangeline Lilly slither through the jungle in a sweat-soaked tank top. Even if you're not the best she's ever had (but maybe you are!), you're absolutely the one she most enjoys making love to. And that's even better.

I know Valentine's sex shouldn't be the same old roll in the hay. Got a move to make my girl happy?

All it takes to make big-night foreplay sufficiently special is to smooch her in some surprising places. Plant soft kisses down the length of her spine, across her collarbones, up the back of her thighs, and anywhere else that seldom gets attention. This'll send the message that you love her—and her body—more than ever.

I'm always the one who initiates sex. How can I get my wife to take the reins?

To get your wife to take control, you need to understand the female sex drive. For starters, it can be influenced by a number of factors, including the time of the month, emotional state, and physical ailments. The emotional factors are particularly important, as a woman's desire to initiate sex depends largely on how satisfied she is in her relationship, how she's dealing with life's stressors, and how she feels about herself and her body. From a physical standpoint, fluctuating hormone levels and such medications as birth-control pills and antidepressants can affect her sex drive. These factors can cause a woman to take a more submissive role in sex, but we urge you not to confuse a lack of initiation with a lack of desire.

If she's receptive to your sexual suggestions and advances and enjoys the subsequent sexual encounters, her libido is most likely intact, and her lack of initiation is probably a result of her own discomfort with sexual expression. Many young girls are raised to believe that sexual assertiveness is the same thing as promiscuity, and they often carry this belief into adulthood. Tell her how you feel, and ask what she enjoys during sex; use her response to segue into your interest in having her initiate often. Finally, be spontaneous. A handwritten note expressing your attraction to her and your desire to be devoured by her could work wonders.

How can my girl and I get the thrill of public sex without being arrested?

Be smart. Use your backyard, go for a hike in dense woods, or find a hotel room with thin drapes. Any of these will spike your risk sensors and increase your body's awareness of all sensations, from a housekeeper's knock to your girlfriend's slightest touch. Another option is to go digital. Putting yourselves on camera can give both of you the same highs—the heavy breathing, the increased heart rate—that we associate with the fear of being caught.

O, MY

Yes, making love is better than masturbating; researchers in Scotland feel compelled to rub this in. A study in *Biological Psychology* found that orgasms during intercourse are four times more satisfying than those from masturbation. Researchers drew postorgasm blood samples from participants (beats a cigarette) and measured levels of prolactin, the hormone that infuses us with contentment. Levels were higher after intercourse than after masturbation.

The complete physiological experience of intercourse—and possibly an emotional component as well—may explain the difference, says study author Stuart Brody, PhD. The surge of prolactin may also be evolution's way of "differentiating a potentially reproductive activity from one that is not," he says. Want to improve your orgasms? Pay emotional attention to your partner, breathe well, and stay comfortable, says Brody. And make sure she's in bed with you.

TRY SOME RISKY BUSINESS

It's no secret that dopamine, the pleasure hormone released by the hypothalamus, is responsible for the euphoria we associate with food, drugs, and sex. The problem with sexual euphoria, as most honest men will admit, is that it tends to fade in direct proportion to the length of a relationship. But a new study in the *Journal of Neurophysiology* offers long-term lovers an invigorating alternative to Levitra.

Researchers found that sharing thrill-inducing activities—think roller coaster instead of romantic comedy—activates dopamine-rich areas of the brain and just might reignite your inner porn star. "Novelty and excitement are the keys to improving a long-term relationship," says psychologist Arthur Aron, PhD, of the State University of New York–Stony Brook and a coauthor of the study. So get out of the bedroom and have sex somewhere new. Log flume, anyone?

GET SATISFIED

There's a good reason some people feel sleepy after sex, say researchers reporting in the journal *Biological Psychology*. Their study of 19 men found that levels of the hormone prolactin surge following orgasm, countering the energizing effects of dopamine (released during sex). Levels of the hormone were also 400 percent higher after intercourse than after masturbation, which is why you're more likely to feel sleepy and satisfied—and less likely to have another erection—after sex than after masturbating.

AVOID BAD BREAKS

Wearing polyurethane condoms might feel better during sex, but a review of 11 studies by the University of Alabama found that breakage rates for non-latex condoms are up to five times higher than those for latex.

SEX: THE HEADACHE MEDICINE

Best news for migraine sufferers . . . and their spouses: When she says she has a headache, she may actually want sex. That's right. Migraine headaches are associated with increased libido, according to researchers at Wake Forest University. Their study of 68 people found that those who suffered from regular migraines reported sex drives 20 percent stronger than those who had tension-type headaches. Researchers believe the phenomenon may be due to low levels of serotonin in people with migraines. High levels are associated with decreased libido.

TRY IT, YOU MIGHT LIKE IT

She likes it, and you might, too—if you'd ask. According to a new survey, 82 percent of women—but just 52 percent of men—are aroused when their partner stimulates their nipples. The survey of University of Texas students, published in the *Journal of Sexual Medicine,* found that only 17 percent of guys have actually asked for such stimulation. That compares with 59 percent of women who aren't shy about asking. If she doesn't mention it, assume she's among the 38 percent who want their nipples or breasts stimulated but don't want to ask. (Twenty percent of guys admitted that they would like it but were too shy to ask.) Men should go slowly—women generally prefer that you start gently.

"Direct nipple stimulation immediately upon initiating sex can be a turn-off for women," says Laura Berman, PhD, president and director of the Berman Center and author of *The Passion Prescription.* "Begin with the side of the breast and graze over the nipple." The study said that previous research has shown that after puberty, the sensitivity of all areas of a woman's breasts becomes "significantly greater" than that of male breasts.

TURN OFF THE TV

Viewing action flicks in bed could curb action between the sheets. In a recent Italian study, couples with TV-free bedrooms had sex twice as often as those with screens to stare at. If you can't give up late-night TV, at least avoid violent films—they were most likely to kill the mood.

>>A MAN'S GUIDE POLL

**The more exclusive attention she gets,
the more likely she'll reach orgasm**

TECHNIQUES	PERCENTAGE OF WOMEN WHO REACH ORGASM
Manual and oral stimulation	90
Manual and oral stimulation, and vaginal intercourse	86
Manual stimulation only	79
Oral stimulation and vaginal intercourse	73
Manual stimulation and vaginal intercourse	71
Vaginal intercourse only	50

PART 5

GET BETTER

It's our hope that you can just skip right over this section of the book. That's because here's where you'll find information and advice about dealing with problems. But hey, we're realists, and the sad truth is that at some point in a man's life, problems are likely to crop up in his sex life and relationships.

So, turn here for the lowdown on oils and lubes to solve dryness problems and make sex slicker than ever. Looking to make your girl a live-in? You'll come to grips with the six realities of cohabitation, before they hit you like a Mack truck. Encountering some problems in the bedroom? Five top sex experts solved five couples' sex problems, and they can help you, too. Need to put some sizzle back in your sex life? You'll find dozens of tips, tricks, and techniques right here.

Even if you don't have any problems—let's say you simply want to get better—here is where you'll find the ways to turn your most important sex resolutions into your greatest success stories. The bottom line: No matter what the issue is, we hope it gets better soon.

SLICK SOLUTIONS

WITHOUT BEING CRUDE, READ ON FOR THE LOWDOWN ON OILS AND LUBRICANTS FOR SEX

BY COLIN MCENROE

Accompanying my teenaged son in 2002 to the cinematic masterpiece *8 Mile,* I almost had to clap my hand across my mouth during the semifamous factory sex scene, in which the distinguished thespian Eminem engages in amorous congress with his leading lady, Brittany Murphy, while standing up in his steaming, clanking workplace. Before he does, Ms. Murphy moistens her hand with her own saliva and then applies it to the area of interest.

I wanted to shout, "She's 16! You can't get her wet? You loser!" It seemed the antithesis of eros. But then, I am hardly the target audience for this film, as evidenced by my own piquant longing not for Ms. Murphy, but for Eminem's boozy, blowsy, disengaged, trailer-park mom played by Kim Basinger. But that's a separate issue.

The point is, when we are young, our partners are usually reliably damp. As our partners edge into their thirties and forties, it's a slightly more complicated question (and it often fluctuates with the menstrual cycle), but then, our technique improves. Our foreplay is more subtle and less rushed. Often, nobody notices any change. (Or maybe we men don't, and our lovers, sore after a night of vigorous love, don't really want to tell us.)

As we men move into our fifties, so do our women friends. Perhaps you have consoled yourself with a 26-year-old, but if not, there's a pretty good chance that the woman in your bed may, occasionally, need a little lubrication beyond the Chianti you served with dinner.

Fortunately, we live in lubricated times. What's your pleasure? Strawberry-flavored Astroglide? Water-based, glycerine-free Sliquid Swirl Piña Colada? Grrl Toyz Passion Dew Flavored Spray?

I could go on. I could really go on. Lube, as it's called in the trade, is big business. New products come on the market every week, it seems.

"The current 'older generation' is more comfortable with sexuality," says sex therapist Sandor Gardos, PhD, founder of www.mypleasure.com, a Web site that sells lubricants and other sex aids. "They are not expecting, like their parents and grandparents maybe did, that sex winds down after 50. Various companies are only too happy to service that market. And they're not portraying it as something you use because you have to, but as something you use to make your sex life better."

The cultural shift is nowhere more evident than in the marketing of K-Y, once upon a time the old gray lady of lubricants, kind of an all-business product for people who just weren't squeezing enough juice out of their persimmons.

"It was like this icky medical cream," says Gardos. "Now it's being marketed as a wonderful, sensual product."

True enough. K-Y is still pretty much the gateway drug of lubricants. The average CVS or Walgreens will have a shelf of different K-Y formulations in different flavors and sensations. They advertise the stuff during *Law & Order,* although they half pretend it's a massage product. Indeed, I have a little orange-capped bottle of K-Y "warming liquid" on my bedside table.

You get what you pay for, says Ellen Barnard, co-owner of A Woman's Touch Sexuality Resource Center (www.awomanstouchonline.com). "Cheaper ingredients tend to dry out faster and get sticky," she says. Most of the stuff you find on store shelves is glycerin based, because glycerin is the cheapest way to make lubricant. Read the label of any product, says Gardos. Sensitivity-increasing products often employ menthol or peppermint oil to create a tingle, but using one of those products is also a great way to end up with an itchy vagina, he says.

Gardos says he even saw one product that is made with an ingredient contained in pepper spray. "I told the CEO of that company about a rule in sexology: Never put anything in your vagina that you wouldn't put in your eye," he says. "Then I asked him if I could put some of his product in his eye. He just about ran out of the room."

That's the bad news. The good news is, if you start using some of the good stuff, which you're more likely to get online or at an adult boutique, you'll never go back to the cheap stuff.

As I write this, I am savoring fond memories of last night's long, slow, slippery encounter with Ms. A., enhanced by Kama Sutra Royal Bengal Super-Rich Silicone Lubricant (which I actually bought at a faux New Age store at the mall). Lube is like motor oil. You can buy it in grades, and I'm finding that the really heavy stuff is fun. Rather than reducing friction, it almost builds in a sense of fuller, snugger contact.

"We call that cushiony. Some people find it does create more sensation," says Barnard.

The stuff I bought set me back $30 for 3.4 fluid ounces. A little of it goes a long way, but I could probably get something similar for about eight bucks less if I shopped online.

If you're having a long lovemaking session, a heavy silicone product will keep her from becoming sore and will probably never dry out. Water-based and glycerin-based products, on the other hand, are eventually absorbed into the skin, says Gardos. The silicone molecule is too big for that, so it stays in play. If there's a downside, he says, it's in the area of cleanup; a water-based product is less messy. Gardos recently reviewed a water-based spray-on lube, which he says might be good for frequent touch-ups and is less likely to make some kind of ineradicable greasy stain.

YOU LUBE

Choosing a personal lubricant on a sliding scale

All of these lubes are safe for use with condoms.

O'My Piña Colada Lubricant: tasty, water-based, moderately slippery; special features: sugar free; stand-up pump bottle; also in strawberry-cheesecake flavor

K-Y Touch Massage 2-in-1 Warming: highly slippery, good for body massage, tastes bad, water-based; special feature: creates a warming sensation on contact

Probe: water-based, highly slippery, tastes bad; special feature: comes in thin and "thick, rich" formulas

Gun Oil: highly slippery, tastes bad, good for use in tub or shower, silicone-based, good for body massage; special features: made from long-lasting dimethicone; military-style bottle

Astroglide Sensual Strawberry: tasty, moderately slippery, water-based; special features: very light lube; strawberry scented

Slippery Stuff: highly slippery, water-based, tastes bad; special feature: glycerin free

Durex Play Tingling: silicone-based, tastes bad, good for body massage, moderately slippery, good for use in shower or tub; special features: made from dimethicone; menthol creates tingling sensation

It seems there are as many flavors and smells as Baskin-Robbins ever offered. Ms. A and I prefer natural smells, but for people using condoms, especially for oral sex, flavors can be a godsend, says Barnard. "Latex condoms don't taste great," she says. "And for men who are uncomfortable performing oral sex on a woman, a flavored lubricant gives them something tasty to enjoy."

Barnard recommends that a man put a little lubricant on his fingers before he even touches a woman. (Are you paying attention, Eminem?) For penile-vaginal intercourse, the most important thing to coat is the penis, she says.

Gardos says the ideal is to get lubricant on both surfaces so that each part is lubricated as it rubs against the other.

Lubricants have all kinds of practical aspects. They're the best way to ensure that a condom does not break, says Barnard. For couples who still want to have sex during or near menstruation, when any woman may run a little dry, they're essential. And for women in perimenopause or menopause, lubricants are a fact of life.

Mainly, though, they're fun. I'm chagrined that I reached the age of 50 without knowing that.

"If you want to experience that warm sensation," says Barnard, "you can always put a tube of any lubricant in a bowl of warm water for a few minutes beforehand."

"Who can plan that kind of thing in the heat of passion?" says Ms. A. "I can barely get the top off the container."

Amen to that.

THE SHACKING-UP SURVIVAL GUIDE

COME TO GRIPS WITH THE 6 REALITIES OF COHABITATION

BY NANCY WARTIK

It used to be called "living in sin." Now it's the status quo. According to the U.S. Census, nearly 5 million unmarried couples wake up together every day. As for everyone else, the majority of husbands and wives had the same address before walking down the aisle. And the CDC (Centers for Disease Control and Prevention) reports that more than half of women have lived with a significant other at some point by age 30. When you're in love, it makes perfect sense. You save money by splitting the bills, your favorite person is around to talk to every night, and best of all, there's sex on tap.

But people rarely talk about how surprisingly stressful moving in together can be. "It's about more than sharing a bed," says Marshall Miller, coauthor of *Unmarried to Each Other*. "It's about making intricate, complicated decisions about money, housework, and time." To keep your love thriving under the extra pressure, take these six realities of cohabitation into consideration.

REALITY #1: IT DOESN'T SEAL THE DEAL

Moving in seems like a natural precursor to marriage, but you shouldn't count on it. In fact, only 45 percent of couples who cohabitate get hitched, says Susan Brown, PhD, a sociologist at Bowling Green State University. And research has linked living together before tying the knot to an increased risk of unhappy marriage. One theory as to why: People who live together often swap rings not because they're right for each other but because they feel too invested in the relationship to break up, says Paul Amato, PhD, a sociologist at Penn State University.

STRATEGY #1: TALK ABOUT THE FUTURE. If marriage is what you want, make that crystal clear even if—scratch that, especially if—it requires an uncomfortable conversation. A recent study in the *Journal of Family Psychology* found that couples who get engaged before setting up house are happier pre- and post-marriage than couples who do so after the move. "Make sure you understand each other's reasons for wanting to move in," advises study author Galena Kline, a research associate at the University of Denver Center for Marital and Family Studies. Even if you don't go shopping for a diamond, agree on a time line for how the relationship is going to unfold.

REALITY #2: ALL ROOMMATES ARE IRRITATING

Just because you're hot for each other doesn't make living together easy. Annie Sargent, 34, a lawyer in Seattle, says she's frequently been on edge since her boyfriend moved in a year ago. When he washes dishes, "he's a whirling dervish—soapy water gets all over everything," Sargent says. She gets so annoyed she yells at him, and then he gets upset because he was trying to help. And that's just one example. "I want him there," she says. "But now I'm irritated all the time."

STRATEGY #2: CHOOSE YOUR BATTLES. Yes, she's annoying. But she'll always be annoying! And so will you, by virtue of sharing the same space 24/7. "You need to let go of the little things that bug you but aren't meaningful," says Noelle C. Nelson, PhD, psychologist and coauthor of *The Power of Appreciation*. Easier said than done, so try this: Whenever she's driving you up the wall, try to think of three nice things she's done for you lately. It should defuse your irritation just enough to keep you from lashing out.

REALITY #3: IT'S NOT JUST ABOUT YOU ANYMORE

You want to grab a drink with an ex after work. Or apply for that amazing job in Newfoundland. But now your decisions, from trivial to momentous, will affect another person's routine, lifestyle, and bank account. "Everything I did suddenly involved an extra step," says Bill Schmidt, 36, who moved in with his girlfriend 8 years ago. Formerly speedy grocery runs now required remembering what kind of yogurt, cookies, or bread she liked. "It took a while to adjust to not just thinking about myself."

STRATEGY #3: BE A BETTER HALF. As corny as it sounds, moving in together really does mean becoming a team, and that means giving up a lot of the autonomy you've been reveling in since you were 18. Before making decisions that could affect her, ask yourself how you would feel if she did the same to you. Then proceed accordingly even if it makes you groan. "If you don't do that, you won't stay together, or you'll stay together and be miserable," says John W. Jacobs, MD, a psychiatrist and author of *All You Need Is Love and Other Lies About Marriage.*

REALITY #4: LOVE DOESN'T SOLVE MONEY PROBLEMS

You might be saving a bundle on rent—unless, of course, you moved into a bigger, more expensive place together. But money problems are as inevitable as basement drafts and broken toilet-bowl handles. According to an April 2006 *Money* magazine survey, 70 percent of couples admit to arguing about finances. "Money is so entwined with power and control, it's seldom something you can talk about objectively with your significant other," says Deborah Knuckey, author of *Conscious Spending for Couples.*

STRATEGY #4: DECIDE NOW HOW YOU'RE GOING TO HANDLE FINANCIAL STUFF. Don't wait until the bills start clogging your mailbox. Some ideas: If one of you earns more than the other, that person should contribute proportionately to the bills. A lot of couples divvy up money chores pretty traditionally: He handles investments, she takes care of bills and daily expenses. "But there's no right or wrong; people decide these things very differently," Knuckey says. Come up with a plan and put it in writing: If arguments arise later, it'll help clear up any fuzzy memories.

REALITY #5: THE SEX WILL CHANGE

According to the 1997 Durex Global Sex Survey, people who live together but aren't married report the greatest frequency of sex. So that's a plus. The minus? The sex can lose its "wow" factor. A 2004 ABC News poll found that 58 percent of people who are married or have lived together for less than

GOAL TENDING

Why do you want to move in?

To increase your chances of being happy under the same roof, you should each know why you're there in the first place. Ideally, your intentions are the same. A recent study by sociologists Lynne Casper, PhD, of the University of Southern California, and Liana Sayer, PhD, of Ohio State University, identifies four types of live-in couples. Any of 'em sound familiar?

1. Knot-Tiers: 46 percent

They're in love and plan to get married.

Lasting power: high

2. Cohabiters of Convenience: 29 percent

They've shacked up mainly because it's easier than living alone. "They're not sure if they want to get married—in fact, some are sure they don't," Casper says.

Lasting power: low to medium

3. Test Drivers: 15 percent

They're doing a trial run.

Lasting power: low to medium

4. True Disbelievers: 10 percent

They plan to do the "forever" thing, but don't like marriage as an institution.

Lasting power: high

3 years report "very exciting" sex lives, compared with 29 percent of couples who've been at it more than 10 years.

STRATEGY #5: KEEP SEARCHING FOR NEW TRIGGERS. A new body in bed might be a bigger source of excitement, but when it comes to truly satisfying, orgasmic sex, nothing beats knowing each other well, says Susan Heitler, PhD, a Denver marriage therapist and author of *The Power of Two*. Take pleasure in the fact that she knows exactly where and how to rub. Just don't assume that there's nothing left for each of you to learn. "Keep trying different kinds of touching, different times to fool around, different ways to turn each other on," Heitler says. Use what you already know to find out more—if she likes your tongue in her ear, she'd probably love it on her upper thigh.

REALITY #6: EXPECT THE UNEXPECTED

When Melissa Haroza, 36, and her boyfriend, Chris, shacked up 3 years ago, she had a cat, but Chris was against pets. "Then one day before a vacation he said he was worried about the cat," says Haroza, who married Chris last year. "He thought she'd get lonely and suggested taking her with us." And it wasn't because he wanted to toss her out of the plane. He'd actually started to care about the kitty. Never underestimate the power of a solid relationship to bring out surprising new sides of a person.

STRATEGY #6: STAY THE COURSE. If the basics are there—trust, shared values, good communication—don't give up when you hit a rough spot (and you will). To keep the going as smooth as possible, build a support system of friends and family members whom you can count on as a couple, Dr. Nelson says. As for major brawls, sometimes just letting time pass can give each of you a chance to sort out your feelings. That's one of the great things about moving in together. You can go to bed mad, and, chances are, you'll still wake up happy to see each other.

SEX HOMEWORK

STUDY HALL WAS NEVER THIS HOT. READ ON TO SEE HOW TOP SEX EXPERTS SOLVED 5 COUPLES' SEX PROBLEMS

BY JAMYE WAXMAN

The fundamentals of sex never change: Insert tab A into slot B. But no matter how long you've been doing it, there's always more to learn, whether it's a move you didn't know would turn you on or a spot on your partner's body you haven't licked before. To prove it, we found five real-life couples whose sex lives could use a firm tap with a wooden ruler and sent them back to school. Each couple confessed what they wanted to improve. Then we asked top sex experts to create the perfect assignment. The result wasn't always a headboard-rattling orgasm, but our eager students learned something new every time. We hope it'll inspire you to play "hot for teacher" with your woman. Bonus: Anyone who reenacts all five lessons gets a gold star.

LESSON #1

The students: Louise and Nat

New York, New York

Both 36

Event planner and graduate student

Dating since May 2005

WHAT NEEDS AN UPGRADE: Nat and Louise think about trying new things in bed, "but seldom get around to it," Louise says. "We've lost the urge to branch out and explore."

ASSIGNMENT: A racy sexual experience that renews their passion, reminding them that wild sex is worth the trouble. "Doing it outside will help them break free from the bedroom and add the exciting risk of getting caught," says

Jay Friedman, a certified sex educator in Seattle. (Actually getting caught isn't a good idea.)

Nat and Louise went to a wooded area in an upper Manhattan park where they couldn't see anyone and were fairly sure no one could see them. But given that it was New York City, people could have stumbled upon them at any moment. "I'd say we had a 25 percent risk of getting caught," Louise says. "We didn't think much about the police, but I would have blamed [the magazine] if we'd gotten arrested!" Louise was nervous about getting naked with people around, so to help her relax—and crack up—Nat did a little striptease. "After she went down on me for a few minutes, we started having intercourse," he recalls. "It lasted about 30 minutes, but we didn't have anything to lie on, so we were limited to standing positions, and that got tiring. I'd bring a blanket next time." The standing sex gave Louise a serious hamstring stretch. "I was bending almost all the way over, and my head was pushing into a tree!" she says. "I didn't think I'd get turned on, and I was pretty surprised that I had an orgasm. It was sexy to see it all happening in broad daylight." Nat didn't make it to orgasm, but he didn't regret the field trip: "I loved the feeling of being completely free and naked with the air against our skin."

Make It Work for You

MIX IT UP. "The best way to get the edge back in a relationship is to try new activities that force a change in your neurochemistry," says Joy Davidson, PhD, a New York–based sex therapist and the author of *Fearless Sex*. A novel experience ups your level of neurotransmitters, including dopamine, the excitement hormone. The catch? If you repeat the activity, it will become as routine as new reality shows on Fox, and those neurotransmitters go into been-there-done-that mode. So try something fresh every so often, even if it's relatively tame, like French kissing on the street or copping a feel in the car.

LESSON #2

The students: Stephanie and Michael

    Clifton, NJ

    26 and 27

    Writer/marketing coordinator and copywriter/Web designer

    Dated for 2 years before getting married in June 2007

WHAT NEEDS AN UPGRADE: Stephanie easily has orgasms with her trusty vibrator, but she has trouble letting go completely when she has sex with Michael. "Mike always initiates sex, then I lose my libido because of the pressure," she says. Because they don't talk about it, Mike feels left in the dark. "She doesn't give me clues as to what she wants, so it's one big guessing game. I want us to enjoy sex together," he says.

ASSIGNMENT: Since Stephanie is comfortable with using vibrators, trying one with Michael is an ideal first step to bridging their sexual gap. Shopping for one together will help Michael feel more involved and give them both a chance to open up with each other. "The best lubricant for great sex is communication, and toys can be a catalyst for talking about sex," says Patti Britton, PhD, a sex coach, president of the American Association of Sex Educators, Counselors, and Therapists, and the author of *The Complete Idiot's Guide to Sensual Massage.*

Stephanie and Michael headed to Babeland, a sex shop with a cheery vibe, in lower Manhattan. "I felt at ease there because the atmosphere and employees don't make sex feel dirty," she says. After browsing the shelves, debating the pros and cons of different toys, and discussing what would turn them both on, they zeroed in on a vibrating ring, a circular piece of silicone worn at the base of the penis that has a buzzing nub for clitoral stimulation. "After we left the store I was really excited. I'm eager to try anything that will help me overcome my intimacy issues, and Mike is open to trying anything with me," Stephanie says. "I don't know why we didn't think of this before." Michael was thrilled at the idea of seeing Stephanie really turned on, and he wasn't disappointed. "She kept pulling me closer and was really into the experience. I guess we found what we needed!" Alas, Stephanie's orgasm remained stubbornly elusive. Nonetheless, she's still happy with the toy: "A fabulous invention, in my opinion! He gets to feel a new sensation, and I get to enjoy the power of a vibrator and a penis all at the same time," she says.

Make It Work for You

GO SHOPPING. Even if she has no trouble scoring Os, shopping for a sex toy together can be a blast. Try this: Browse separately and pick out one toy you love and one you think your partner would love. Meet back up and exchange picks.

LESSON #3

The students: Kristin and Matt

    Jackson, Tennessee

    Both 28

    Registered nurse and mechanical engineer

    Married 5 years

WHAT NEEDS AN UPGRADE: Kristin wants to try new positions, but body-image woes hold her back. "I'm super self-conscious about my body from the waist down," she says. Matt wants to get back to when their just-met sexual hunger overruled self-criticism. "It'd be nice to rekindle the passion we had when we first started dating," he says.

ASSIGNMENT: Use Liberator Shapes to make sex more fun and alleviate anxiety. The soft wedge-shaped foam cushions prop you up and elongate your body so you can relax. "The shapes will help Kristin let her guard down and focus on how she feels as opposed to how she looks," says Ducky Doolittle, author of *Sex with the Lights On*.

    Kristin and Matt ordered the Liberator Wedge/Ramp combo ($185/www. liberator.com): two large triangular pillows that you can fit together or use separately. The shapes are designed to give you the right support, and the angles are consistent with how your body moves naturally during sex. Matt was so excited to try them that he'd stick his head out the door every hour to look for the delivery truck. "Once we got them in the house, we tried an altered version of missionary, where Kristin lay back on the wedge combo so her hips were raised and her legs rested on my shoulders," he says. Success! "I didn't think about how I looked because I was relaxed and not contorted," Kristin says. "I focused on the sensations instead, finding new ways to hit my G-spot." As an unexpected bonus, the pillows got them talking more. "We'd talk about what to try next or how to do something differently," Matt says. The only downside: interrupting foreplay to grab the pillows.

Make It Work for You

IF YOU DON'T WANT TO SHELL OUT THE DOUGH FOR SEX PILLOWS, toss couch cushions on the floor and use them to inspire new positions. Better lighting can also boost body confidence, says Candida Royalle, author of *How to Tell a Naked Man What to Do*. "None of us is perfect," she says, "but bright white bulbs are particularly unflattering." She recommends replacing them with amber-colored lighting, which casts a warm, sexy glow.

LESSON #4

The students: Mariana and Mark
    San Francisco, California
    33 and 31
    DNA applications scientist and software engineer
    Dating since January 2006
    WHAT NEEDS AN UPGRADE: Mark and Mariana enjoy a super-hot, high-intensity sex life. "But Mark has two jobs and a 7-year-old son, which makes it difficult to find time to connect emotionally," Mariana says.
    ASSIGNMENT: To appreciate a sexual encounter that's about intimacy, not orgasm. For couples like Mark and Mariana, who don't get a lot of time together, "the trick is to keep from always leaping into goal-oriented sex," Davidson says. "Touching without climaxing is often the key for couples to connect [emotionally]," Britton says. "This exercise allows them to demonstrate to each other that eroticism can be so much more compelling than just crossing the finish line."

Step one was setting the mood, which Mark and Mariana accomplished with candlelight, sexy music, and massage oil. "I blindfolded him and massaged his body with my hands, lips, tongue, feathers, and even with my body," Mariana says. "That felt exceptionally erotic. I loved that he couldn't anticipate what I was going to do next." The slow, careful touching was very different from their usual get-naked-and-go M.O. "I really liked the feeling of just being in the moment," Mark says. "It was a huge turn-on to be teased, and then to tease, but after a while it got frustrating and I wanted more!" Then it was his turn to blindfold Mariana. "Mark was tender and playful," she says. "I got so aroused that I tried to get him to forget about the homework. I told him we could even lie about it. But we stuck to our guns—well, he did, so I did, too." When Mariana was about to hit the point of no return, they dialed back and cuddled until they fell asleep. "When we woke up we decided we were done with our homework," Mark admits. "So we went all the way, and it was intense." They gave the exercise an A+. "The tension from the buildup was enormous," Mariana says. "I'd never experienced anything like it."

Make It Work for You

MAKE UP SOME SEXY RULES TO SLOW THINGS DOWN. "Really hot sex depends on the amount of pleasure and the height of arousal, regardless of whether you orgasm or not," Dr. Davidson says. To shift the focus away from goal-oriented sex, try "creating specific scenarios in which you only use certain parts of your body to pleasure each other," she says. "For example, use only your mouths, or hands, or even toys." Take turns imposing playful limitations on each other.

LESSON #5

The students: Stacey and Bryce
   Brooklyn, New York
   32 and 34
   Teachers
   Dated for 3 years before getting married in November 2007

WHAT NEEDS AN UPGRADE: By the end of a stressful day in the classroom, Stacey and Bryce say their energy levels are about as high as Kevin Federline's IQ. To unwind, they park in front of the TV, and by the time they get around to sex, they're falling asleep. "When we do have sex late at night, it can feel routine," Stacey says.

ASSIGNMENT: Multitask their TV viewing by watching skin flicks during prime time. "Studies have shown that both men and women watching sexual imagery have increased blood flow to their hot spots," Doolittle says. In other words, it's a reflex—one with a very practical purpose: to promote the survival of the species. "It directs your attention to sex when you're distracted and pressed for time," Doolittle says. "If porn gets Stacey and Bryce focused on sex, then they can turn their attention back to each other."

Following the recommendations of a female friend who enjoys porn, Stacey brought home three movies. At 10 p.m. she popped *Playgirl's Burning Lust* ($22/www.cduniverse.com) into the DVD player, and before long she and Bryce were both laughing and rolling their eyes. "We weren't into the beefcake/Barbie-doll sex," Bryce says. "It was weird to see so many fake boobs and unnatural bodies." The next night, a second title, *Playgirl's Erotic Encounters* ($22/www.cduniverse.com), got an equally bad review. "We fast-forwarded right through it," Stacey admits. "The sexual acrobatics were awkward." The third flick, *Xana and Dax* by Comstock Films ($25/www.comstockfilms.com), was different. "This was our favorite," Bryce says. "There was no plot; it's a real couple having sex. They looked like people we would know and be attracted to." Stacey agrees. "I loved *Xana and Dax* because they're a real couple, with genuine orgasms and a sincere admiration for each other," she says. "We watched it straight through, and even though we were as tired as usual, we had sex right after." And they changed their usual routine by trying a new position from the video. "Now we're starting to incorporate more porn in our sex life," Stacey says. "We even brought some on vacation right after doing this assignment."

Make It Work for You

USE SEXY IMAGES AND THOUGHTS TO KICK-START A SLEEPY LIBIDO. "If you're open to erotic movies, watch a DVD—even for just a few minutes—to get in the mood when you're tired," Dr. Davidson says. "Or wake up early and watch a scene to inspire morning sex." If adult movies aren't your thing, e-mail each other lascivious ideas or sexy pics during the day (how about one of you?), then talk about it when you get home. If you flirt throughout the day, you're more likely to put sex on the plate—even before dinner.

BROWSE FOR BOOTY

You'll find plenty of online options like www.babeland.com, www.blowfish.com, and www.goodvibes.com to point and click your way to ecstasy, but you'll miss out on a sexy hands-on experience—and a chance to talk as you explore the aisles. If the only adult boutique in your neck of the woods is that neon-lit novelty store off the interstate, get some thrills by browsing for hidden erotica at these mainstream shops.

Bookstore

Take your girl to the sexuality/erotica section and flip through tawdry tomes until you find something tempting. Some to check out: *The Sex Bible,* by Susan Crain Bakos ($30); *She Comes First* and *He Comes Next*, both by Ian Kerner, PhD ($23 and $24); *The Ultimate Guide to Sexual Fantasy,* by Violet Blue ($15); and *A Year of Spicy Sex: 52 Recipes to Heat Up Your Sex Life,* by Gabrielle Morrissey, PhD. ($15).

Lingerie Boutique

It's easy enough to pick out lingerie together, but to make it extra sexy, shop between dinner and a movie. Then, wear the stuff out of the store. He gets the anticipation of undressing you, and you get to feel the silk against your skin. Frederick's of Hollywood Smooth Sensations bras and panties ($10 to $28/www.fredericks.com) are sexy but wearable outside the boudoir.

Grocery Store

Skip the obvious phallic vegetable and whipped cream clichés. Instead, run to the baking/spice section and look for a bottle of cinnamon sugar. Once you're home, sprinkle on skin and lick clean. Serves two.

Home Improvement Center

Hit the home decor aisle for a full-length mirror. Most of them come with, er, mounting hardware. Tip: Instead of installing it vertically, stick it horizontally on a wall next to your bed. Nothing makes missionary sexier than seeing head-to-toe action.

SEX: THE COMPLETE INSTRUCTIONS

WE ASKED 10,000 GUYS WHAT THEIR BIGGEST SEX RESOLUTIONS ARE. TURN YOUR MOST IMPORTANT RESOLUTIONS INTO YOUR GREATEST SUCCESS STORIES

Who says resolutions are to be made on January 1st and abandoned on January 10th? Any time is a good time to make a resolution. No matter what the calendar says, pick one and work at it!

LAST LONGER IN BED

First, take one adult-size dose of reality—you may feel better: The average guy lasts 5 to 10 minutes. So maybe you're perfectly normal but have been brainwashed by sitcom jokes and porn. Sex therapist Brian Zamboni, PhD, suggests shrugging off an early emission with some extra attention to her arousal (yes, it means staying awake), then getting back in the saddle. Most men last much longer the second time around. And the more you practice, the longer that first time will last.

If your doctor signs off on it, you could try Viagra: A study shows that it can help reduce your refractory period for that second go-round, and confidence leads to endurance. Also, do the following:

PLEASE HER FIRST. Then she won't care so much about your hair trigger. Use your hands, mouth, or sex toys to bring her to orgasm before you take your turn, says Ian Kerner, PhD, a sex and relationships counselor in New York City and author of *She Comes First*.

LET HER CLIMB ON. When she's on top, your penis is less stimulated. And ask her to go slowly. "Long and fast thrusting is hazardous to a man's endurance," says sexologist Robert W. Birch, PhD.

PRACTICE. When you masturbate, don't let yourself come quickly. It will train your body to finish fast, says Zamboni.

If it usually takes you 2 minutes, try to stretch it to 5, and so on. Pay close attention to your arousal, Kerner says. If you can learn to sense when you're about to ejaculate, you'll know when to pull out and take a breather during sex.

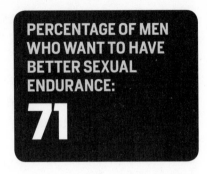

HAVE MORE SEX

Focus on better sex, and the frequency will take care of itself, says Joy Davidson, PhD, a sex therapist and the author of *Fearless Sex*. One way is to add quickies to the equation . . . while redefining "quickie" in a way that works for both of you. Think of it more as an unplanned event than a brief one. Try a new environment where daring and spontaneity are part of the act—a department-store dressing room, your garage before you leave for dinner, under that tiny airline blanket in 35A and 35B. If more places are available, more sex is, too. "If it's exciting, she won't need as much time to be aroused," says Joel D. Block, PhD, a sex therapist and the author of *The Art of the Quickie*. "Quickies that work will energize any sexual relationship. You'll have captured her imagination."

TELL YOUR CRUSH HOW YOU FEEL ABOUT HER

"Rip off the proverbial Band-Aid and get it over with," says Nicole Beland, *Men's Health*'s Girl Next Door. "Until you ask, you're never really going to know." Talk in person, call, or e-mail (yes, e-mailing is fine) on a Thursday afternoon—that's the golden hour for confessing a crush. "It's late enough in the week that a girl will be thinking about the weekend, but she won't be rushing out the way she might on Friday," Beland says. And keep it short. "Tell her you have to get something off your chest, and then blurt it out just like they do in the movies," she says. "It's the most painless and romantic way. Then back off and give her time to think."

IF SHE REJECTS YOU . . . Stand up straight, smile, and say something like, "I'm glad you're honest, and it would be great if we could be friends." Above all, stay classy. She'll remember that.

IF SHE'S ON THE FENCE . . . Lay low and don't try to win her over with flowers or gifts. "If she's waffling, a grand gesture would only overwhelm her," Beland says.

IF SHE SAYS, "OH, ALL RIGHT" . . . Send flowers the next day—something small and basic. Then plan the date.

"It takes balls," Beland says. "Will she jump into your arms? You're about to find out."

FIGURE OUT WHAT YOU WANT IN A WOMAN—AND THEN FIND HER

That's a lot of pressure you've put on yourself there, pal. If you use that as your primary relationship goal, you're probably overreaching. "Stop looking for a serious relationship," says John Gray, PhD, author of *Mars and Venus on a Date*. Instead, aim for good dates—no higher. Set a goal to meet a new woman every week, or ask a pal or mutual friends to set you up. (You heard right—request blind dates.) It doesn't mean one of them will be The One. But as you accrue what Gray calls "positive dating experiences," you'll feel more comfortable and start to understand what you're really looking for. "Beginning a relationship should be like visiting a friend's house, not house shopping," Gray says. "You want to appreciate the details, not criticize."

REDUCE YOUR PORN HABIT

Your problem may not be a bad jones (and overworked johnson), but boredom. If you transform spare time into quality time, you won't be running to your computer every 10 minutes. "Join a hockey club or play in a basketball league at your gym," suggests Scott Haltzman, MD, author of *The Secrets of Happily Married Men*. "Engaging in sports will help relieve pent-up physical needs."

And kink up your real-life sex life. "Porn is a quick fix," says Ian Kerner, PhD, a sex and relationships counselor in New York City. Tell your girlfriend a sexy fantasy you had about her. "Women are into role playing just as much as men are," says Kerner. It'll turn her on, and you'll have the naughty nurse of your dreams—no flat-screen required.

MAKE SURE SHE REACHES ORGASM—EVERY TIME

This one's easy: Downgrade that resolution. "Put a woman under that kind of perceived pressure and you're pretty much guaranteeing that she won't climax," says Laura Berman, PhD, president and director of the Berman Center and author of *The Passion Prescription.* "It's one of the main reasons women fake it."

PERCENTAGE OF MEN WHO WANT TO TAKE HER TO THE PEAK EVERY TIME:

80

Remember John Cleese in *The Meaning of Life:* "What's wrong with a kiss, boy?" A survey conducted by the Berman Center and K-Y Brand found that couples who kiss often in nonsexual situations are eight times less likely to feel stressed than those who don't. The key: "Kiss her in a way that doesn't feel like a quick stop-off on the way to getting undressed," Berman says. "Massage her, rub her all over her body, and give her the opportunity to quiet her mind before having sex." Yes, all that before you go stampeding toward her clitoris.

And once you do get to her clitoris? Toning down your intensity during sex may help her relax. "Unlike men, a lot of women find it easier to have an orgasm if they're receiving slower, more consistent stimulation," says Berman.

PERSUADE YOUR WIFE OR GIRLFRIEND TO EXPERIMENT MORE IN BED

Here's the problem: Whatever you suggest, she'll know why you'll enjoy it, but she'll wonder what's in it for her. (Note: Her chance to play "horny chiropractor" is not an incentive.) So start with bringing out her fantasies, says Gloria G. Brame, PhD, a sex therapist and the author of *Come Hither: A Commonsense Guide to Kinky Sex.* One night a month, be her do-anything male escort. She decides what happens. It could be the hot naughty. It could be dinner, one long kiss, and sending you off all excited. It could be shopping attentively with her—stick with us here—so every other woman in the store is jealous (never a small thing in her world). At the end of the evening, she pays you with an IOU for whatever she thinks you were worth—so she'll have a chance to exercise her racy imagination. Whatever happens, you gladly play along and then reap the benefits. "Once a man shows he can be tolerant and eroticize her fantasy, she'll offer up more variety," Brame says.

APPROACH WOMEN MORE EASILY AT PARTIES

Make encounters unavoidable by finding a role to play. Volunteer to take the coats or make the drinks for a while. This will make the initial approach easier, says psychologist Bonnie Jacobson, PhD, author of *The Shy Single*. And if your first attempts fizzle, don't fret. You may have to mix a few martinis before you stir someone's interest.

SPEND MORE TIME WITH YOUR WIFE OR GIRLFRIEND

Which one? Make up your mind! Seriously, you have to start planning for the relationship. Set up a romantic dinner date the way you'd schedule an office meeting and you'll thrive at home and at work. "The classic mistake busy men

MAN'S GUIDE PRINCIPLES

Here are a few rules to live by:

Start foreplay in the morning. Jump-start her libido with a morning compliment, followed by a flattering midday e-mail, and finish with your secret weapon: Do a household chore. She'll melt.

Invest the extra 10 minutes. The time you devote to oral sex or manual stimulation will make her eager to come back for more.

Choose the win-win position. Coax her on top: more stimulation for her, more staying power for you.

Convince her she's a sex goddess, and she will be. Drop naughty compliments when she's clothed, and before you know it, she won't be.

make is putting all their planning into their workdays and none into their personal lives," says Julie Morgenstern, a time-management consultant. "It may feel like career suicide, but the only way to keep your creative and strategic edge at work is to allow yourself to recharge at home." Making your partner a priority may boost your health, as well: Studies show that spending time with a supportive spouse can curb work-related stress and lower blood pressure.

Set up a simple, specific schedule for spending time together. If that means a weekly gig for the babysitter, go for it. You'll be surprised by the payoff: "A routine is not so much confining as it is liberating," says Morgenstern. It's a guilt buster. "You won't feel guilty spending time with business associates on a Monday night because you'll have planned other times to go out with your wife or girlfriend. It frees you to live in the moment."

HAVE FREQUENT SEX WITH HOT WOMEN

What you're really saying, then, is, "I want to manage several relationships at once without being perceived as a womanizing jerk." There are dangers here. Women in sexual relationships sometimes like to include monogamy in the program. But if you want to try, then the best advice, says Dean Mignola, author of *The Single Guy's Survival Guide,* is to remain genuine without being predatory. Let each woman know that you're seeing others. Say this: "I want to make sure when I choose someone, I really know her." She may dump you then and there. But maybe not. Her competitiveness may kick in, which could result in extra nakedness.

PROPOSE TO YOUR GIRLFRIEND THIS YEAR

Congratulations! May she always have the wit of Sarah Silverman and the body of Laetitia Casta. To ensure that this is the last proposal you'll ever have to deliver, first make the moment all about the two of you. That means you should resist the urge to tell everyone you know before you propose, says Judy Kuriansky, PhD, author of *The Complete Idiot's Guide to Dating.* This includes

PERCENTAGE OF SINGLE MEN WHO PLAN TO POP THE QUESTION THIS YEAR:

22

her best friends. The next step is setting up the occasion. You don't need an audience; renting a hot-air balloon or securing space on the Jumbotron will only be a distraction. Instead, plan a day that demonstrates how well you know her, and propose then. Pick a place you've enjoyed together before, or choose a significant date, like the anniversary of the day you met. When she says yes, all that's left to do is pucker up . . . and kiss your independence goodbye!

TURN A FRIEND INTO A LOVER

Making a move on a good friend requires more careful work than defusing a pipe bomb. One false move and, well, you know. Avoid devastation and fallout with these four expert-approved strategies.

1. **SET THE SCENE.** Choose a place that's comfortable for both of you, says Logan Levkoff, a sex educator in New York City. And don't make it a big production. "A lot of guys try to take cues from sappy movies where friends become something more," says Levkoff. "Don't stand outside her window with a boom box over your head."

2. **READ HER BODY.** Talk less, do more. "Kiss her," says Levkoff. "Sometimes it's easier to break down the barrier physically instead of verbally." But how do you know to go for it? "If her face is close enough that you can lean in, then that's a good sign," she says.

3. **LEAVE YOUR GAME AT THE DOOR.** She knows about every girl you've dated and every pickup line you've ever used, so no fancy come-ons, Levkoff advises. Look her in the eyes and say, "You know all about me and my past, and I don't want the other girls I've dated. I want you." Yes, it's formal, but say it anyway. "It works because it shows her you're sincere," says Levkoff.

4. **RETREAT.** If it doesn't work out, follow these three words: Let it be. "Eventually, your friendship can, and will, return to normal," says Levkoff.

HAVE HARDER ERECTIONS

Legendary erections are all about great blood flow, like you had when you and all your blood vessels were in your teens. Regular exercise will always help with that, and here are some other hardening strategies you should be aware of.

LOSE SOME WEIGHT. If you're looking to turn your weeping willow into a mighty oak, just add testosterone. Building muscle will stoke your he-man hormone supply. The surest way to deplete it? Gain fat. A study from Weill Medical College at Cornell University shows that as men gain weight, their testosterone levels shrink accordingly. The really good news: Muscle is the best fat incinerator around. Add some and you stiffen your resolve in two mutually reinforcing ways.

GET BERRIED. The antioxidants in berries may combat free radicals in your bloodstream that could put a damper on your erection, Indiana University researchers found. Add as many as you can to your presex diet.

TUNE YOUR TICKER. Yeah, yeah—heart disease is the number one killer of men. But let's talk about something important: The blood-vessel scarring that threatens your heart also threatens the tiny vessels that harden your erection. So eat an apple and a bowl of oatmeal every day: Fiber is a great blood-vessel scouring agent.

GET OVER YOUR EX AND MOVE ON

Strip clubs and buddies can be your first line of defense, but as therapeutic as they are, you have to go back to that empty home sometime.

BE SERIOUS ABOUT IT. "Treat a breakup as if you're overcoming an addiction," says anthropologist Helen Fisher, PhD, author of *Why We Love.* Banish evidence of your ex—cards, photos, that cursed jug of Woolite. They're the equivalent of a dime bag in the glove compartment, says Fisher.

TAKE A 90-DAY HIATUS FROM NEW RELATIONSHIPS. Enjoy your unencumbered life: "If you've wanted to go to South America or take sailing lessons, now's your time," says Fisher. Before you know it, you'll be ready to dash yourself on the jagged rocks of love all over again.

THE PRECIPICE

BRING YOUR RELATIONSHIP BACK FROM THE BRINK
WITH LESSONS LEARNED BY THIS COUPLE

BY DAGNY SCOTT BARRIOS

The way my husband and I arrived on the brink was not unique. Clinging to a mental list of irritants, after a few years of "You never . . . " and "I always . . . ," there we were.

"I just don't know if it's worth it anymore." I was a thousand miles away in a hotel room on a business trip. I'd left in a snit—called "goodbye" from the bottom of the stairs, gotten in the car, and driven off. Without waiting for him to answer, without waiting to exchange our customary hug and kiss.

It was rotten of me, leaving like that. But didn't I have cause? Hadn't he lain in bed while I raced around in a predawn huff, getting our daughter her breakfast, even while I was the one trying to get to the airport? Wasn't I fed up with being responsible for everything all the time? Didn't I feel like he was no help at all . . . like I'd be better off without him?

Well, didn't I?

As I sat attempting to justify my fuming, I knew I'd crossed some line, leaving without so much as a peck on the cheek. Ice cold.

And so: "Go concentrate on your work," came my husband's soft voice. "We'll talk when you get back."

I closed my phone and stared at the flowered nylon bedspread. So this is where my marriage ends, I thought, curling and uncurling my stockinged toes.

A TEAM DIVIDED

When I got home the next night, my husband and I verbally thrust and parried. It wasn't exactly a fight, more a series of accusations thrown back and forth as we alternately followed each other from room to room and stomped off, unable to resolve anything, unable to let it go.

I had wondered if I would be better off alone—not always, but from time to time. The thought was like a virus that sat just under my skin, erupting in times of stress. If we didn't have a child, I told myself, I could walk away. But we did, and she was so young—2, then 3, a baby still. Yet when the resentment bubbled up, I felt ready to leave, despite our daughter. We survived each bout of fighting, but I grew cavalier, assuming I could walk away.

Now we lay on our backs staring at the ceiling. I began to envision what was to follow: the grim packing of boxes, a sterile white-walled condo, shuttling our daughter back and forth, Christmases and Hanukkahs divided in half.

The silence ticked by. He was saying nothing. My husband is cast in the old mold—tough, impervious, stoic. These things I'd loved about him when I thought they came from a place of strength now turned against me. He would never be the one to back down first.

As neither of us spoke, it dawned on me that he wasn't alone in that role: We'd each worked so hard to avoid being weak. Without realizing it, after years of stubborn accusations, we had chipped away at any foundation of trust, any sense of being a team. The only thing that could save us was a new strategy—one that didn't stem from that place of mulish certainty, but rather of yielding and resilience.

I closed my eyes. I swallowed my pride, that hard, immutable thing. "This is not what I want," I began. "Listen, if you really want to leave, that's one thing. But I think our problem is that we're not trying to be on the same side. I'm willing to try if you are. Believe it or not, I don't want you to be miserable."

He rolled from his back and faced me. "It's not what I want, either."

NOT AN OPTION

A few weeks later, a man I didn't even know walked us farther away from the precipice. I was interviewing J. for a project when he began talking about his relationship. He had been married for 25 years. The first two decades had been ideal, he said, but now he and his wife had grown distant. "I hardly know who she is anymore," he mused.

My mind raced ahead to the predictable conclusion: that he must be dreaming of leaving, starting anew now that the children were grown. But instead he said something remarkable.

"I'm not going to have an affair, and I'm not going to leave. That's not an option. So we have to work on redefining what we mean to each other at this stage."

"I'm not going to leave." Why did I find that so shocking? Isn't that what marriage really means? Not leaving is the most basic precept of the institution. And yet how many couples truly play by those rules? I realized that I couldn't have made the simple statement this stranger just had. In truth, for me, leaving had always been an option.

He went on: "People get into a difficult time in their relationships, and so they find the new girlfriend or the new wife. And instead of working through things, they just keep repeating the same cycle over and over. But it's those difficult times where growth happens."

When a woman leaves a relationship nowadays it's virtually a badge of honor, a sign of healthy self-respect. And to me, not considering that possibility had always seemed, well, weak. Until now. Could it be that finding a way to stay put was actually the tougher thing to do?

When I returned home from this trip, I told my husband about the conversation, how stunning it was to hear a married man say that leaving was simply not an option.

"We should sign a contract," my husband said. "That we'll never leave."

I laughed. "We already did. It's called a marriage license."

But I knew what he meant. Perhaps there should be another stage to the wedding vows. After a year, or 5, or however long it takes to acknowledge the possibilities that lie in wait. "Here," the document would say. "Now sign on the line and say that you're in this for good."

IN IT TOGETHER

We haven't signed any new document. We haven't needed to. Now that we're not so busy eyeing the escape route, the brink grows more distant. We focus on remembering what we love about each other, letting the petty complaints slide. In the bargain, the big things have gotten better, and we are happier. He's more willing to help out; I'm less likely to snipe and fume.

We still argue, of course. But we're better at it. No longer feeling vulnerable, we don't slip into threats. We've learned to give each other the benefit of the doubt.

Recently, when a remark he made upset me, a smile flitted on his lips as my voice rose.

"What's so funny?" I demanded.

"We're going to be together anyway; why fight about this?"

So our simple disagreement remained just that—a thunderstorm blowing through quickly, instead of twisting into a referendum on our future together. The difference was that we'd finally shut the window, the one we'd always kept cracked open as an escape route. We were finally in this marriage together.

KEEP SEX EXCITING

If, like most men, you're feeling too overworked and overextended to take a few days off, you're probably feeling something else, as well—a lugubrious lack of sexual excitement. All work and no play can make Jack a dull boy; they can also make Jill a divorcée. To keep the woman in your life happier—and a happier her is a much happier you—make arrangements for a weekend getaway now.

Consider these stats:

Nearly 40 percent of couples report having better sex than normal on the weekends, when they are on vacation, or on special occasions, according to the Berman Sexuality Center's 2005 Intimacy Index.

Women who take two or more vacations a year with their husbands are twice as satisfied with their marriages than women who don't get away—and 50 percent less likely to suffer from depression. Makes sense, when you consider a new study from the University of North Carolina at Charlotte, which found that workaholic men are three times more likely than the general population to become separated or divorced.

Couples who are sexually adventurous (role-playing, sex toys, acrobatics) are 26 percent more likely to have sex several times a week than are their more conservative peers who, according to the Kinsey Institute, may have sex just twice a month.

TAKE HER, OUTDOORS

Need to put some spark back in your sex life? Add some sizzle by risking a little exposure.

ON THE BEACH. You've both thought about it, so expectations are high. "Beaches connote both sex and romance," says sex educator Ellen Kate Friedrichs, of www.sexedvice.com. Bring up the idea early in a trip to heighten anticipation. And don't be impulsive; pick your spot and bring a blanket. "Wait until long after sunset, then get away from the ambient light of the boardwalk or pier," suggests Lorelei Sharkey, one half of the sex-advice duo Em & Lo. Steer clear of the dunes; "you won't be able to hear an interloper until he or she is on top of you."

ON A CAMPING TRIP. Don't confine your primal urges to the tent. (Though a stealth shag in a campground with nearby neighbors is hot.) On a hike, it's worth carrying the extra weight of blankets and a pad like the Big Agnes Air Core pad (www.rei.com). It's cushy, but durable, and doubles as a raft for skinny-dipping. Then get off the trail, find a sheltered spot, and let it happen. In camp, try the Sweetie Pie Sleeping Bag Doubler (www.functionaldesign. net) to turn a regular bag into one big fun house for two.

IN THE HOT TUB. It's at once private and out in the open; you can both be stark (or half) naked without feeling exposed, thanks to the churning water. "Hot tubs are social spaces, relaxing, but they also represent sexiness," says Carol Queen, PhD, author of *Exhibitionism for the Shy*. And she'll love those jets. Emma Taylor, the Em of Em & Lo, suggests a silicone-based lube for whatever you have in mind; her natural lubrication will wash away.

ADD UP THE COST OF HAVING AN AFFAIR

Uh oh, big trouble. For your relationship—and for your wallet.

$595

A membership to and the related services of www.alibinetwork.com: The secrecy of an affair is what tends to interest men at first, but keeping it quiet can be costly.

$499

A trip to the doctor for antibiotics—paid in full to keep it off insurance forms: Adulterous men usually don't use condoms with the missus or the mistress; an STD is bound to pop up.

$4,300

Your annual raise: Men in rocky marriages are more likely to take their at-home stress to work, causing productivity to dip.

$264

A gym membership to boost your mood: Affairs tend to make men especially prone to depression.

$1,050

Legal fees: Between 46 percent and 62 percent of cheaters dip their pens in the company ink. Watch out for a harassment suit.

$3,600

Family therapy: Infidelity is one of the hardest hurdles to clear in couples therapy, and it's especially hard on adolescents.

$163

Blood-pressure meds and a digital BP monitor: Marriage trouble has been shown to significantly raise a man's blood pressure.

TOTAL: $10,471

HEAL A BROKEN RELATIONSHIP

Every 5 seconds, a woman shells out cash for a cheesy novel with a Fabio look-alike on the cover—that's $1.2 billion worth of ripped bodices every year. Why? Women drink up romantic fantasy the way you put down Johnny Walker Blue. Keep that in mind when you have something to say to a woman in your life—whether she's your main squeeze or tantalizingly out of reach. To turn anger into forgiveness or disinterest into passion, grab a thick sheet of that résumé paper you haven't needed in years and focus on her specific, unique qualities. "If your love letter could be sent to your neighbor's wife, it's the wrong love letter," says Jason Tesauro, coauthor of *The Modern Lover*. "The little moments you remember are much better than just a generic phrase of love." Here's how to pen a note that will end up at the top of her lingerie drawer, not the bottom of her birdcage.

THE PRESENTATION: "Handwritten on decent stationery, with anything but an ordinary ballpoint pen," says Tesauro. Even better, use the back of the hotel receipt from your weekend getaway at the bed-and-breakfast, or the inside cover of a playbill from a show you saw together.

THE WORDS TO USE: Every pencil pusher, once on the romantic hunt, begins to think he's Robert Browning, which leads to stomach churners like "hearts beating as one" and "eyes like limpid pools." Instead . . .

KEEP IT SIMPLE: Tell her exactly why you love her and why you think she's sexy (i.e., show, don't tell). Things like, "I love the way your body looks when we're in the shower together," or, "You're irresistible in that black dress you wore on our anniversary" will let her know she's still beautiful.

PROPER DELIVERY: If you're going to send it by mail, seal it with a wax stamp. (A few drops of candle wax and the imprint of a foreign coin will work.) It's a small touch with a big romantic effect. Otherwise, tuck it into her briefcase, on her dashboard, under her plate, or into her luggage if she's traveling without you. Discovering the note in an unexpected place ensures that your love story stays a page-turner.

AVOID BEDROOM BLUNDERS

One more reason to love orgasms: They mask pain, thanks to the endorphin flood. The rub? While in the throes, you might not notice a sensation that would normally hurt. Learn from our not-so-fun nooky accidents and get off without getting wounded.

OUCH #1: BRUISE

Overly enthusiastic thrusting, groping, kissing, or sucking can result in an unwelcome shiner or the dreaded hickey.

RX: It's a bummer—a bruise usually lasts a couple of weeks. But decreasing blood flow to the area will limit its size, says Jeffrey R. Bytomski, DO, a physician at Duke University Medical Center. To do: Ice bruise for 20 to 30 minutes three times a day for the first 2 days and wrap it with a bandage.

NEXT TIME: There's no preventing the odd bruise in the sack. But if your slender beauty's pelvic bone juts into you, place a folded fleece scarf at the point of impact (use it later around her wrists). And if she attacks your neck like a vampire, break out the garlic and run.

OUCH #2: OVEREXTENDED MUSCLE

You contorted Ringling Bros.–style last night, and today you feel like you scaled Mount Rushmore.

RX: Rest and stretch. To ease any soreness still lingering 24 to 36 hours later, apply heat for 20 to 30 minutes two or three times a day, Dr. Bytomski says. But if you're too lame to even consider bedroom gymnastics after 24 hours, see a doc to rule out a torn muscle.

NEXT TIME: Stay limber with this full-body move four times a week, says yoga instructor Kristin McGee. Frog Pose: Squat, bending your knees out to the sides at 90-degree angles, and rest your forearms on the floor. Gently press your butt down. Hold for 30 to 60 seconds.

OUCH #3: RUG BURN

Carpets aren't the only offenders. Wood floors, sheets, and even the backseat of your Ford can rub skin the wrong way.

RX: Clean the wound with soap and warm water, air dry, and apply an antibiotic ointment like Neosporin. Cover with a nonstick bandage to keep the spot clean, Dr. Bytomski says. Change it daily, removing it for good once a scab forms.

NEXT TIME: Switch to high-thread-count sheets. (Higher equals softer.) Or toss a cushy blanket like the Fascinator Throe ($85/www.liberator.com) over any surface you tumble on. Avoid anything made from terry cloth or scratchy wool.

OUCH #4: VAGINAL IRRITATION

Obviously, this one's for her. It happens when (a) she isn't lubricated enough, (b) she has a bad reaction to a lube or a vibrator, or (c) you didn't wash your hands well enough after slicing a chili pepper (true story—yikes).

RX: Thanks to its cell-shedding process and natural cleansing acids, the vagina is self-healing. She should avoid inserting anything (including your penis, tampons, or vibrators) for 48 hours—the time it takes to mend. Soothe discomfort with a warm water bath (no soap) twice a day, says Hilda Hutcherson, MD, assistant professor of obstetrics and gynecology at Columbia University Medical Center in New York City.

NEXT TIME: Demand generous foreplay: It takes anywhere from 30 seconds to several minutes once she's aroused before she naturally lubricates. Test a new lube on her inner labia and wait a few hours for a reaction before a full-on slather. And, if jalapeños are involved, vigorous hand washing with a washcloth and warm, soapy water is in order. Avoid: jelly rubber toys containing phthalates, chemicals that irritate tender tissue.

OUCH #5: WOUNDED WILLIE

Wild sex could put your johnson in jeopardy. If an enthusiastic thrust misses its mark and hits her pubic bone instead, you could tear your tunica albuginea (erectile tissue). You'll hear a pop—followed by an unprintable verbal outburst. Get to the ER, pronto. You'll need a surgical procedure to repair the tear and prevent scar tissue, says Drogo K. Montague, MD, head of genitourethral reconstruction at the Cleveland Clinic Foundation. Luckily, a broken banger is rare, but younger guys, take note: Harder erections are more likely to snap.

THE HONEST TRUTH ABOUT WOMEN FROM OUR LOVELY NEIGHBOR

My ex is a nut. How do I explain the situation to the girl I'm now dating?

First of all, wait at least a month. The more time your new girlfriend has to get to know and trust you, the less likely she'll be to bolt. That said, don't wait much longer than that, or she'll consider it a lie of omission. Bring the bad news up casually, over dinner: "I don't know if you've ever had an annoying ex, but I'm dealing with one right now." Give her a brief account of the relationship (which paints you in the best light, of course) and how it went south. Then change the subject as quickly as she'll let you. You want to send the vibe that this is an issue, yeah, but it's nothing the two of you can't handle.

I hooked up with a gorgeous girl but was too drunk to perform. How do I get a second chance?

Did you call her the next day to say that you wished you'd been sober? If not, a softy is the least of your problems. Women are perfectly aware that a long night of drinking will turn a one-eyed snake into a gummy worm, and we seldom hold it against a guy. We know you may be too embarrassed to call. But if a week goes by and we still haven't gotten a post-hookup hello, we're pissed. If you want to see her naked body again, you'd better start with a good excuse. Try, "I've wanted to get in touch with you every day this week, but work deadlines hit hard and my life has been crazy. . . ."

My girlfriend says she doesn't enjoy receiving oral sex. Is that possible?

Can you imagine a guy not wanting his knob polished? Probably not, but think again. What if she used her teeth and chomped down like it was an Italian sausage? It could be that your girlfriend has had a few bad experiences that have made her reluctant to be the recipient of a tongue bath. She might also just be saying that she doesn't like it because she doesn't feel, you know, fresh—because of her period or any number of things that might be going on down there, none of which you want to know about. And then there's that self-consciousness that could be left over from her days in the convent with Sister Mary Immaculata. Either way, I suggest waiting for a night right after she's had a shower, and gently kissing your way south. If/when she protests, ask if she'll grant you just one chance to change her mind.

Even though she's clearly trying, my girlfriend isn't so great at giving oral sex. How can I prompt her to improve her technique?

You need something that will make the experience more pleasurable for her, something that will encourage her to treat your penis like a lollipop, something that will prompt her to get her hands involved. You need flavored lube. Sure, whipped cream and chocolate sauce are more readily available, but they're too messy. There's a lube called Sliquid Swirl Green Apple Tart ($12/www.babeland.com) that has a slippery, water-based consistency and tastes pretty good. Squeeze one drop on the palm of her hand and one on the tip of your rod, and prepare for liftoff.

The last woman I tried to have sex with doggie style said it was offensive. Do most women feel that way?

No. Most women enjoy a variety of positions, including that one. But if I were having sex with someone for the first time and he quickly maneuvered me onto my hands and knees, I'd be bothered. You can't see each other's face. You can't kiss. It's not offensive so much as extremely unromantic.

Is tantric sex bullshit?

Yes . . . and no. "People get a lot of misconceptions when they hear Sting say that it allows him to have sex for 8 hours straight," says Ian Kerner, PhD, a sex and relationships counselor in New York City and the author of *She Comes First.* "It's not going to turn you into some kind of sexual superstar." What it might do, however, is foster a heightened sense of spirituality and a deeper level of connectedness with your partner—at least that's the conclusion reached by studies of couples who practice the art. Tantric-sex practitioners reach those states through meditation, massage, and yogalike positions. Other tantalizing benefits include the ability to stay erect for hours and the enjoyment of multiple whole-body orgasms (minus the ejaculations, of course). "In that sense, it might also help men with premature ejaculation and erectile disorders," says Kerner. "But the fact that it takes a while to learn and that it's fairly complicated, spiritually and philosophically, turns people off pretty quickly. I'm all about making sex easier for people, not more difficult." For more information, visit www.tantra.com.

My girlfriend is really uncomfortable when I hit her G-spot. Does it need to warm up, just like the clitoris?

G-spot stimulation is tricky, because it sometimes makes a woman feel as if she has to pee. She may put on the sexual brakes, even if it feels as if orgasm (yours or hers) is close. If she likes G-spot stimulation but simply needs time, ask her how she wants to start (for example, kissing, clitoral or breast stimulation, G-spot stimulation with your fingers), and go from there. Remember: For some women, it will still be too much.

Sometimes my girlfriend has pain during sex, and we have to stop. What am I doing wrong?

She may just need more lube. Our bodies can only get so wet on their own. Lube helps make marathon sex a reality. Other times, women feel pain during deep-thrusting positions that hit the cervix. Try giving her more control (woman on top—forward or reverse cowgirl). If lube and a position switch don't help, she should visit her doctor. Check out the National Vulvodynia Association's Web site (www.nva.org) for resources related to genital pain that doesn't go away.

I know the G-spot is on the front vaginal wall. But is there any extra stimulation from aiming toward other areas when I'm thrusting?

Sure—and finding what works is half the fun. Thrusting that hits closer to the cervix, where there are more nerve endings, can feel great. So can pressure about 3 or 4 inches farther out, around the entrance—particularly if it touches parts of the clitoris.

GET STIFFER WITH A STATIN

New research shows that Lipitor can help with erection problems if Viagra alone doesn't work. Taking both drugs simultaneously improved erection quality in men with erectile dysfunction by 76 percent, according to a study in the *Journal of Sexual Medicine*. Lipitor improves the function of the endothelium, the lining of blood vessels where erection-producing nitric oxide comes from, says study author Howard Herrmann, MD, a cardiologist at the University of Pennsylvania. This allows the Viagra to do its thing—prevent the breakdown of nitric oxide. In theory, he says, other statins should also work with Viagra. But don't try anything without a doctor's okay.

AVOID NASTY SIDE EFFECTS

Best new reason to take aspirin: If you regularly use pain medication, consider taking aspirin instead of a nonsteroidal anti-inflammatory drug (NSAID), such as ibuprofen. A study in the *Journal of Urology* found that middle-aged men who pop an NSAID every day double their risk of developing erectile dysfunction. Researchers speculate that NSAIDs may reduce nitric-oxide synthesis, a process essential for maintaining an erection.

Best new reason to garage your hog: Riding a motorcycle, like riding a bicycle, can cause erectile dysfunction (ED), say Japanese researchers in the *International Journal of Impotence Research*. They studied 234 bikers and found that an alarming number of them—nearly 70 percent—had erectile dysfunction, and there was a correlation between its prevalence and the number of years the men had been riding. The researchers believe that the compression and vibration of the saddle may cause ED.

> **PERCENT MORE LIKELY A MAN IS TO HAVE ERECTION PROBLEMS IF HE SMOKES A PACK OF CIGARETTES A DAY THAN IF HE DOES NOT SMOKE:**
> **40**

TAKE A PILL TO LAST LONGER

A drug to fight premature ejaculation (PE) seems to be working, but it's unclear when it will become available—if ever. A new study of 2,000 men with PE found that a form of antidepressant tripled the length of time men lasted during intercourse. The drug, dapoxetine, is similar to antidepressants like Zoloft and Paxil. These drugs—called selective serotonin reuptake inhibitors—delay ejaculation, but they can also lower your libido, which kind of defeats the purpose. The new drug enters and leaves a man's system more quickly, largely avoiding that side effect, says Jon Pryor, MD, a *Men's Health* urology advisor and the study's lead investigator.

In the placebo-controlled study, men who took the pill increased time to ejaculation from less than a minute to nearly 4 minutes, on average. SSRIs make serotonin more readily available to the body, reducing anxiety and delaying orgasm. Dapoxetine was rejected last year by the FDA for

❯❯ He Said/She Said

WOULD YOU BE THIS FORGIVING?

A survey says men are more tolerant of lying and cheating in a relationship.
Percentage who would forgive their partners for . . .

HE SAID		SHE SAID
59%	Lying about the number of sexual partners they've had	50%
54%	Kissing someone else	37%
47%	Having cybersex with someone else	24%
20%	Having sex with someone else	12%

undisclosed reasons. Johnson & Johnson declined to say when it would reapply for approval.

GIVE NEW MEANING TO "CLARITIN CLEAR"

When spring is in the air, your interest in sex may decrease, report researchers in the *Annals of Allergy, Asthma & Immunology*. In the study of more than 80 people, men with seasonal allergies were more likely to report a decrease in erectile function, intercourse satisfaction, sexual desire, and overall sexual contentment than men without allergies. Treatment with an oral antihistamine returned their sex drives and erectile function to normal.

SPOT HIDDEN PE TRIGGERS

According to a study of 153 men published in the *Journal of Sexual Medicine,* an inflamed prostate may be the cause of premature ejaculation in some men. Researchers found that 64 percent of participants with PE also suffered from prostatitis, an inflammation of the prostate gland that may be caused by trauma or an infection. The swelling of the gland can put pressure on the surrounding nerves and trigger ejaculation.

Another hidden cause of PE is thyroid problems. Problems below the waist might originate in the neck, according to Italian scientists. In a study published in the *Journal of Clinical Endocrinology and Metabolism,* the researchers found that 50 percent of men with hyperthyroidism (overactive thyroid) suffered from premature ejaculation and 64 percent of those with hypothyroidism (underactive thyroid) had below-normal sexual desire. Erectile dysfunction was common in both groups.

PART 6

SURVIVE RELATIONSHIPS

Anyone who says marriage is easy hasn't been in one. Yet 70 percent of men (and 68 percent of women) describe their marriages as "very happy," and 96 percent of men (and 91 percent of women) would marry their current spouse if they had it to do over again. So, despite rumors to the contrary, the institution isn't dead after all.

In this section, we offer our very best tips for building a strong relationship and keeping it together year, after year, after year. After all, isn't that what marriage is all about? Here you'll learn how to keep your home fires burning brightly. You'll read how to battle-proof your relationship, or at least win her over with fiendishly simple strategies. In a bit of a pickle? See if you can pass our forgiveness test and learn how to wriggle your way out of any relationship woe. Then discover the best ways to keep in touch throughout your day and always be in her hottest thoughts.

We hope these tips help make your life together one of happiness, harmony, and great sex.

BURNING-HOT HOME FIRES

KEEP THE EMBERS HOT WITH THESE 7 INCENDIARY STRATEGIES

BY MATT BEAN AND DENNY WATKINS

The heat of a new relationship is a chemical reaction, and it can fade with time. Here's how to rekindle the flame.

PLAY GAMES WITH HER

Boosting her dopamine levels outside of the bedroom could pay dividends between the sheets. "Your brain can't differentiate between the external anxiety caused by a novel situation and the internal anxiety caused by being attracted to someone," says Victoria Zdrok, PhD, a clinical psychologist (and former *Playboy* playmate—wowza). "A boost outside of the bedroom can carry over for when it matters most."

The best way to increase her anxiety, sans cardiac arrest? Competition, says Zdrok, which also helps release sex-drive-boosting testosterone. Sign up for a couples adventure race (www.usara.com) or just belly up at the local pub's trivia night; by competing on the same team, you'll also improve communication and cooperation, the two behavioral foundations of sexual success.

WAX NOSTALGIC

Revisiting that bed-and-breakfast romp of 3 months ago isn't just an exercise in nostalgia. Recalling the relationship's formative moments can stir up the hormone norepinephrine, which helps the brain shine an emotional klieg light on memories. "You'll unlock her passion," says sex therapist Laura Berman, PhD, president and director of the Berman Center and author of *The Passion Prescription*, "and intensify the new memories you're making, too." The brain's internal archivist responds best to strong contextual cues—smells, environments, music, textures, even certain foods—so orient her mental rearview mirror by concocting a smorgasbord of evocative sights and sounds.

LIE DOWN ON THE JOB

The monogamous prairie vole might not be your sexual role model, but researchers found that the creatures are literally addicted to their mates, thanks to their receptivity to oxytocin. That hormone battles stress and increases arousal (it's released by orgasm, after all), so the lesson here is clear: Up her dosage and she'll be hooked on you. Physical contact (cuddling!) and muscle massage both unleash the chemical, so give her this sensual massage in the postcoital glow: Ask her to lie facedown, and, straddling the backs of her upper thighs, apply rotating thumb pressure to either side of her lower spine, says Linda Banner, PhD, author of *Advanced Sexual Techniques*. By the time you reach her shoulders and neck, the oxytocin jets should be firing full force.

LET HER LEAD YOU

It pays to be her sexual party doll every now and then. A study at the University of Michigan found that female rats receive a dopamine boost (there it is again—that euphoria-inducing neurotransmitter) only when they control sex. But don't just offer her the blow-up valve. "Make sure she's not just hearing, 'Do me the way I want to be done,'" says sex therapist Gloria G. Brame, PhD, author of *Come Hither: A Commonsense Guide to Kinky Sex*. Instead, Brame suggests role-playing a scenario in which she's in a position of authority and you're the sexual novice. The fantasies women said they liked most: professor/student and nurse/patient.

PERCENTAGE OF WOMEN WHO SAID THEY'D BE GAME FOR A LITTLE PLAYACTING:

76

BECOME A STRANGER

Reinvent yourself outside the bedroom, and you could help refresh her passion inside it. According to researchers at the Massachusetts Institute of Technology, we keep a sort of neural dossier on a person tucked away in our brain, just above the temples. This case file is overhauled when we meet their friends or develop deeper relationships with those we've already met, says William Pollack, PhD, an assistant clinical professor of psychiatry at Harvard medical school and a *Men's Health* mental-health advisor. "She'll see you through their eyes, and it will bring out different aspects of your own personality," says Pollack, "stimulating love and lust neurotransmitters." So introduce her to Jack and Mona from your cycling group at a dinner party: It could encourage her to attack your body anew.

LEARN NEW MOVES

Trying new sex positions isn't just a new way to fit the key into the lock. "Anything novel or exciting is likely to drive up the levels of dopamine in her brain," says anthropologist Helen Fisher, PhD, author of *Why We Love*. Magnetic resonance imaging scans at Oxford University found that learning a new motor skill—whether it's fingering bar chords on your guitar or plucking a new sexual harmonic in bed—sets off a flurry of activity in many of the same brain regions activated during orgasm. Sold?

RECLAIM VIRGINITY

Send your sex life back to square one. "If you've learned how to pleasure her, it's too easy to forget about foreplay and all the other things that keep sex fresh," says Debby Herbenick, PhD, the *Men's Health* "Bedroom Confidential" columnist. Start with a 3-day sex break to build anticipation, pooling dopamine behind her sexual Hoover Dam. Then spend a night necking like teenagers, clothes on. Wait 2 days and spend another one touching each other sensually—everywhere but the genitals. Take 2 more days off and then use your lips instead of your fingertips to do the same. By this time, your dopamine will be redlining, and both of you will have a surplus of arousal-boosting testosterone. Bonus: The heightened physical sensitivity can unearth long-neglected erogenous zones when—finally—at the 2-week mark, you blow the dam.

THE BATTLE-PROOF RELATIONSHIP

WHEN SHE PICKS A FIGHT, YOU CAN PUT UP THE USUAL DEFENSE—OR WIN HER OVER WITH THESE SIMPLE STRATEGIES

BY KRISTINA GRISH

Truly passionate sex beats obligatory makeup sex any day. Maybe men don't feel the difference, but we women do. We hate fighting. It makes us feel alienated, confused, and downright disappointed.

But the next time we bite your head off, don't rush to pack up your CDs. Experts insist that squabbling (but not screaming) is a healthy sign. It's silence that should scare you. "The guy might think everything's okay since they're not arguing much, but that can really mean she's over the relationship and planning her exit strategy," says Karen Sherman, PhD, coauthor of *Marriage Magic! Find It, Keep It, Make It Last.*

You need to know what her fighting words mean. What follows is classified intel from behind enemy lines—code breakers that can lead to a cease-fire, then pay off in a peace treaty that will make everyone happier. If we feel closer and more intimate after each resolution, that's more naked for you.

THE ATTENTION FIGHT

OPENING VOLLEY: "We don't go out anymore."

IT MEANS: She's nostalgic. "I want my husband to sit across from me, think I'm attractive, share my food, and realize we still feel what we did before I became a wife and mother," says Jennifer Jeanne Patterson, author of *52 Fights: A Newlywed's Confession.*

BATTLE TACTICS: Once a month, surprise her with a real plan. "If you've gone a whole month without proffering flowers, compliments, or a special date, you'll have a problem," says Carol Ritberger, PhD, author of *Love . . . What's Personality Got to Do with It?* "Do something she'd like, but give it a spontaneous twist. Go for a walk, but take her to a sight she's never seen. Or book a babysitter, then lead her through a night of surprises—without prompting." Men like familiar places, "but women respond best to novelty."

WHAT YOU WIN: Dinner counts as foreplay. Really. "Women like to be shown off," says Charles Sophy, MD, a psychiatrist and an associate professor of psychiatry at UCLA. "Men should hear this as a compliment. Avoid getting defensive, and realize she needs attention or loves PDA with you. You'll come home and have a great evening."

THE FRIENDS FIGHT

OPENING VOLLEY: "What's with the morons in your fantasy baseball league, anyway?"

IT MEANS: She's questioning your judgment. "Criticizing how men spend time with their friends implies that they're irresponsible in making choices," Ritberger says—meaning your partner is nervous about your decision making with regard to the two of you.

BATTLE TACTICS: When she disses your buds, it feels like a personal insult because friends are directly tied to identity and ego. Hold your ground and try this sneaky attack: Invite her to an event with your friends, suggests David Wygant, a Los Angeles–based dating coach and the author of *Always Talk to Strangers: 3 Simple Steps to Finding the Love of Your Life*. "She wants to spend time with your friends, but a lot of this has to do with her not wanting to be the invisible girlfriend and knowing you're not cheating on her."

WHAT YOU WIN: Peace. "Once she's out, she'll realize your friends are harmless geeks, and she'll never want to join you again," Wygant says. Sherman has a trick play that works: Include her in one of your regular pool or bowling nights—and let her pick her team. Competition—either with or against each other—is well established as an aphrodisiac.

THE MONEY FIGHT

OPENING VOLLEY: "Do you really need another gadget?"

IT MEANS: She's implying a lack of responsibility on your part. This raises issues of control and insecurity, and highlights both partners' need for order, Sherman says. Women tend to be more security-minded than men, adds psychologist Warren Berland, PhD, so you probably have different tolerance levels for spending.

BATTLE TACTICS: Schedule budget talks. Have a sit-down with paper and pencil (or computer and software) to go over spending and debt levels. Negotiating lets her discuss the issue—but as you sympathize, make your case. Use "and" statements rather than "but" ones. ("I understand you're nervous, and I also want to buy this new plasma TV. How do we figure this out together?")

WHAT YOU WIN: You get the TV—as long as you set aside a few hundred for something she wants. Wygant warns that women can view a big purchase as something that will compete for your attention. If ever there were a time to splurge on a pair of $200 jeans for her, this is it. "She'll think of you every time she wears them," Wygant says, "which lets you make love to your plasma all you want."

THE INTIMACY FIGHT

OPENING VOLLEY: "Why does everything have to be sex, sex, sex all the time?"

IT MEANS: It's not about sex. She's lacking intimacy, excitement, novelty—all those things that made your early days so darn carnal. She may feel that sex is now more about your enjoyment than something mutual.

BATTLE TACTICS: Research shows that the female snuggle impulse is also her aphrodisiac, so take an honest look at your attempts at intimacy. Do you assume that a shoulder rub must always lead to the bedroom? Ask what she needs from you in order to feel close—it could just be more snuggling or listening. And leave sex out of the discussion. Berland suggests speaking in "feeling" and "wanting" terms, without accusation. "Don't assume you know what 'affection' and 'love' mean to her," he recommends. "Simply say, 'What do you want? Please tell me, because I want to give it to you.'" Find out what intimacy means to her, then provide it.

WHAT YOU WIN: More sex, of course!

THE KIDS FIGHT

OPENING VOLLEY: "Why can't you spend more time with the kids?"

IT MEANS: She feels like she's doing all the work. "The typical scenario is that the woman feels as if she's lost her wits dealing with the kids all day, and her husband comes home from work at night and shuts down," Sherman says. "He removes himself from household responsibility and doesn't understand she's been working all day, too."

BATTLE TACTICS: If she's punchy from a long day, don't plant yourself in front of the Pistons game. Nothing will change until you help with dinner, laundry, or homework. When it comes to chores, both of you should act the way you would at your jobs: Delegate, budget, and set deadlines. "Men have the ability to prioritize like this at work, so why not apply these sensibilities

CUT THE RED WIRE

Here are five ways to defuse an explosive argument:

1. Don't ask "why" questions. This creates an emotional response and puts her in fight-or-flight mode, says Carol Ritberger, PhD. Other questions are fine, especially if they show an interest in "how" or "when" the two of you can solve the problem.

2. Don't assume she's basing her decisions on emotion. There may be plenty of logic behind her reactions, though these reactions may be charged with stress and contention. And for goodness' sake, don't tell her she's being emotional.

3. Don't cross-complain. Countering her bickering with your complaints won't work. If you're fighting to be heard, someone's bound to lose. It might be you.

4. Don't interrupt. Actively listen to whether she uses kinesthetic ("I feel"), auditory ("I hear"), visual ("I see"), or cognitive ("I think") terms—and respond in her language. She'll hear it more clearly.

5. Use body language. Touch her, lean forward, and maintain eye contact to show that you're in the moment with her.

at home?" asks Sherman. "If your report isn't handed in on time, the boss will ask for it. If you aren't contributing to a meeting, your team will be livid."

WHAT YOU WIN: A calmer home, kids who actually like their father, and, after they go to bed, the last quarter of the Pistons game. Which is the best part, anyway.

THE FORGIVENESS TEST

YOUR KEY TO ROMANTIC BLISS? PASS THIS SIMPLE 6-QUESTION QUIZ

BY SARAH MILLER

First, two generalizations: men screw up, and women have unholy tempers. (The opposite can also be true, so save your breath.) How lucky for men that we women also have a weakness for seeing what's best in you, believing your lines of bull, and giving you a second chance. For the following exercise, imagine yourself in the doghouse. Let's see if you're man enough to get yourself out.

1. You and Heather have plans to meet at a restaurant at 7:00. When you show up—at 7:30—Heather is on her way out the door. How do you get her to stay?

A. Explain to Heather how, in your book, a half hour really isn't late.

B. Insist that you were actually supposed to meet at 7:30. Refuse to give in until Heather concedes that this may in fact be true.

C. Deliver a compelling, detailed monologue explaining all factors that led you to be late.

D. Run in breathless and, before Heather can utter a word, say, "On the way over here, I kept thinking about what you said the other night, and I think I totally agree with you."

The answer is D. It's natural to want to soothe Heather's rage. What's more important, and easily capitalized upon, is that she's been feeling sad and hurt. Male lateness plays into women's abandonment issues, which, be assured, are considerable. She was worried you weren't going to show up at all, and the only thing that grew more rapidly than her anger was her craving for attention. Give her an adrenaline shot of it: immediate and total focus on her, her ideas, her needs, her day, her clothes. She might just get high enough to forget you were late.

2. You are heading to a birthday party for a new girlfriend. You have no gift. The only place nearby is a 7-Eleven. What do you do?

A. Buy her a bunch of silly things—a six-pack of beer, some Slim Jims, a Waylon Jennings CD. She'll think your gift is offbeat and cool—and that you are, too.

B. Tell her you haven't gotten her anything yet. You've been looking, but can't find the right thing.

C. Call a friend who's going to the party and see if you can sign on with his or her gift.

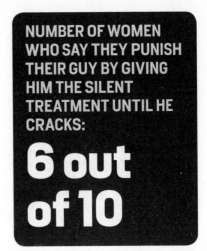

NUMBER OF WOMEN WHO SAY THEY PUNISH THEIR GUY BY GIVING HIM THE SILENT TREATMENT UNTIL HE CRACKS:

6 out of 10

D. Tell her you ordered something but it hasn't come yet, then order something when you get home so it's sort of true.

The answer is B. If you've ever found yourself giftless on the way to a party, you are perhaps not in tune with the expectations of civilized society. Maybe this girl likes that about you. Still, there's a fine line between anti-establishment and totally lazy (A), unimaginative and insensitive (C), and passive and ineffectual (D). Don't shun option B just because it's a big, fat lie.

Lesson: It's never about what happened; it's about what could have happened. Tell her about all the time you've spent looking, that you had a few near hits, but that, ultimately, nothing's been perfect. She's going to want to believe you so much that she will. Convincing someone she's so special that it was hard to find an object worthy of her is a gift in itself.

3. You cheated on your girlfriend. For whatever reason—photographs, cell phone records, your sobbing admission—she knows. She says it's over. You stand the best chance of getting her back if you . . .

A. Call her twice a week, telling her how miserable you are. She'll take pity eventually.

B. Enlist a mutual friend to talk to her. When she sees how desperate you are to get her back, she'll forgive you.

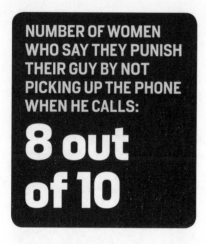

NUMBER OF WOMEN WHO SAY THEY PUNISH THEIR GUY BY NOT PICKING UP THE PHONE WHEN HE CALLS:

8 out of 10

C. Call her once when you know she won't be home. Leave a message saying that you miss her and you hope she'll call you soon. Don't call her again until she calls you.

D. Sleep with a lot of people and see that word gets back to her. She'll be so jealous, she'll be begging you to come back.

The answer is C. Guys seem to go for A, figuring the more times you tell her how sorry you are, the greater the chance that she'll believe you, right? Wrong. Cheating is not just about what you did with your johnson. It's about character. And whereas before you were just a cheater, now you're a whiny cheater with stalking tendencies. As for B, people who run relationship interference with friends usually have vaginas. Keep it mannish, please, though not enough to carry out D, which could backfire, and either way, what are you going to do about your 34 new girlfriends, one of whom, we guarantee, has passed on an infection?

C lets her know you are there and gives her a chance to miss you. Her decision to come back won't be based on whether she forgives you so much as how much she can't stand being away from you. Make yourself scarce and she'll be forced to remember you as the guy she knew before all this happened, whom she used to love and maybe still does.

4. You're going to be an usher in your brother's wedding. One of the bridesmaids, Nina, is totally hot and, for some reason, totally wants you. But your new girl, Tina, is dropping hints about being your date. You . . .

A. Go to the wedding by yourself and hope that Tina doesn't bring it up again.

B. Tell Tina that you would invite her, but it's going to be the most boring thing ever.

C. Take Tina. Slip Nina your phone number.

D. Wait until the last minute. Tell Tina you want her to go, but you have to make sure it's okay. Take as long as you can to find out, hoping she'll make other plans. If she doesn't, tell her that you're really sorry, but you're actually not allowed to bring a date.

The answer is D, for dirty. Let's start with A. Tina is female, so not only is she going to ask you how the wedding was, she's going to want details—details that you, having spent the majority of the festivities in a pool cabana with 4 pounds of Nina's purple satin dress over your head, will be unable to provide. You could try your hand at B, but only if you have a handy response when Tina says, "Oh, I'm never bored when I'm with you." (No guy does.) Try C, and Tina will get a whiff of Nina's designs on you. Nina will do that weird chick thing of trying to impress the girlfriend of the guy she wants to have sex with. Next thing you know, they're having a 3-hour conversation about manicure injuries and horseback-riding camp, and that's that for furtive number swapping.

So lie, and lie big. Once you've made up your mind to crawl on your belly like a snake, you should be a big, smart, stealthy snake that snares his prey, not a wimpy little green snake that tries to dart across the driveway and gets crushed by a Big Wheel.

5. You swear not to get a lap dance at a bachelor party. You come home and swear you didn't. Pictures emerge months later: you, getting a lap dance. Your defense?

A. You were so drunk you don't remember.

B. The girl kept coming over to you. No one was asking her for a dance, and you felt sorry for her. You didn't say anything because you didn't want to upset her.

C. It wasn't a lap dance. The groom called for photo ops for each guy. She was in your lap for like, 5 seconds, and you forgot about it.

D. Your friends made you get it, but it was totally boring. And you didn't tell her because you didn't want to upset her.

> **NUMBER OF WOMEN WHO SAY THEY PUNISH THEIR GUY BY WITHHOLDING SEX UNTIL HE GROVELS:**
>
> # 4 out of 10

The answer is C. Never blame anything on being drunk. B and D sound like such classics as "My wedding ring makes my finger itch." C will work if you believe deep down inside that you really haven't been caught. You have to walk a fine line between breezy ("I didn't think to bring it up") and matter-of-fact ("That's what happened"). Now it's turned from a conversation about your lack of morals into one about whether she really wants to be mad at you for making a tiny little gesture to please your friend. Nice work.

6. You're enjoying dinner at home. All of a sudden she starts screaming that she's miserable and it's all your fault. You . . .

A. Just be quiet. You probably can't make her feel better anyway.

B. Spend the rest of the evening listening to her cry about all her problems.

C. Call 911 and ask for a guy with a net.

D. Run.

The answer is B. Fix yourself a big drink and settle in for an evening of convincing her that you're going to do whatever it takes to make her happy. Don't worry about the fact that she's expecting miracles. In this case, it really is the thought that counts. However, if this happens more than, say, once a month, try C, followed by D.

SHELLFISH DECISIONS

SOME COMPROMISES IN A RELATIONSHIP CAN BE TOUGH TO SWALLOW.
BUT KNOW THAT WHAT YOU GET BACK CAN BE EVEN BETTER
THAN WHAT YOU GIVE UP

BY LYNN HARRIS

Bacon. Oh my God, bacon. Any food in the world is better with bacon, including bacon. Also, can we talk about shellfish? Fried oysters, steamed clams, shrimp with garlic. Funny crustaceans you can get only in Spain. And while we're on the subject: a nicely charred burger with Cheddar. And bacon.

I love them all. I will love them forever. And because I love my husband, I have given them up. David, you see, is a Reform rabbi. This did not faze me when I met him, as I'd grown up with rabbis I liked and admired. (You might say I'd always been rabbi-curious.) Also, he was hot.

There was only one thing that worried me: Would he eat lobster? In other words, just how kosher did he keep?

Actual culinary practices vary widely among denominations and individuals, but the basic kosher cuisine trifecta is no pork, no shellfish, no combining poultry or red meat with dairy (see "burger with Cheddar," above). In stricter observance, animals must be slaughtered in accordance with Jewish law: a quick knife slash believed to be painless. Those who really get jiggy with it use separate utensils and dishes for meat and dairy and do not eat in restaurants (or homes) that aren't officially kosher.

If you're thinking, "Lighten up, sister, there's always Fakin' Bacon," hear me out. For Shakespeare, music was the food of love. For me, food is the food of love. So this kosher thing looked like it could be a problem. And sure enough, I fell for David—even though he was never going to hide a diamond in an oyster or peel me a shrimp. We talked about it: He never told me what not to eat in a restaurant or on my own, but he did ask that we keep his apartment—

which, I should admit, I practically moved into after our third date—free of treyf (nonkosher items).

Oh, mixed feelings! Of course, technically, I can live without mussels. Emotionally, I'm not so sure. I've always associated my appetite with adventure and associated picky eaters with a lack of imagination and an unwillingness to enjoy life. I know kosher and picky are different, but I worried that keeping kosher would feel like a major compromise of my try-anything, unpicky spirit. As a serious cook, I feared a cramp in my blowout dinner-party style. And think of the children! If things got serious with David, I'd never be able to salute my daddy's Southern heritage by fixing grits with Jimmy Dean sausage. I'd never teach Junior how to eat a lobster—a rite of passage in my native Boston. This was about more than holding the butter. Reject family tradition? Rein in my spirit? I wasn't sure I could do it.

Then again, I knew that people gave things up all the time in relationships. I know tons of people, male and female, who've moved to be with their mates. My friend Beth gave up a friendship with an ex when she got engaged to someone else. My friend Meredith gave up her beloved cat for her farm-raised fiancé, who was adamant that animals live in barns, not houses (or microscopic New York City apartments).

SQUID PRO QUO

In other words, if I were to marry David, steamed clams would be only one of many things we'd negotiate—simply by virtue of being together for the long haul. "Compromise is part of every relationship. When you're a grown-up, you don't always get your way," says Sharyn Wolf, a therapist and couples counselor in New York City. She's one of several experts who cautioned me against using the word "sacrifice" in the context of relationships. "The concept of sacrifice belongs in the Middle Ages," she says; it's too easily associated with being a martyr. Instead, she suggests, rethink it as "cooperation between two people."

Yes, even when one of them is giving something up. The key is that it can't always be the same person surrendering. "In a particular situation, the give/

take could be 70/30, but at the end of the day, or month, or year, it should balance out to 50/50," says Renée Cohen, PhD, a psychologist in Los Angeles. So I might give up calamari, but he'll give up the freedom to sleep until noon that only a bachelor can get away with.

But negotiating compromise in relationships can be trickier for women than it is for men. That's because on the one hand, society still expects us to be the caretakers of a relationship, to "do what it takes" to make it last. On the other, as independent women—even when a compromise makes utter practical sense—we may still think twice, for fear of slipping into the dreaded Doormat Zone. "I never thought I'd move anywhere 'for a guy,'" bemoans my friend Aliza. Whom I called in Alaska. Where she had moved to be with her husband.

"It made sense deep down," Aliza says. "His career—wildlife biologist—offers only certain options. And in the big picture, I wasn't doing it for him; I was doing it for us." His job—unlike her freelance consulting work—provided the stability, and insurance, they'd need for their new baby. And Aliza knows she has freedom to maneuver, too . . . should they be asked to move again. "I said I won't go anywhere until the baby is born, and he agreed," she says. In a relationship that feels balanced to begin with, it's easier to say yes when you know you could say no, and that he'll meet you halfway—or be the one to give in next time.

KEEPIN' IT KOSHER

Of course, that doesn't mean a move to Alaska—or an equivalent deed—is always the right, generous, balanced option. My friend Lara regrets removing a mole that a former boyfriend of hers didn't like: "I still miss it, like a little phantom limb," she says. And I hit the roof when a friend of mine, a brilliant writer, gave up a weekend MFA program to spend more time with her boyfriend's kids—the same kids who once asked her, "Why does Daddy make you do all the chores?"

If you think you might be letting go of more than you should, says Susan Hendrick, PhD, professor of psychology at Texas Tech University, ask yourself: "Am I compromising so much that I don't know where I end and where my partner begins?" And check in with your gut: "Am I balking at this because I just don't feel like skipping my super-fun girls' snowboarding day for his Cosmically Important Work Event or because it's really too much for him to ask?" And then check in with him. Let's say he wants you to give up your standing Sunday tennis date with college friends, some of whom are still-single men. Ask him why. Maybe he has a jealousy problem . . . or maybe he just wants to spend more time with you.

The first time David and I visited my parents in Massachusetts we were warned that family friends were bringing live lobsters for dinner. Oh, no. I love David; I live for lobster. David wouldn't have minded if I ate it. But this time, I thought, I'll see how it feels to put love over lobster. I asked if they could bring us some fresh Maine halibut. And I held David's hand under the table as everyone cracked their claws. I can't say I didn't salivate over what I was missing, but the sense of got-your-back partnership that I discovered was equally delicious.

Today, we keep kosher both in and out of the home—making an exception, at least for me, of the entire state of Maine. Have I lost something essential in myself? Nah. It's easy enough to go fish or veggie in restaurants without making a fuss. And it has always been my choice, day to day. What have I gained? A practice that's become meaningful to me and to our partnership. And a balanced, satisfying marriage I wouldn't give up for anything. Only in some sort of culinary gangster nightmare would I have to make this choice, but I now know I can live without bacon, not without David.

A BABY AT ANY COST

READ ONE COUPLE'S STORY AS THEY EMBARKED ON THE MOST DARING
ADVENTURE OF ALL—A QUEST TO FIND THEIR CHILD

BY BROOKS HANSEN

The day my wife and I were to meet Ilya for the first time was very breezy and
sunny. It was late July 2004, and we were over on the far side of the world, in
a college town in western Siberia called Tomsk. We'd just come off 2 days of
solid travel from New York City, so we were day-for-night tired, disoriented,
and both numb with anxiety.

Ilya was 6 months old. We were there to adopt him.

Six years of pain and heartache had led up to that moment. That's about
how long Elizabeth and I had been married, and we had spent the whole time
trying to have children—first "naturally" (that had lasted about 6 months),
then for about 4 years with the help of so-called reproductive technologies,
which is all that business with fertility drugs and needles, plastic cups and
petri dishes. Nothing seemed to work, and our subsequent efforts to adopt
hadn't gone much better, so we were feeling pretty broke (I, being a novelist;
Elizabeth, a schoolteacher), pretty old (39 and 41, respectively), and very discouraged as a couple.

But all the way over in Siberia, we were ready to put our troubles behind
us. Finally, all our prayers and hard work were about to become real, and
warm, and human.

The orphanage was tucked away on a shady side street and had a beaded
curtain for a door. A pair of nurses led us down a hall into the office of Dr.
Vinskaya—a tall woman with cropped, bleached-red hair and cat glasses. She
spoke no English, but she seemed very smart and gracious. She sat us down
and through Alina, our translator, started going over all of Ilya's medical
information:

Weight, good; head circumference, above average; muscle tone, good. All ideal, actually, though I'll admit I was in a little bit of a fog. I don't think I really heard a thing until the knock at the door came and the nurse brought him in, a small swaddled package in a white bonnet.

A beautiful baby. His looks were very refined, in fact, and handsome.

His eyebrows had a distinctive shape, the same as Elizabeth's.

"An old soul," I said to our translator. She nodded obligingly. Elizabeth played with him while I took some photos we were supposed to send back to the pediatrician we had standing by stateside, just to get the official thumbs up, but I wasn't worried about his health.

Ilya rolled over. He gurgled. He examined his own hands. He smiled when we lifted him high, giggled when we brought him down. He was alert, but calm. He was what every adoptive couple dreams of.

And yet I felt nothing.

WRESTLING WITH MY INNER ARCHIE BUNKER

There is a kind of collective urban myth that circulates among adoptive parents (and those who'll listen to them) that despite all the bureaucracy and randomness of the adoption process, when they first meet their child, they somehow know that they were meant to be together.

All the fears and uncertainties vanish when they lay eyes on their true, spiritual son or daughter.

The first time I ever heard this was at an introductory meeting for international adoption, held in a handsome brownstone on the Upper East Side, home to one of the most highly respected agencies in New York City. Elizabeth and I had already decided that domestic adoption wasn't for us—too many stories about biological mothers reneging on their agreements, which they can do with virtual impunity in the United States. Also, there seemed to be a growing tendency here toward what's called open adoption, where biological mothers are granted a degree of access to the child—through update letters, report cards, scheduled visits, and the like—that, at least to Elizabeth's and my way of thinking, made the whole thing sound like one giant babysitting scam. We wanted our own baby, free and clear, so we'd gone to this meeting not far from where we lived to get the lay of the land.

It was a perfectly civilized affair, complete with cookie trays and coffee urns and a dozen other couples like us—attractive, nicely dressed, and looking as if they just ate a plate of bad clams. We sat in our folding chairs and listened to the various agency representatives give their presentations about adoptions in Asia, Latin America, and Eastern Europe and Russia. Then they invited a few of their recent clients to show off their beautiful new children, and that was my first taste of the myth. In each case, they said how there'd been no doubt the moment their child was handed to them.

"It was like destiny," they said. "A miracle."

I wasn't going to argue. That's what I wanted to hear. The parents were all clearly glowing, and the children were certainly beautiful. There was one intensely cute little Korean boy. Plump and serene, and a little Buddhaesque. He looked right at us a couple of times and smiled, I swear. We'd have snatched him right there and made a run for it, if Elizabeth hadn't been wearing heels.

But it wasn't going to be that easy. That was the other purpose of the meeting: In addition to assuring us that someday soon, if we worked hard, we would know that glowing feeling, too, the agents wanted us to understand the nature of the road ahead. We needed to know that between all of us and those little bundles of joy across the room lay a gauntlet of paperwork, petitions, notarized financial forms, medical forms, home studies, and, maybe worst of all, a nasty list of choices that, frankly, no couple is in a position to make, but which must be answered or they don't get past square one.

Questions like, How much money were we willing to spend? How much health risk were we willing to take on? How long were we willing to wait? How old did we want our child to be? What gender did we prefer? What race? The kind of stuff you can't think about for 2 seconds without feeling like Archie Bunker. Granted, we'd had to make a lot of tough decisions during our years at the fertility clinics, but at least there had been doctors around to advise us, experts with certificates on the wall. Now it was just going to be the two of us trying to navigate our way through the labyrinth, and I'm not too proud to say that after 4 years of having every tack we tried denied, denied, and denied again, my faith in our judgment was at a pretty low ebb. I wouldn't have put us in charge of ordering a pizza.

We sought guidance in all the usual corners: counselors' offices, chat rooms, psychic tables, park benches. Elizabeth and I were both raised Catholic, so there were a lot of pews thrown in there, as well. I'd actually been thinking a lot about Jesus' father, Joseph, ever since our fertility treatments started, just because it seemed to me that he might have gone through some similar stuff with Mary, feeling a little shunted to the side, trying to figure out how he fit into this whole sexless-begetting business. Had he ever balked at all? Did he worry that he and Jesus might not connect? Or had he always known that this was how his life was supposed to go?

We were living up near Columbia University at the time, in a neighborhood chock-full of young people and all the different ethnic types we'd just been given to consider. Now when I headed out for lunch every day, this city, my home—this heretofore blessed sea of complete strangers—transformed into a kingdom of potential heirs. I'd head up 107th Street and turn right onto Broadway, and now every baby in every carriage, every little girl feeding pigeons, could for all I knew be an eventual dead ringer for my son or daughter. Waiting for the light to change, I'd look left at the Latino boy heading to the park with his soccer ball. "Son!" I'd think. "Let me take that for you."

Or the Chinese girl beside him—so quiet and demure. "Did you get your paper done on time? Of course you did. I'm proud of you."

The restless Filipino on the delivery bike. The Ukrainian driving that cab. Was my child going to grow up and have that guy's nose?

Or those bowed legs over there? More to the point, did I have it in me to be the father of every single one of these people, to be equally calm and open and patient, to be as fierce in my love as a parent should be? You never know until you try, I guess, and I did my best to keep an open mind, but I'll be honest with you, those couple of blocks never did wonders for my appetite.

THE CALL OF THE COLD PEOPLE

Then one day, I had what felt like a semilucid moment while inline skating in Central Park. Up to then, Elizabeth and I had been leaning toward Korea. The process was quick, the kids were generally young and healthy, and the orphanages had an excellent reputation. And all that sounded nice after everything we'd been through. But I'd been cutting east to west that afternoon—late fall—when I passed by the statue of Jagiello, King of Poland, Grand Duke of Lithuania, and it struck me that speed and health just weren't valid bases on which to be making this decision. They were ways of avoiding what we still feared, but maybe it was time to set our fears aside and go for what felt right, what felt like an adventure, and looking up at the scowling iron mask of Jagiello, it made more sense emotionally to try to get a baby who looked like us.

The agencies had made it clear, however: Adopting from Eastern Europe was a much dicier proposition. There was a lot of red tape, the orphanages were overburdened, and there was more drug abuse in the general population, so the risk of things like HIV and fetal alcohol syndrome was much higher.

Still, Elizabeth agreed with me. For whatever reason, this made more sense emotionally. So for a little extra money, we hired a private lawyer (instead of an agency, that is), thinking we might benefit from the personal attention of someone who had working relationships over there, who understood all the paperwork and was familiar with the various orphanages.

She herself was from the Old World and confirmed the fact that the Eastern Bloc could be slippery. Laws changed. Countries shut down and opened up again for various and sundry political and legal reasons. Adopting couples had to be flexible, but she claimed to have been having a lot of luck in Romania recently and might we be interested?

We thought about it, but not long. If Romania was where the action was, then Romania it would be.

Of course, we didn't want to get our hopes up, but we thought we should be ready. We moved to a new apartment next to the park with an extra room, set up a crib, bought baby clothes. I listened to a lot of Dinu Lipatti records, and every Saturday afternoon at 4:30, Elizabeth and I curled up on the couch to watch the Romanian news on channel 25.

Not that we understood a word. We just wanted to get a look at the people and see if we could convince ourselves that this might finally be the answer. This might be what would work for us.

Nope. Reports of corruption in Romanian adoption began to surface in the news not long after we signed our checks. There was even talk of a moratorium—meaning that all foreign adoptions would be suspended until the system could be cleaned up. Elizabeth was profoundly nervous about the whole thing, but our lawyer did a good job of reassuring us with talk of pending legislation in the parliament and special "exception" lists for couples who were already in the pipeline, and we were trying with all our might to be optimistic.

But Elizabeth was right. After about 14 months of waiting and hoping and nothing making much sense, we started combing the Internet and talking to people at the embassies, trying to figure out what was really going on over there. The more we learned, the more clear it became: There were no children coming out of Romania. No exceptions. No lists. The whole thing had been a complete waste of time.

That was a low point—realizing we were apparently just as inept at adopting as we were at conceiving—but we didn't give up. On the contrary, we went into a kind of manic, flailing, full-throttle panic mode. We started placing ads in upstate weeklies for domestic adoption: LOVING COUPLE WANTS BABY. We got back in touch with our fertility doctor and started up another cycle of stimulative drugs, just because, what the hell, you never know. We were even looking into surrogacy—that's where you hire a woman to carry your fertilized eggs—even though that can cost eighty grand and we were flat broke.

We were desperate, but there was one bright spot. Elizabeth had managed to track down an out-of-state agency that seemed to be doing good work in Russia. We'd been turned off Russia early on by the fact that the children tended to be toddler age before you could get them out of the country, but this agency said that wasn't necessarily true, and the truth was, Russia was the first place we'd have turned if we'd just gone with our gut. Maybe it was all those great writers, maybe the hockey players—more likely the composers and what they'd been doing to me since I was a kid, but I really did feel like Russia and me, we'd had this date coming for a while.

It meant a ton of paperwork—Kafka wasn't kidding—but that just made the thing seem more real somehow, like it actually might happen. And in fact, almost as soon as our "dossier" was finished, we started getting what are loosely called "referrals" on actual children. These can vary in kind, depending upon the country or the region you're dealing with, but basically they're medical evaluations of available orphans, sometimes including little postage-stamp photos and (if you're lucky) videos. In our case, the information was minimal, but we had already secured the services of a medical consultant, a well-known expert on babies and international adoption who helped clue us in on the sorts of things to look out for.

The first few referrals we saw all contained one glaring red flag or another: premature birth, hepatitis, traces of heroin in the blood, things like that. Then in midsummer came word of Ilya. Six months old and apparently as healthy as a horse. That's pretty much all we were told, but our agent said that the region he came from was her favorite in all of Russia. She knew the local coordinator personally and trusted her.

"I really think this is the one you've been waiting for," she said.

TO RUSSIA WITH LOVE

But Ilya didn't feel like the one we'd been waiting for when we held him that first time in Dr. Vinskaya's office.

Elizabeth was the first to admit it. We were scheduled to see Ilya twice that day, morning and afternoon. Between visits, we went back to the hotel to grab some lunch, and that's where Elizabeth confessed to me that she'd felt a weird distance. She blamed herself. She said she felt like she wasn't being open enough, and she wanted my help.

I was caught off guard. Part of what had gotten me through that first meeting was the idea that my wife could finally be happy now. But I did what I could: I said all the commonsense things you'd expect—that of course there would be a certain distance at the beginning; that no moment could withstand the expectation we'd brought to this one; it was silly to expect fireworks, that wasn't the point. The point was to be thankful and open ourselves. Let the feelings follow at their own pace. And yet I knew damn well what she was talking about.

When we returned to the orphanage that afternoon, we took him to a little yard out back. There was a small gazebo, some half-buried tires, and, over the fence, a pair of teenagers shooting BBs at a tree stump.

We paused beneath the shade of a tree, and while Ilya looked up into the dappling light, I felt myself go completely empty. It was as if all the hairline cracks of doubt that Elizabeth had pointed out now opened into large, spilling fissures. I was stunned. Here, now, finally holding a child, a jewel of a child, my hands felt numb. Could I be this boy's father?

I supposed. Be kind and caring? Sure. Make sure he's safe? Yes. But there in my arms he felt purely, sickeningly, accidental.

I didn't let on to Elizabeth until afterward. We went and took a walk by the river, just the two of us—high on a white stone esplanade, buffeted by a stiff warm wind. I had to tell her what I'd just gone through, and I was hoping maybe she could rally me now, make me see that I was only panicking and this was still the right thing, adopting him—it had to be. But all that emerged from that extremely slow, painfully pause-laden conversation was that Elizabeth apparently wasn't doing any better than I was. We were both lost, and horrified—at ourselves. We had no idea what to do or how to flip the switch that was going to fix all this, because it was still unthinkable that we should even be hesitating.

We found our way to a restaurant, a Greek ethnic place with an indoor courtyard and a small grotto and waitresses running around in quasi-medieval garb. There was what sounded like a Russian wedding band playing inside, loudly, and one very persistent fly.

"I don't know," said Elizabeth early on, around the time our beers arrived. "I don't know what we're going to decide, but I really do feel like whatever it is, someday we're going to look back on this, and we're going to know it was the toughest decision we ever made, but we will know why."

All I could say was I hoped so, but first things first.

And how we finally did decide, I'm not even sure. In the midst of all those tears, I don't think we ever said it out loud. We didn't have to, I guess, not if we both really felt that way. That little boy deserved better, and we knew we were lucky in that respect, that Ilya was as impressive as he was. If he had been in any way feeble or sick, there's no way we could have made the choice we were making. But we knew that soon—in 2 weeks, or a month—some couple was going to fly in and meet him and know in an instant: "Here he is, this is him, we found him," and they were going to count themselves blessed for the rest of their lives. They were going to see him and feel all the things we didn't.

A MOMENT OF CLARITY

The following morning, we met in our hotel room with our adoption team—the local coordinator, the translator, and the attorney. They were nearly as confused as we were. They wanted to make sure we understood, though. The chances of there being another referral here in Tomsk were nil.

"Ninety-nine percent," as our translator put it, "against."

We said we understood. We'd spoken to our stateside agent the night before, and she'd made it clear that we would most likely have to take all our paperwork back to Moscow and wait there to see where the next referral would come from, though just the thought of that—flying to a whole new region, meeting another helpless little boy or girl, and running the same risk— withered me.

The lawyer had brought some paperwork, a form that we had to fill out to explain why we weren't accepting the referral. We did the best we could, but it wasn't easy, in our shell-shocked state, to justify a decision that basically defied explanation and then to have that justification translated into Russian and reduced to some 2-inch phrase to fill in a blank on a page.

Things weren't going well. Elizabeth was weeping, and I was trying to make sure that whatever did get written on that form couldn't be held against us in the future. At that moment, the lawyer cleared her throat to interrupt. She was on the phone with someone at the Ministry of Education, and she said a new referral had just come in. A 3-month-old over at the children's hospital. A preemie. Another couple must have just passed on him, but we could go see him now if we wanted.

Elizabeth and I were both still bleary. When it's taken all your mettle to back off one diving board, it's not exactly welcome news when someone says, "Hey, look, another!" But there was also part of us that just wanted to get this over with, because I think we both understood that if we went to this hospital, met this other boy, and felt the same emptiness inside, then maybe it was really time to take a step back, admit that the whole idea of our making a family together might have been a mistake. Maybe we just weren't meant to be parents.

From the outside, the hospital looked abandoned. There were no cars in the lot, no lights on inside, no doctors or nurses in evidence until we got into the office of the chief physician in the ward. The same as the day before, we sat and listened while she ran down the boy's medical record. The facts were indisputably grim: born 10 weeks early, 3 pounds. He'd suffered anemia, kidney trouble, and a heart arrhythmia. I could already imagine our doctor back in New York shaking her head, and I'll admit a part of me felt relieved. We had our excuse—maybe this wasn't make-or-break—but then the door opened and they brought him in, in a little pink bonnet. All they had, I guess.

Elizabeth held him first. His eyes were blue, and his hair was an orange-red, but that color could have been from the anemia, they said. The back of his head was flat on one side from lying in a crib with no one there to turn him, but he also had little elfin features and flashing eyes. When Elizabeth handed him over to me, he trembled briefly and spat up, but then he curled right into my shoulder. He craved warmth and contact, but he wasn't frail. He was strong, the way you'd have to be to make it from 3 pounds to 9, alone. He had dancing brows and a curl at the edge of his smile. He was the most riveting thing I'd ever seen, and looking down at him, I felt something I hadn't felt in years, something I wasn't sure I'd ever feel again. Clarity. I thought to myself, If this little boy can grow up to experience even a fraction of the personality, a fraction of the emotion and the life that this face was clearly created to reflect, well, that'd be something to see. I wanted to be there for that. Holding him for that first time, I realized the reason that Elizabeth and I had been having such a hard time of it since we'd left New York: We'd been asking the wrong question. The question wasn't, Does this child belong to us? The question was, Do we belong to him? And the answer was yes.

Yes.

And I guess it might be pushing things to call what happened there in Tomsk a miracle, except I know that for as long as I live, I'll never be able to make sense of how it all turned out. More had been asked of us—both Elizabeth and me—than I could ever have dreamed possible, but there in that office, even more was given back. Just like that, the past 24 hours made perfect sense, and so did the 6 years of struggle that led up to it. All in the time it takes a child to fall asleep on his father's shoulder, I remembered what it feels like to be sure, to be blessed and grateful, and to know that as unbelievable as it may seem, my old friend Joe had been right: This was how it was supposed to go all along.

CAN YOU HEAR ME NOW?

You can't be with her every moment of the day. Banter wisely over the phone, via e-mail, or in text messages, however, and you'll always be in her hottest thoughts, no matter what the medium.

THE MEDIUM: PHONE

CHOOSE YOUR MOMENTS.

She says: "I'm actually out with my friends right now."

You say: "Cool, I was just folding my laundry and trying to figure out *Lost*. Anyway, you want to go to the movies or see a show on Friday?"

The problem: She can't be expected to turn attention away from her friends and make plans just because you happened to call. Hear a lot of noise in the background or have a bad connection? Ask if there's a better time to call.

BAG THE BRAGGING.

She says: "I'm really looking forward to the summer."

You say: "That's funny, because I was talking to buddies from Princeton over the weekend about a trip . . ."

The problem: Gratuitously mentioning status-related details (alma mater/car/summer house) comes off as insecure and bragging, two qualities that don't exactly win over the ladies. Letting her stumble across your secrets (or coax them out in more personal moments) shows confidence, says Ann Demarais, PhD, a psychologist and coauthor of *First Impressions: What You Don't Know About How Others See You*. When she mentions summer, ask what she's most looking forward to . . . and more conversation will ensue. Questions show interest, a quality with melting power.

PERCENTAGE OF WOMEN WHO HAVE DEEP PROBLEMS WITH THEIR PARTNERS' COMMUNICATION SKILLS:

64

FIND COMMON GROUND.

She says: "Yeah, I love music. I saw U2 last year. They were great."

You say: "Bono is such a tool. The only thing worse than his music is the windshield-sized sunglasses."

The problem: The point of banter is to find commonalities; people don't want their opinions dissed. Stuck on a mismatch? Be positive and creative, and show humor. The first things you say will be the filter she sees you through, Demarais says.

Better banter: "I missed U2, but I did catch Springsteen."

She says: "I've never been that into him, but I loved Bruce's cameo in *High Fidelity*."

You say: "That was cool. I'm a big Nick Hornby fan."

She says: "Oh my God. I love his stuff." (And that's how Bono can bring people together.)

SPEAK IN SOUND BITES.

She says: "I teach high-school social studies. There's never a boring day at that place."

You say: "You know, I was reading an article in the *Times* about education policy, and . . ."

The problem: Sounds like a lecture is coming. Bad move. Keep the back-and-forth banter flowing by speaking in short sound bites—any less, you're boring; any more, you run the risk of seeming like a bore, says Robyn Landow, PhD, a clinical psychologist in New York City. Stay light on details and throw in compliments when possible. "I hear working with teenagers is difficult. How do you do it?" picks out something that matters to her—always a powerful aphrodisiac—while also moving along the conversation with a question, you suave devil.

THE MEDIUM: VOICE MAIL

You say: "Hey, it's me. Um, I'm just having some dinner and then chilling, so if you want to, um, talk, I should be around. So hopefully we'll talk soon. . . . Oh, yeah, I just rented *Closer*. You were right. It's good. . . . That's it, I guess. Bye."

The problem: You were rambling and indecisive. The purpose of voice mail is to make a point clearly and decisively. Go for brevity with a positive tone, says Demarais.

Better banter: "I had a great time on Thursday. I'd love to see you again. I was calling to see if you want to have dinner on Friday. Give me a call when you get this message and let me know what you think." Always be prepared to leave a direct, simple message when you call. Let her know you'd like to make plans, and tell—don't ask—her to call you back. "Nine times out of 10, if she has even a passing interest, she'll call," says Eve Marx, author of *Flirtspeak*. "Her subconscious is hardwired to respond to simple instructions."

THE MEDIUM: TEXTING

She writes: "How ya doin'?"

You respond: "Okay."

The problem: She's hoping you've been thinking about her. You're saying that you haven't, says Landow. If you actually care, try "Doing well. Great to hear from you. Will definitely call tonight." Her read: She made your day. There's a future.

You write: "Can't chat right now—I talk to you too much anyway."

The problem: Sarcasm rarely translates between screens. "It's nearly impossible to convey nuance with 155 characters," says Regina Lynn, author of *The Sexual Revolution 2.0*. Be clear now so you don't have to explain later.

She writes: "Whatcha doin?"

You respond: "Out w/friends."

The problem: Vagueness signals secrets, Landow says. Texting "At the Burger Shack with buds. Looking forward to tomorrow" will keep her anticipation high and her phone in one piece.

CHOOSE THE PERFECT GIFT

Birthday, anniversary, or Valentine's Day coming up? Don't panic! Here are some gifts she'll love.

WINE-LOVER PICNIC BASKET

There's nothing quite like spreading a blanket under the wide-open sky and feeding each other gourmet treats. This summer, indulge her with a sophisticated picnic basket; every time she sees it, she'll remember the first time, whether it was fresh baguettes and Camembert in the French countryside or an elaborate four-course spread in your own backyard. Invest in a British classic built to last as long as your relationship: The handcrafted willow hamper sold by Williams-Sonoma comes stocked with everything you need for sophisticated pleasures, including a tablecloth, earthenware, stainless-steel flatware, a cutting board, and an insulated wine tote and glassware. We guarantee she'll give you an excuse to play hooky on a sunny day. ($200/www.williams-sonoma.com)

ANTIQUE JEWELRY BOX

Sure, jewelry will make a woman's eyes dance, but she's not going to see the diamond studs you bought her when she's paying the bills. And it's while she's in the midst of the mundane that a woman most needs her romantic battery recharged. The perfect solution: an antique jewelry box that's not only a romantic gift in itself, but also a reminder of all those other tokens of love inside.

To find the right piece, head to a reputable antiques dealer. To check for authenticity, make sure all of the hardware is matching and operable and that the box itself is in pristine condition. Or leave the hunt to an expert and head directly to Sallea Antiques in New Canaan, Connecticut. The spacious gallery is stocked with antique boxes made out of opaline, cut crystal, tortoiseshell, and exotic woods. (from $1,000/www.salleaantiques.com)

PAGE TURNER

Remember that photo-booth picture the two of you took on your second date? She still keeps it in her wallet (along with ticket stubs and cookie fortunes from your first dates). Upgrade her portable memory stockpile with a made-to-order moving image of the two of you. For a measly eight bucks, you can have 6 seconds of your favorite digital clip—say the moment the two of you kissed at your wedding or a mini-movie you record specifically for this occasion—converted into a full-color, pocket-size flip book.

The process is simple: Download the free editing software from www.flipbooker.com, select a 3- to 10-second video, and upload it directly onto its server. In 7 to 10 days, a one-of-a-kind, 4-inch-by-1¾-inch flip book will land in your mailbox.

Every time she flips through the 60-page, old-fashioned moving picture, it will remind her that you harbor a nostalgic streak, and it's handy evidence of your creativity.

START A PILLOW FIGHT

You're 20 minutes late, you forgot the dry cleaning, and she's utterly apoplectic. This can go two ways: a war of the roses or a prelude to makeup sex. For the latter, begin by rethinking your body language: Align your torso with hers, maintain eye contact, and avoid crossing your arms. "It's a stance that signifies a willingness to listen," says David Givens, PhD, a nonverbal-communication expert in Spokane, Washington, and author of *Love Signals*.

The next step: Agree when she calls you "insensitive." This demonstrates emotional empathy. Then place your hand on the small of her back, whisper an apology, and watch. Researchers have long known that the adrenaline rush that comes with fighting can also spike arousal. "It's a heightened state," says New York psychologist and former *Playboy* playmate Victoria Zdrok, PhD, "that makes makeup sex the most passionate." Chalk one up for the defensive line.

AROUSE HER INTEREST

There was a time when even the slightest graze of your hand could produce a shudder of anticipation in her. Today, familiarity has made your touch less potent, and you're both busy—leaving almost no time for an elaborate at-home seduction. Since "attention is the most important thing that you can give to your partner," according to Lou Paget, author of *The Great Lover Playbook*, you need a strategy to get her aroused in public. Try touching one of these six erogenous (and perfectly legal) zones the next time you're out for dinner. Touch them all, and you'll be having dessert in bed.

NECK: Upgrade your greeting with a gentle kiss on the triangle between the bottom of her earlobe and the top of her collarbone. "It's extremely sensitive," says Emily Nagoski, PhD, a sexuality instructor at the Indiana University. Go the extra mile by whispering into her ear how great she looks.

HANDS: Researchers have recently discovered that by holding his wife's hand, a man can automatically reduce her stress. If she's frazzled about her PTA fund-raiser, grab her hand and tell her what an amazing job she has done. Sounds corny, but that touch is just the kind of emotional support she needs.

WRIST: The inside of her wrist is especially sensitive because the nerve endings are just below the skin's surface. Trace small circles there in a clockwise motion. "It's stimulating," says Lauren Slade, president of the Universal College of Reflexology, "versus a counterclockwise sedating motion."

FEET: The sole of the foot has 7,200 nerve endings—nearly as many as the clitoris. Engage in dinner-party footsie. Or apply pressure to the heel region: "That area is linked to the pelvic and sex gland reflexes," says Slade.

BACK: "[The area] just above her derriere is one of the most sensitive areas on a woman's body," says Paget. The reason? Areas of skin rarely exposed to the sun are more sensitive to touch. Place your hand there often—whether it's at a party or just walking down the street. It's instant arousal disguised as a gentlemanly gesture.

HEAD: "Your head is one of the greatest concentrations of all of your neurons," says Paget. "Shy of orgasm, it's one of the few times she'll close her eyes and focus on the sensation." When you're out in public, place your hand on the nape of her neck and massage the base of her scalp with extended fingers. Watch her turn to putty.

RESUSCITATE YOUR RELATIONSHIP

Going on a weekly date with your wife will improve your marriage; you don't need to be told that. But in case you need convincing, a new study at Idaho State University found that couples who go on about six dates per month are more likely to be satisfied with their marriage. "Having those few hours to reconnect with your wife can bring back that flush of energy that originally sparked your relationship," says Gina Ogden, PhD, a marriage and family therapist and author of *The Heart and Soul of Sex*. The Idaho researchers found that the more dates you go on, the happier you'll be, regardless of whether you spend the night on a blanket on your living room floor or at the Four Seasons. Here are new ways to invest in a stronger relationship and a steamier love life:

COME BEARING GIFTS, BUT JUST NOT FLOWERS. Surprise her instead with an archived newspaper from the day you had your first date. If you can't remember, try your wedding day (www.newspapersremembered.com).

AMBUSH HER AFTER WORK. Plan a date, but don't tell her where you're going, or anything about it, until you get to your destination. The anticipation alone will make for a memorable night. Blindfold optional.

RIDE IN STYLE TO AND FROM A RESTAURANT BY HIRING A CAR SERVICE. This way you both can enjoy a night of drinking and dancing. Or, rent a convertible and just cruise around the town—you'll get that new-car excitement, without crippling your bank account.

SNEAK OUT OF THE OFFICE FOR A LUNCH DATE. Enjoy some afternoon delight by getting a hotel room for afterward.

GO FOR THE ABSURD BY MAKING DATES AT PLACES YOU WOULD NEVER ORDI-NARILY VENTURE TO. Check out the local biker bar, go to a rodeo, or find a Medieval Times dinner theater in your area (www.medievaltimes.com). The crazier, the better. It will help break up the monotony of dinner and a movie.

THE HONEST TRUTH ABOUT WOMEN FROM OUR LOVELY NEIGHBOR

My wife changed jobs. Now she's always stressed and rarely in the mood for sex. What can I do?

Endure the drought as patiently as possible. I know a guy whose wife wasn't interested in sex for a full year during medical school (partly because of stress, partly because of the stench of formaldehyde), but when that year ended, things were hotter than ever. New jobs, kids, illnesses—they're bound to come up at some time and suck the life out of one or both of your sex drives. You could draw her a hot bath before bed or plan a 4-day weekend, but until she settles into her new routine, you'll probably remain underserviced. I can only send my condolences and suggest you reacquaint yourself with the joys of masturbation.

My wife just lies there during sex. How can I encourage more action?

First, a question: Is she loglike outside of the bedroom? Because if she doesn't exercise, stretch, dance—anything—it's going to take some effort to bring out her inner sex bunny. Before she can enjoy your body, she has to start enjoying her own. Invite her to go hiking, or buy her a gift certificate for yoga classes. Anything that will get her blood flowing is likely to liven up her sexual M.O. by raising her confidence in her body. If she's already active yet carnally comatose, try to reconnect with her in a sensual way. Suggest taking a long, soapy shower together or trading full-body rubdowns in bed, and lavish her body with attention. Nothing softens a woman up or turns her on like a little pampering.

Where did the sex vixen I married go? And how can I get her back?

She's still there. She's just stressed, tired, and horrified by the 5-plus pounds of flab she's gained since the wedding. Your mission: Make her forget about all that and romp like a newlywed. A few things that will help: drinking margaritas in the middle of the day; installing dimmers on all the lights in your house; watching a slow-burning, sexy film like *Girl on the Bridge*; reaching over to rub high up on her thigh in the car; copping a feel in an empty aisle at Home Depot; chasing her around after she steps out of the shower. Treat her like a sex kitten so often that she starts to believe it.

My wife wants a baby, but I'm not ready. How do I stall?

Unfortunately, women suspect that most men won't feel prepared for fatherhood until their kid is graduating from college. Give her one or two honest reasons why holding off would be the best thing for the baby. See, it's not about you: It's about bringing the bundle of shared DNA into your universe under ideal conditions. Maybe you want to build an addition to the house so the tyke can have his or her own room. Or wait until you've earned 4 weeks of paid vacation so you can spend the first month at home to help. Make sure you give her a specific time frame—like 6 months or a year—after which you'll be happy to get her preggers. Her nagging should subside.

My wife says I don't seem interested in her anymore. How can I reassure her that I'm still smitten?

Being a man, you can't recall exactly how you behaved before you'd slept with her a thousand times. She, meanwhile, has logged how intensely you gazed into her eyes, how eager you were to tear her clothes off, and all those things you said and did just to make her laugh. If you make an effort to reenact that initial passion, she won't have any doubts about your level of commitment or attraction. Think back, good and hard—did you call her in the middle of the day just to say hi? Did you snake a hand up her sweater the second she walked in the door? Did you wax on about all the trips you wanted to take with her? Bring some of that back and you'll have a happy wife.

My wife dreams that I cheat, then gets angry. Normal?

She's being ridiculous, but don't groan and roll your eyes. When she's finished describing her latest nocturnal drama (brought on by watching too much *Desperate Housewives,* probably), tell her what she needs to hear: that you love her and would never cheat on her. Then turn the tables. Look her in the eye and get all sincere. Say that it really bothers you—no, hurts you—that she has these dreams, because you deserve to be trusted. And that if a random, meaningless dream could upset her so much, it must mean she has doubts about you. Doubts that are completely unfounded. (Sniff.) If you can make it through that little speech, she should be stroking your back and apologizing to you in no time.

My wife is a slob. Asking doesn't work, so how do I get her to clean up?

This situation calls for some below-the-belt matrimonial bargaining. There has to be some little thing you do around the house that bugs her just as much as crumby carpet bothers you. Whatever it is, start doing it every day until she complains. Then offer to make a genuine effort to stop if she, in turn, tries harder to pick up after herself. Warning: This method could backfire if there are dozens of things about you that drive her crazy, versus the three or four complaints you have about her. If that's the case, you'll just end up right back where you started. But it's worth a try.

My wife calls me at work to talk about our toddler and gets ticked off when I'm too busy. Help me out.

You call her a few times in the early morning. Ask how the kid is doing. Ask how she's doing. Then tell her you have to go. Hanging up first won't seem so cold if you're the one who called. What she really wants is to not feel so darn isolated at home.

HANG UP

Your cell phone may be straining your relationship. In a new study in the *Journal of Marriage and Family*, researchers analyzed cell-phone usage of 1,367 couples for 2 years and found that relationship and family satisfaction both drop as cell-phone usage goes up. That's because always being available to your employer can blur the boundaries between work and family time. Cell phones can cause work worries to "infiltrate other parts of our lives," says study author Noelle Chesley, PhD. Let the calls go to voice mail or screen them more strictly, she says.

DON'T BE EXTREME

Thinking in extremes can signal trouble in a romance. If your opinion of a woman swings wildly—she's the greatest; she's a pig—your relationship may be rocky, new research suggests. A study published in the *Journal of Personality and Social Psychology* found that people who view their partner in absolute terms are more likely to have lower self-esteem. Seeing a partner in extreme terms "can't be good for a relationship. It would make the relationship seem unpredictable to both partners," says study author Margaret Clark, PhD, of Yale University. Better to find virtues in her faults, Clark suggests. Instead of whining, "She's so flaky," try, "She's disorganized, but creative."

CHOOSE YOUR WORDS CAREFULLY

"We" can save your marriage. University of Pennsylvania researchers say the pronouns couples use when arguing influence the resolution of their fights. They asked couples to discuss heated issues facing their relationships and coded each word used as positive, negative, or neutral. The arguments in which spouses used more second-person pronouns, such as you and me, tended to be negative, while those that included first-person pronouns we, us, and our tended to result in positive outcomes.

WIELD A PEN

If you want to make sure your girlfriend hangs around, grab a pen or find a keyboard. Relax—you don't have to write a love letter, and spelling doesn't count. New research from the University of Texas shows that writing a journal about your relationship can make it last. In a study, some dating couples wrote about their relationships for 20 minutes a day, 3 days in a row, while other couples just wrote about daily activities. Checking back in 3 months, researchers found that those who wrote about their love lives were three times more likely to still be together. Why did it work? It's a practice run. "You can sort out how you feel before you talk to your partner," says lead study author Richard Slatcher, PhD. "It smoothes communication, which strengthens the relationship." You can reap the same benefits by writing occasionally—for instance, when you're working through problems, he says. "Writing just once may help get those nagging thoughts about your relationship out of your head," says Slatcher.

SEXUAL HEALING

It takes longer for an injury to heal if you're arguing with your spouse, according to a weird experiment documented in the *Archives of General Psychology*. Researchers inflicted blisters on the arms of 42 couples on two separate occasions, one before an argument between spouses, and the other before a less-stressful social interaction. After an argument, it took a day longer for the blisters to heal. Relationship stress can lower the production of proinflammatory cytokines—proteins that help cells heal—at the site of an injury.

GLOSSARY

afterplay

No, we don't mean watching the game highlights on *SportsCenter*. And by the way, though it's not called after*work,* if she hasn't yet joined you in the land of bliss, you do indeed have some work cut out for you. Even if the Big Unit is temporarily on the DL, you owe it to your partner to use alternative methods to bring her, too, to that happy place known as orgasm. Or at least make sure that she's fully satisfied with her lusty layover. She won't feel very playful if she's uncomfortable from not having climaxed.

But assuming that the sex was mutually good and both of you emerged from the afterglow feeling a bit frisky, this is the time to nurture your intimacy and move the pleasure in new directions—by goofing around.

So tickle each other like little kids, or trace your initials on each other's tummies. Words of love? Well, compliments are fine, but a lighthearted tone is what you want—not contrived lines or a loaded pop quiz, like, "How was it for you, babe?" Activity? Feed each other peeled grapes. Take a bubble bath together. Do anything that feels good, as long as you do it together.

Afterplay is a kick for its own sake, but it also helps settle the two of you into a nice, relaxed groove. If she's a fairly new partner, that's going to pay dividends the next time the two of you get it on.

Which could be sooner than you think, since afterplay sometimes leads to a new round of, well, play. (Oddly, when this happens, you don't seem to worry much about that early meeting.) Then you can both fall happily asleep.

anal sex

The opening of the rectum is loaded with nerve endings, making it a sensory-rich venue for sexual play. Since you and your partner each have one, the opportunities for anal pleasure are doubled. Sexual contact can be limited to the outer area or proceed into the canal itself and, in your case, all the way up to the prostate. Anal intercourse—penetration of the anus with the penis—is only the best known of an array of anal activities. The stimulation can also come from a finger, a tongue, or a sex toy.

Anal sex is more common among heterosexuals than you may think. Probably at least one in four straight men has tried it. Some male/female couples find anal play exquisite. Some avoid it because they consider it nasty, while others do it precisely *because* they find it nasty. Still others think it enhances sex because it fits into a role-playing or power game.

Of the millions of opinions about anal sex, only two matter—yours and your partner's. If the two of you like it and feel fine about it afterward, do it all you want.

But do it right. You can't just slide in the back door one night on a whim. As with any new sexual foray, the two of you should reach an understanding ahead of time. Decide what anal variation you might like to try first. Then, if you're going to insert anything, have plenty of water-based lubricant on hand; the anus doesn't self-lubricate, so friction can be too painful without it. Take it slow. Probe, don't thrust. Keep checking in with each other. How does it feel? Pull out—slowly—if there's any sharp pain.

You can move from the vagina to the anus, but you can't go back again: The anus hosts bacteria that you don't want to introduce elsewhere. And when using a condom, you should wear a *different* one for each activity. Finally, to make the experience that much more pleasurable, consider mutual bathing as mandatory foreplay and afterplay, with special attention paid to the featured orifice.

aphrodisiac

There's no such thing, but there are plenty available to you. Contradictory? Only because the word *aphrodisiac* is thrown around so wildly. Is an aphrodisiac something that improves your physical sexual functioning? Then Viagra is certainly an aphrodisiac for men with erection problems (as is good health for everybody). Is it something that makes sex more likely? Alcohol qualifies, then, insofar as it reduces the inhibition that may stand between attraction and consummation. Is it anything that makes sex a better experience? If so, this book is full of aphrodisiac possibilities, from A to Z. Or is it something that makes you feel sexy? Again, tons of things work for one person or another. For you, it may be confidence. For her, it may be chocolate.

But let's get real here. The aphrodisiac that man has been searching for throughout history isn't any of those things. It's a potion that will make a particular woman want to have sex with you and only you, right here and right now. *That's* what's had folks grinding up rhinoceros horns and extracting sheep testicles all these centuries. We're here to tell you that such a thing doesn't exist, will never exist, and shouldn't exist.

Sex is too complex to be distilled into a single potion. Sexual desire alone involves physical, psychological, social, cultural, and situational components, and no two people combine those components in the same way. Even if some mad scientist were to come up with a formula that would influence all those factors simultaneously, he would have to learn about the specific target's sexual makeup and customize the potion. Good old-fashioned courtship or seduction would work a lot faster.

The best aphrodisiac advice is like the best financial advice. To have money, you can work steadily, spend frugally, save faithfully, and invest wisely. Or you can try to win the lottery. To have sex, you can pay attention to who she is, learn what she wants, make her comfortable with you, and then go about creating the conditions most likely to lead to her arousal. Or you can hunt for an aphrodisiac. The first strategy may not always work. But the second probably never will.

beard burn

Straight men aren't often on the receiving end of a sandpaper beard, so we seldom appreciate how much it hurts. And you know when it bothers a woman the most? During oral sex. Her thighs are soft. Her thighs are sensitive. And her thighs are getting scratched at a time when she should be focused on the pleasure she's feeling in between them. It doesn't matter that you're aware of your 5-o'clock shadow and you promise to be careful. You can't be careful enough. Besides, careful is the last thing you want to be. You should be able to let yourselves go crazy without worrying about your cactus face getting in the way.

This one is a no-brainer: Leave the 2-days'-growth look to the empty-headed teen idols who started it. Either shave it smooth or grow it out. (Once it reaches the true beard stage, facial hair is far more tolerable. It's the stubble that makes women homicidal.) And if you're clean-shaven and planning on getting lucky tonight, shave again in the afternoon. It's a small price to pay for unbridled sex—and to avoid having your ears yanked off just as you're getting into it.

bras

A sadistic killjoy's evil invention, serving no purpose but to separate us from two of life's most exquisite gifts. Still, women are attached to their bras in more ways than one. Or even two. (Who could blame them?) So treat a brassiere with as much respect as you do its contents. It matters to her.

De-bra her with reverence. Don't yank or pull or otherwise rush to get it the hell out of the way. Remove the garment as if unwrapping a priceless treasure, which is exactly what you're doing. Prolong the thrill as the twin marvels of her flesh slowly present themselves for your viewing and fondling pleasure.

All this, of course, is dependent upon getting those famously uncooperative bra hooks apart. Give yourself to the count of 10 to get the little buggers unfastened. Any longer and you're merely fumbling. If you run out of time, look her in the eye and tell her how wonderful it would be if she would do the honors herself. She should be delighted to oblige; if she's not, you didn't have much going in the first place. Realize, too, that many bras nowadays unclasp in the front—a helpful little technological advance that enables us to see what we're doing while we're doing it.

As you may have noticed, there are bras and there are bras. If you're dying to see her in a nice little black lace job, by all means pursue the matter. But do not—repeat, do not—buy one for her as a gift. For a woman, form and function matter at least as much as aesthetics. Bras have to be tried on. And, as mentioned, a woman relates to her bra on a deeply personal level; buying one is something she just has to do herself.

Instead, just happen to come across your choice in a catalog or store display in her presence. Tell her you think she'd look great (or "marvelous" or "sexy," but *never* "better") in that one. Repeat this process until she gets the hint.

breasts

Mammary glands that produce and deliver nourishment to newborns. That's one definition. Here's another: proof that God loves us.

Why do we adore them so? Because they're beautiful—exquisite hanging sculptures of soft flesh in varying shapes, sizes, and hues. Because they're unique—nothing on our own bodies (or in the universe, for that matter) feels quite like a female breast. Because they're the essence of femininity—at least in our society. Because they're erogenous—contact with them can create a two-way charge of excitement. And because of the intrigue factor: Most of the time, they're at least partially hidden and taboo to touch.

Having said this, we remind you that a woman's breasts are fundamentally different to her than they are to you. Men get so much pleasure out of female bosoms that we sometimes forget that they're attached to a whole person. The most accomplished breast men are sensitive to each woman's feelings about her own breasts. Is she proud of them? Ashamed? Indifferent? Turned on by their erotic potential? Uncomfortable with the attention they get? Gather this kind of intelligence, along with the more specific information you need about how (or whether) she likes them touched. Not only is this a more considerate approach, but it also deepens the pleasure and intimacy of breast play for both of you.

chlamydia

Probably the most common sexually transmitted bacterial disease that most people have never heard of. In women, untreated chlamydia can lead to pelvic inflammatory disease, chronic pelvic pain, and ectopic pregnancy. It can cause infertility in both women and men. Antibiotics knock it out quickly, but you won't seek treatment if you don't know you have it, and about 85 percent of women and 40 percent of men with chlamydia notice no symptoms. If symptoms do show up, they'll probably include mild pain when you urinate and a slight discharge from your penis. If you notice any of these problems, immediately have them checked out, and tell your partner. (We hope you'd have sense enough to do both of these without our telling you to.) If your lover complains of pain during intercourse or if you notice that her vagina is producing unusual discharge or an unpleasant odor, she may be infected.

clitoris

This supersensitive nub of flesh above the vaginal opening exists for one reason and one reason only: to get her off. It (not the vagina itself) is where her most intense sexual pleasure comes from. That makes the clitoris the answer to every man's prayer: a magic button for pleasing a woman.

So why isn't it pushed more? Lots of reasons, the most curious being that intercourse only sometimes gives the clitoris direct stimulation. You may curse this as a flaw of evolution, but you'll be happier if you take it as a cue to engage in sex play that will indeed include the clitoris, such as using your (or her) fingers or your tongue or a sex toy. This you can do before, during, after, or instead of intercourse. (Quick tip: You may have some difficulty using your tongue during intercourse.)

There's another reason for clit neglect: Like a properly prepared martini, a good clitoris is hard to find. It's not very big. It's seldom where you think it should be. And even though arousal leads to engorgement of the clitoris—a kind of female erection—the organ has a counterproductive habit of retracting into its surrounding hood of flesh exactly when her stimulation is peaking. Many a finger or tongue has withdrawn in confusion at this point, so tantalizingly close to paradise—not a pleasing development for her. And then the hidden treasure is hard to relocate.

There are two good solutions. One is communication. *She* knows where everything is, and she probably also knows when and how she wants you to touch her. All she has to do is tell you . . . or show you. The latter, for the record, can be an incredibly sexy experience in its own right.

Meanwhile, all *you* have to do is ask. Clitoral attention provides a fine opportunity to refute the charge that men won't ask for directions. Or see for yourself: On your next trip downtown for cunnilingus, leave a light on and check things out. Every vulva has its own beauty, and here's your chance to explore this one. One part of you or another will be spending a lot of quality time here. Why not know the terrain?

contraception

Talk about taking things for granted: Technological advancement has given us contraception that's safe, easy, available, and effective. So what do we do? We complain. About the cost. About threats to spontaneity. About the few remaining risks. About the general hassle of it all.

The truth is, contraception—the prevention of unwanted pregnancy using birth control devices or agents—has changed the way we think of sex. For the better.

Modern contraceptives work in lots of ways. *Barrier methods*—such as the diaphragm, the cervical cap, the female condom, and the sponge—are temporarily placed inside the vagina to block sperm from reaching an egg. (The male condom, of course, keeps the sperm out of the vagina in the first place.) *Spermicides* are substances that actually kill sperm once they're in the vagina, and they're typically used to supplement other methods. *Hormonal birth control* prevents ovulation so there's simply no egg to impregnate; the Pill is by far the most popular, but there are also longer-lasting implants and shots, as well as the morning-after pill.

The type of contraceptive that's best is up to you and your mate. But we can tell you two things, the first of which you've probably heard before: The responsibility for birth control is not hers, or yours, but shared—just as the consequences of an unwanted pregnancy are shared. In practice, that means you should be just as unwilling to participate in unprotected intercourse as she is. Our second piece of advice may sound radical: Consider contraception a part of sex, not a sidetrack from it. Think of the birth control (and safe sex) conversation with a new partner, not as an anti-romantic obligation but rather as a thrilling prelude to pleasure. After all, talk is a turn-on, and what could be a sexier topic than arranging to have great, carefree sex with each other? The same holds for applying a birth control device—your condom or her diaphragm, for example. Don't approach it as an imposition. Make it a mutual rite of pleasure. Foreplay, if you will.

crabs

They're really lice. But when they infest your pubic area, they certainly make you feel crabby. That's because they also make you feel intense itching as they feed on your blood and lay their tiny white eggs, or nits, in your pubic hair.

The tiny lice can live outside a host for up to 2 days, which means that they can be spread by simple contact, not just by sexual intercourse. So you and your sex partner don't have to suspect each other of infidelity if the little buggers show up.

cunnilingus

Now here's a medical term for oral sex that really sounds like what's going on. As you probably know, it's the sexual stimulating of her genital area (labia, clitoris, and vaginal opening) with your lips and tongue.

The secret here is to enjoy it. Don't do it "for" her. Don't "give" it like a gift. Go down on your partner in the spirit of mutual pleasure. Get into the sensate experience of cunnilingus instead of just trying to bring her off. Make yourself comfortable and settle in for a good time. Look for ways (like music, scents, positions) to heighten the pleasure—*your* pleasure. Sound selfish? On the contrary, you'll be a more enthusiastic and generous oral lover. You'll be less likely to get impatient about just how long you have to do this before she's had enough. And you'll find it easier to get creative—to explore, experiment, and stumble upon new ways to please her. When you're having fun, it's easier for her to have fun.

Then again, maybe you just don't like the idea of getting your face down there and going at it. Give it a chance. Give it a few chances. It's worth the effort, since a lot of women are crazy about cunnilingus and since it gives you a fine opportunity to pleasure your partner without needing an erection. But look, if it remains clear that this thing isn't for you, don't do it. Just be forewarned that for some women your disinclination in this area is a deal breaker.

dildo

What's the difference between a dildo and a vibrator? A penetrating question. In general, they're both sex toys. And from a woman's point of view, both have the advantage of never getting tired, never losing the mood, and never watching baseball on television. But the joys of vibration are best applied externally, exciting the pleasure-packed nerve endings of the vulva, clitoris, anal opening, or penis head. The nonvibrating dildo, on the other hand (or even on the same hand), is like Roger Clemens—it likes to work inside and is most effective when it keeps moving in and out.

This brings up another question on your mind: "Why would she want a fake penis in her vagina if she can have mine?" Well, she's better qualified to answer that than we are. Ask her. You'll probably find that it has nothing to do with your penis size or your performance, nor with any problem in your sex life together. A dildo, like any sex toy, isn't for "fixing" one or both partners. It's for enhancing sexual pleasure. So don't think of it as just her thing; think of it as a toy for two. She can play with it in your presence, while you watch or participate (by, for example, orally pleasuring her). Alternatively, you can do the inserting, leaving her hands and mouth free for reciprocal favors. And if you've both learned to like anal stimulation, two more orifices become eligible receivers. In that case, she can use a special harness to mount the dildo on her pelvis so she can experience doggie-style intercourse from what is usually your point of view, as the two of you engage in some serious role reversal. The possibilities, as they say, are endless.

An added bonus: A dildo is a good safe-sex option. Just make sure you wash it thoroughly or put a condom on it before transferring it from the anus to the vagina or mouth. And always use a lubricant for anal insertion.

If you're intrigued, start by shopping together online, via mail order, or at one of the modern, nonsleazy sex shops where you can actually see what will be getting into you—and the options abound. A veritable cottage industry of dildo designers has come up with numbers that look like dolphins, mythical figures, hands or feet, or simply abstract forms that are pleasing to the eye. Some day, the Museum of Modern Art may offer a retrospective on Non-Penile Representation at the Dawn of the Dildo Revolution: Form and Function. Meanwhile, you and your lady can choose between a dildo that looks just like an erect penis and one that doesn't.

Check the material. Silicone-based dildos are much better than the predominant mystery-rubber kind. They're easier to clean (you can pop them in the dishwasher—top rack only), and they last longer. Size, though, is your main concern. Too big will be uncomfortable, especially if it's going up an anal canal. Too small might be disappointing, especially if it's going into a vagina. How do you know what size is just right? After all, test-inserting a dildo is impossible online, and it's frowned upon at the sex-shop display shelves.

You can try using the finger-comparison test, but by far, the most accurate solution is produce. Finish laughing, then go on down to the supermarket, select zucchini and cucumbers in lots of sizes, go home, wash them, insert them one by one (using a condom and, if you're testing them for anal use, a water-based lubricant), pick her favorite (and yours, if applicable), and then measure its circumference. You now have a size guideline, without having done anything that folks haven't done for thousands of years. And you'll both be smiling during the salad course tonight.

doggie style

Zoologically accurate slang for intercourse wherein you enter her vagina from behind. Variations abound, of course, but the most doglike rear-entry position has the two of you on your knees.

One drawback here is the nomenclature. *Rear entry* sounds coldly mechanical. *Doggie style* sounds like a fashion rag for the canine set. Solution: Give it your own name. *Rump bump, over the moon, that thing I really like*—just get creative; it's all good.

douche

Flushing out the inside of the vagina with a jet of water or cleansing liquid is a centuries-old hygiene practice. But if your partner is among the 40 million American women who douche regularly, she's wasting her time.

The very idea of a hygienic douche implies that there's something foul about the vagina. The truth is, it's a self-cleaning organ. A regular bath or shower gets the area plenty clean. Now, if you're uncomfortable with the natural smell and taste of your partner's healthy vagina, that's an issue. But it's not one she can simply wash away.

On the other hand, a persistent foul odor from the vagina could indicate an infection. If that's the case, the woman needs a medical exam, not a douche. In fact, douching often makes things worse—or even causes vaginal problems in the first place—because prepared douching products contain chemicals that upset the balance of the vagina's natural pH and healthful bacteria. The result is often an increase in yeast and bacterial infections.

Douching also has a long, unsuccessful history as a birth control strategy. If your partner uses it as your sole means of contraception, start thinking of names for the baby.

ejaculation

The projection of about a teaspoonful of sperm-containing semen from your penis is so associated with orgasm that we usually consider them the same thing. Technically, they're not, since you can theoretically have an orgasm without ejaculating. Don't count on that, though.

What you can count on is that once you reach what's known as ejaculatory inevitability, nothing in the world is going to stop the semen from coming. What you feel at this stage is the fluids from several glands gathering in the urethra, the tube that the semen rushes through to get out. Then, the urethra and penile muscles contract, the bladder opening closes (so that no urine gets into the mix), and the seminal fluid has no choice but to spurt out the opening of your penis. That, sir, is ejaculation. So do yourself a favor: Once you hit ejaculatory inevitability, don't try to hold back. That just ruins a good time. If you want to delay ejaculation, learn to recognize the feelings that come before you come.

Not being able to ejaculate is another matter. Physical causes might include prostate troubles, diabetes, neurovascular problems, medications, even cancer. If you can come while masturbating but not during intercourse, the cause is probably psychological. See a sex therapist. And there's another offbeat condition, retrograde ejaculation, which results in nothing coming out when you ejaculate. Instead, the semen shoots backward into the bladder because the valve that's supposed to prevent that very thing has been damaged. While this doesn't necessarily ruin the pleasure, it makes it hard to father children. The most important advice about ejaculatory problems? If there's any pain, see a doctor. Orgasm may not always make the Earth move, but it should never hurt.

erection

It's what nature gave you instead of a penis bone, which would've been awkward to have around all of the time.

An erection is a reflex. You can't, alas, will one into existence. (Nor can you will one *out* of existence, as many a mortified 13-year-old has discovered during fourth-period biology class.) Rather, the brain needs to respond to some kind of sexual stimulation. That stimulation can be physical, as when a curvaceous nymph rubs your genitals. It can be mental, as when you think about a curvaceous nymph rubbing your genitals. It can be aural, as when a curvaceous nymph whispers into your ear that she'd like to rub your genitals. Or it can be visual, as when you watch a curvaceous nymph rub her own genitals. Whatever it is, your brain responds by marshaling your body's heavy hitters—the circulating blood, the autonomic (involuntary) nervous system, and chemicals—to work together to create an erection.

This they do by sending more blood into your penis than is allowed to drain away. There, the blood gathers in special erectile tissue, mostly in spongelike cylinders called the corpora cavernosa and the corpus spongiosum. That accumulation builds up a hydraulic pressure, rendering your penis bigger, stiffer, and ready to rumble.

erection difficulties

The essential thing to know about erection problems is this: The erectile dysfunction that those earnest-looking guys in the Viagra commercials are talking about is not the same thing as those occasional episodes of unwelcome limpness. If it's episodic, it's not erectile dysfunction. Erectile dysfunction (or impotence) is a consistent inability to get or keep an erection satisfactory for sexual intercourse. That has nothing to do with the nearly universal male experience of not getting it up from time to time. Occasional power failures are normal. Repeat, *normal*.

In fact, there are circumstances when you're not *supposed* to get it up. Too much alcohol in your system is one of those circumstances. So is outside stress, such as tomorrow's IRS audit. So is stress from the sexual encounter itself, such as performance anxiety or worrying about birth control. So is anything else that interferes with the complicated electrochemical biology and psychology of erectile function. The reason for the system's failure may not be clear at the time, but you can bet there is one. It's your body's way of telling you that this is not a good time for intercourse. It's not your fault.

That doesn't make it any easier to take, does it? But you can handle it. First, remind yourself that it's an isolated case that says nothing about you as a man. You are not your penis. Resist the male urge to tough it out, as if trying harder would change things. Don't ignore what you're both thinking about; that just makes it seem more important than it need be. Go ahead and let her know you're disappointed—but not humiliated. Keep the mood light. Continue paying attention to her. Then, simply do something else together. Bringing her to orgasm orally or manually are two obvious choices, but they're not the only ones. Do whatever you've been doing that you both enjoyed. Focus on the positive things about being together. You can have intercourse some other time.

By the way, sometimes guys create erection problems when there aren't any. It's natural for erections to come and go during a love session. For example, if you divert your attention by going down on her, your erection may take a recess. Relax and it'll come back. Panic and it may not. Like everything else about sex, erections don't appreciate being rushed.

As for true erectile dysfunction, lots of factors—physical and psychological—can cause it, most of which are more likely as you get older. One thing you can do on your own is try to notice whether you get erections in your sleep. Do you occasionally wake up with a hard-on, even though you can't achieve one for intercourse? Can you get erections under certain circumstances and not others? If so, these are good indications that your plumbing is okay and the problem lies elsewhere. Even so, if you're consistently getting soft-ons, you need to see a doctor. Ongoing erectile problems often indicate a more threatening condition, such as cardiovascular disease. Also, a doctor can uncover some other cause, such as medications or diet. And finally, there are treatments—including Viagra—that can get you up and going again.

erogenous zones

Formally, those areas of the body that produce the most sexual excitement or libidinal gratification when stimulated. Traditionally, that means the genitals, breasts, buttocks, anus, and mouth. If formal and traditional sex is what you want, that's all you need to know. But if you'd prefer a rich and varied sex life that's more satisfying to you and your partner, throw out the whole notion of erogenous zones. Think of the entire human body as one giant sexual-pleasure center.

That's not just the sexually correct thing to say. It's a view you can use. Instead of privileging a few body parts, experiment with every square inch of both bodies and see which can give or receive pleasure. You'll find areas that work for both of you. You'll also find plenty of spots that turn on one and not the other. You may discover exquisite joy in a foot rub that only tickles her.

She, in turn, may squeal with delight at a light lick at the back of her neck. And once you're fully aroused, other parts of your body that were ignorable a few minutes earlier can suddenly surprise you with their capacity for sexual pleasure—if you give them a chance. That chance will never come if you confine the action to the traditional erogenous zones. Don't limit. Explore.

estrogen

You don't know women if you don't know estrogen, the principal female sex hormone. More accurately, it's a *class* of hormones from the steroid family that includes estradiol, estrone, and estriol. Estrogen is what makes a woman a woman, starting in early fetushood, when it's instrumental in shaping her vagina, uterus, and ovaries. Later, estrogen is responsible for the mood swings, breast development, and rounding hips of budding female pubescence. Higher-than-usual estrogen levels contribute to various discomforts (for both of you) just before her period. And estrogen manipulation is why birth control pills work.

Most important for her (and therefore your) sex life is a woman's estrogen-driven tendency to seek closeness and nurturing contact as part and parcel of being sexually turned on. We testosterone-powered men aren't opposed to the intimacy thing, but we tend to think that . . . well . . . it doesn't need to be overdone. What we have here is a chemical conflict between the sexes. Accommodating it is the ongoing challenge of a sexual relationship.

Her estrogen production drops drastically with menopause around age 51. From a feminist point of view, there's a certain advantage in this, since her chemically mandated "caretaker" urge is now better able to yield to more self-assertive goals. But sexually, the estrogen decrease can cause some problems, such as drying and thinning vaginal walls, painful intercourse, and lowered libido. What's more, the higher incidence of female cardiovascular disease after age 50 points out the heart-protecting qualities of estrogen. Other postmenopausal problems show that estrogen also protects bones and aids memory. For those reasons, many women in their fifties and beyond replenish their estrogen supply through estrogen replacement therapy, also known as hormone replacement therapy (HRT). There's controversy about that, though, with strong feelings on both sides. The pro-HRT camp sees it as a quality-of-life advantage since today's postmenopausal women can expect to live several more sexually active decades. Opponents see HRT as unnatural and an unnecessary breast and uterine cancer risk since estrogen, amongst all its other qualities, can have a cancer-promoting effect. The overall significance of that effect is part of the controversy.

Estrogen, by the way, influences your own sexuality as well. Just as women manufacture a tad of testosterone to fuel their sex drives, men produce a little estrogen from their testes. And as your testosterone levels dip a bit in later years, your estrogen is freer to encourage the more "feminine" virtues of nurturing and harmonizing. The new chemical balance can give you a best-of-both-worlds sexual persona, and it's one reason why older men enjoy a reputation as better lovers.

faking orgasm

The running gag is that if fewer men faked foreplay, fewer women would fake orgasm. As things stand, lots of women sometimes fake it, and some fake it often. Why might *your* woman do this? To please you. To let you know that she's having a good time. To reassure you that you're a good lover. What better proof of all those things than a smoking climax? And if it's not happening for real, a false crescendo of moans and cries will do the trick. No harm done, right?

Maybe. Even well-intentioned deception isn't exactly a desired ingredient in a sexual relationship. It's certainly not going to help real orgasms happen. And there may be some performance anxiety going on—*her* anxiety about being sufficiently responsive to you. Eventually, faked orgasms may be the only ones she'll have. While you're in the room, anyway.

You don't have to suspect that your partner is faking orgasms to help her not need to. First, destroy the justification for fraud by finding a way to let her know that your ego doesn't depend on whether you "give" her an orgasm during sex. Sure, you want her to feel good and be satisfied, but the idea that you're a good lover if she comes and a bad one if she doesn't gives you too much credit either way. Getting that important point across is a step toward encouraging more mutual trust about each other's sexual needs. She should feel comfortable letting you know that she hasn't come yet. And you should feel comfortable receiving that information.

Also, take to heart that one-liner about foreplay. Women do need more time for arousal. And they're much more likely to climax during sex if there's generous stimulation.

But that still avoids the real issue. If your woman fakes an orgasm during intercourse to please you, it implies the following: (1) that sex is a challenge, (2) that intercourse is the playing field, (3) that victory comes with her orgasm, and (4) that winning is so important that she may have to rig the results to do it. The fact is, though, that for most women, intercourse is not a feasible route to orgasm. And trying only makes it harder.

Instead, think about re-choreographing your sexual sessions. Play down the idea of orgasm during intercourse. Help her come via oral sex, manual sex, vibrator sex. Encourage her to take things into her own hands and get herself off—with you there. Any of this can happen before intercourse, after intercourse, or instead of intercourse. All those things are just as much "real" sex as intercourse.

They're certainly more real than faked orgasms.

female ejaculation

There does seem to be such a thing, though what's being ejaculated is something of a mystery. Only some women ejaculate, and only sometimes. The clear or milky liquid they release at orgasm isn't semen, obviously. Experts believe the fluid, which may be part urine, spurts out of two ducts on either side of a woman's urethral opening. It often comes with her second or third orgasm, and some experts believe that it requires G-spot stimulation.

Sorry we can't be more specific about this aspect of female sexuality. But would women be as sexy if there were *nothing* mysterious about them?

foreplay

There's no such thing. The word suggests a pointless preliminary before the main event, like waiting in line to ride a roller coaster. But that makes sense only if you think of sex as no more than penetration and orgasm, with everything else as warmup. That ain't the way it is. Foreplay doesn't come before sex. Foreplay *is* sex.

You knew this in your early teens. With actual intercourse not in the cards, sex was a thrilling combination of kissing, touching, rubbing, squeezing, petting, and all those other interesting things humans do to pleasure each other and themselves. You didn't dismiss all this as just a prelude. It was *action*. It still is.

There are plenty of good reasons to make foreplay an extended action sequence. Yes, a big one is to help bring her along to full arousal. But this is no one-way street. The more turned on she gets, the more turned on you get. The result is an arousal feedback loop that the two of you can exploit for extreme pleasure—regardless of whether you follow it up with coital union.

There's more. Foreplay fosters intimacy, which delivers big payoffs in an ongoing sexual relationship. It also creates that thrilling sense of cresting excitement that a lot of couples leave behind with their dating days. Then there's the obvious: Foreplay is your chance to enjoy, from top to bottom, that fetching female body to which you've earned access.

If you do proceed to the old in-and-out, generous amounts of foreplay will have made your erection and her orgasm more likely to happen. Concentrating on the pure pleasure of foreplay rather than the necessity of an erection or the desirability of an orgasm prompts the latter two to take care of themselves.

Nobody has come up with an all-purpose manual telling you what to touch, where to lick, and how hard to rub. That's a good thing, actually, because the key to foreplay is simpler than that. In fact, it comes down to two words: *Pay attention.* Let her pleasure be your guide. Experiment. If she doesn't let you know—via moans or words or arching her body toward you—whether something feels good, go ahead and ask if it does.

And pay attention to what feels good to you, too. That arousal feedback loop is yours for the asking.

genital warts

Meet the bug behind the most common sexually transmitted disease in the United States: the human papillomavirus (HPV), father to genital warts. And unlike bacterial infections (or that brother-in-law houseguest who finally gets the hint), this virus never goes away.

It's sneaky, too. Many infected people never know they have it because HPV can stay hidden in their bodies without ever showing up as warts. And then they can unknowingly pass it on to someone else. In fact, here's a sobering thought: There's a one-in-five chance that the next woman you sleep with will have an HPV infection.

If it does show up as warts, they'll be little cauliflower-like bumps on your penis or elsewhere on your genital area. They can also show up around your anus and even in your mouth. (You guessed it—they get there through oral sex.) It's a good idea to have your doctor check you during regular exams, especially if you suspect that one of your partners may have had it. Periodic self-exams are wise, too.

It was once thought that these warts were ugly but harmless. Not so anymore. Some strains of the virus have been linked to penile cancer in men and cervical cancer in women. And one recent small study found that genital warts increase men's risk of developing prostate cancer.

Currently, your only treatment option is to have the warts removed. A doctor can prescribe a medication that you dab on your warts a couple of times a day. If that doesn't work, he can fry or freeze them off in his office. The problem is, this solution works only for the visible warts—it won't eradicate warts hidden in the layers of your skin.

Researchers are still trying to find a vaccine for the virus. It's been a tough go since, as with the common cold, there are so many different strains.

If you want to avoid this lifelong hanger-on, your best bet is still a plain old condom. Even though condoms won't entirely protect you—because warts can lie outside the boundaries of the rubber—they can reduce the risk substantially, especially for men. One study showed that failure to use condoms made men three times more likely to develop warts. In women, the odds were about half that.

gonorrhea

Popularly known as the clap, gonorrhea warrants no applause. There are more than 350,000 new cases of the stuff in the United States every year.

You'll know that you're one of them if you experience the following symptoms: One to 7 days after intercourse with an infected partner, you notice a burning feeling when you take a leak. If you milk the shaft of your penis, you'll usually see yellow pus ooze out the end. Say hello to *Neisseria gonorrhoeae,* a sexually transmitted bacteria that's taken up residence in your system. You need to see a doctor pronto for some antibiotics.

Ignore gonorrhea, and you run the risk of becoming infertile. Even so, a lot of guys see the clap as no big deal—go on a round of pills, and it's gone. That may explain why the percentage of men with gonorrhea who get repeat infections within a year hovers between 17 and 22 percent.

The scary part of that attitude is this: Studies have shown over and over that being infected with gonorrhea makes it easier for you to catch the virus that causes AIDS. And the bacteria is growing increasingly resistant to antibiotics. Not such a harmless little bug anymore, huh?

The clap is almost entirely preventable with the use of condoms. Yet another very good reason to wrap your willy.

G-spot

In the 1940s, German obstetrician Ernst Grafenberg began a controversy that continues to this day. He described an area in a woman's vagina that became known as the G-spot. Trouble is, nobody has ever really seen this purported center of sexual pleasure.

The reason the G-spot can be as elusive as the Loch Ness monster is that it's made of erectile tissue that can be felt only when a woman is aroused. So gynecologists are unlikely to come across it, because a pelvic exam is far from arousing, and medical ethics boards prefer to keep it that way. No autopsy has been able to confirm the existence of the G-spot, either.

So where is this legendary happy zone said to be situated? On the upper part of the vaginal wall, 1 to 2 inches behind the back of the pubic bone. It consists of nerve endings and blood vessels that, when stimulated, can grow to be as big as a half-dollar.

Not all women feel something when you stroke the spot; some feel that they need to urinate. But for those who respond well to G-spot wrangling, it can be a source of overwhelming orgasms—sometime even leading to the equally mythic female ejaculation.

You and your partner can figure out how responsive she is to G-spot simulation with a minimum amount of spelunking: Next time you're deep into foreplay, lie face-to-face. Slide your index and middle fingers into the top third of her vagina. Feel for a rougher patch of skin in the above-mentioned location, and stroke it with your fingertips as if you were beckoning someone to come (which, in a sense, you are). If this doesn't produce any sensations of particular interest, wander around the area doing the same thing. She'll let you know if and when you strike gold.

The G-spot is slightly harder to hit during intercourse. The best positions for stimulating it are doggie style and woman on top.

herpes

Think you know what someone with genital herpes looks like? Next time you're in a public place, count off four normal-looking people. One of them has it. That's right, almost 25 percent of Americans test positive for herpes simplex virus type 2. And that's not counting those with HSV-1, another type of herpes virus that generally just causes cold sores around your lips but can also occur on your genitals. A type-1 infection can travel south via oral sex, and a type-2 infection can migrate north the same way.

Condoms offer limited protection against herpes because the virus can be shed from any part of the genitals, not just what's covered in latex. That said, as is stated on the package, condoms do *reduce* your overall risk of contracting sexually transmitted diseases, herpes included.

Obviously, your chances of being infected rise with the number of partners you've had. If you've slept with 2 to 4 people, your odds of carrying the virus are 20 percent. That jumps to 25 percent if you've had 5 to 9 partners, and 31 percent if you've had more than 10.

Here's the kicker: Most people who carry the virus don't know it. The symptoms can take years to show up—if they ever do. That's why some people who have been monogamous or celibate for a long period can suddenly find out that they have herpes.

When symptoms do occur, they include small sores and crusty, blisterlike lesions in the genital area and itching or burning that can be mistaken for jock itch. The first episode is usually the worst and can be accompanied by flulike symptoms. Subsequent outbreaks are milder and generally clear up in about 10 days.

Given the statistics and the uncertainties, you might consider asking your doctor to do a diagnostic blood test at your next checkup. If you test positive, antiviral drugs can reduce or eliminate the painful outbreaks.

From there, it's a matter of responsibility: If you're positive for the bug, please, *please* warn potential partners. You're on the verge of giving them a lifelong disease. Though you're most contagious when symptoms are actually present, you can pass on the virus even if you never have symptoms, or if you had just a single outbreak a decade ago. And even if you don't have serious symptoms, that doesn't mean that the person to whom you give it won't. For one thing, recurrent infections tend to be a lot worse for women than for men. At special risk are pregnant women and those with immune systems weakened by AIDS, chemotherapy, radiation therapy, or high doses of cortisone. For example, a pregnant woman can pass a herpes infection to her infant, causing critical illness or death. Infections have even been implicated in certain cancers, such as cervical cancer.

If your partner already knows that she's positive too, she'll probably be relieved to have found someone to whom she doesn't have to worry about giving herpes. In this situation, however, it's more important than ever to find out whether she's HIV-positive. Having sex with an HIV-infected person while either one of you is experiencing a herpes outbreak makes you up to 32 times more likely to contract the AIDS virus.

impotence

This word meaning "lack of power" is the one that most men use to describe an inability to have erections. While such a problem is indeed serious, it hardly makes one powerless. So instead, let's just use the term preferred by the guys in white coats (and some former presidential candidates looking for second careers as TV pharmaceutical pitchmen): *erectile dysfunction.*

Erectile dysfunction, or ED, has a less permanent ring to it—as well it should. Just about every man who once had erections and who's still taking breath can regain his former capacity. He just has to be willing to work for it.

That said, the 20 to 30 million men in the United States who experience ED will not all take the same route back to firmness. That's because the underlying reasons for the condition vary from person to person.

Once upon a time, it was believed that long-term erectile dysfunction was "all in your head," albeit the wrong head. For some of us, this is still true. Performance anxiety, stress, and guilt are leading psychological causes of ED. Even sleeping with a woman you find intimidatingly attractive can leave you with a soft-on.

Today, however, docs know that ED often stems from a physical problem, especially if your dysfunction has grown steadily worse over the years. The culprit can be anything from diminishing testosterone levels to undiagnosed heart disease. In the latter case, your ability to get stiff is among the first things to go when your arteries clog up. Consider your flagging member an early warning system—one that your life may depend on. Erectile problems can also indicate adult-onset diabetes, so a full checkup is in order.

Whatever the case, the boys with the Bunsen burners have developed some bang-up drugs to help. Most famous is Viagra (sildenafil). The drug works in 70 to 75 percent of men, even if their ED is psychological in nature.

Urologists do say that too many men use Viagra incorrectly. First and foremost, you won't get top results from it if you take it with a fatty meal. That means no burgers, steaks, or corn dogs for a couple of hours before and after you pop one. Have a salad with fat-free dressing or a light pasta dish as your precoital repast.

And remember that Viagra doesn't "give you" an erection, it creates the ideal physiological conditions for one. You still need to be in an arousing environment. That means that you can't just toss down the little blue pill and go watch the Cowboys play—unless you spend most of your time ogling the cheerleaders.

intimacy

You hear a lot about women wanting more intimacy from their men, but what the hell does that mean? Well, according to the triangle theory of love, intimacy joins passion and commitment as one of three key ingredients in a complete, abiding love. It means that you feel free to talk about anything. You're patient and understanding with each other.

As long ago as prehistoric times, women satisfied the need for intimacy by congregating with other women and chatting happily while their men went out to hunt, gather, and visit Paleolithic strip joints.

Nowadays, thanks to the liberation movement, your woman's support system is all off at work. Inevitably, she turns to you to sate her intimacy needs. And you're just not that well-equipped to deal with it.

The best thing you can do is spend a half-hour or so every day just talking with her. About anything. Ask her how her day was, tell her how yours was, talk about what she'd like to do this weekend. It doesn't matter. To her, talking freely is a sign that everything is okay. So put your newspaper aside for that 30 minutes and play the part of a whiskered old woman. Maybe it's not as much fun as the strip joint, but it has its own quieter rewards, and we can almost guarantee that she'll show you greater interest and appreciation in return.

jealousy

There she is, across the room. Talking to another guy. Worse yet, another handsome guy. (We're assuming that you're handsome, too; if we're wrong, you're even worse off than we thought.) And damned if she isn't laughing and touching him on the forearm the way she used to touch you.

On the other side of the world, in the Polynesian Islands, the Kiribati people know what you're feeling. They call the worst form of jealousy *koko,* "a murdering thing."

While jealousy is a normal emotion, no one disputes that it can have a destructive effect. In one survey of 651 university students, more than one-third said that jealousy was a significant issue in their present relationships, causing problems ranging from loss of self-esteem to bitter arguing to stalking. It can also cause the very thing a jealous man fears the most: the departure of his woman for another man. That's the irony.

Intense jealousy can strangle a relationship to the point where it can no longer survive. If you pound on her emotionally every time she wears a sexy dress, is a little late getting home, or goes out drinking with friends, you're setting yourself up for a fall. That doesn't mean you can't *feel* jealousy. You just have to keep it in check. Even little passive-aggressive remarks—"Wow, that must have been some line in the supermarket"—can take their toll, depending on the situation and the woman.

What do we mean by "depending"? Simply that jealousy is a paradox. Much like alcohol, it's poisonous when taken to an extreme (or, for some people, to any degree), but in moderation, some people think it can act as a love balm. One study of married couples showed that 40 percent of the women had used jealousy to test their husbands' commitment. For example, your wife may have smiled at another man in full view of you. Or she may have deliberately not answered your phone call when you were expecting her to be at home.

Maybe she was trying to get a rise out of you. In her mind, a jealous reaction is proof positive that you still want her. To her, indifference is deadly—a sign that you want out of the relationship. So, if you should pick up on these little cues, go ahead and address the issue head-on: Ask her if she's feeling neglected. Does she need something you're not giving her? Just be cool about it. No physical aggression, ever.

Kama Sutra

Probably the world's oldest and most widely read sex book, the *Kama Sutra* was written sometime around the 5th century by the Indian sage Vatsyayana.

Kama refers to one of the ancient responsibilities of men in their roles as heads of households: pleasure and love. In other words, a properly educated man of society should know how to take the skin boat to tuna town. Or something like that. *Sutra,* in case you're wondering, loosely translated means "teachings."

Old though it may be, the *Kama Sutra* is far from dated in much of its material—with a few notable exceptions. One is the advice on how to keep your woman from going astray: Sprinkle a monkey-dung potion on her head.

Likely the most famous part of the book is its extensive collection of sexual positions. One of our favorites: A woman lifts her legs up and crosses them while her lover is inside her. It's known, surprisingly enough, as the tight position.

If you and your partner are in a bit of a rut, or if you're feeling sexually playful, pick up a copy of the book and give things a shot. But hold the monkey dung.

K-Y jelly

The grandpappy of sexual lubricants, K-Y jelly was originally designed to ease the entry of your doctor's fat finger during prostate exams, and for related gynecological uses. It wasn't long before it found its way into bedrooms.

The good thing about K-Y is that it's widely available in drugstores, in supermarkets, online, and even at some convenience stores. Since it's water soluble, it doesn't break down a condom like petroleum-based lubes do.

The bad things: The original formulation is not spermicidal (though you can buy K-Y Plus Nonoxynol-9), and no type of K-Y prevents the spread of sexually transmitted diseases. It's also heavy and greasy, and it dries out quickly after you put it on. You have to keep adding more if the use to which you're putting it lasts more than a few minutes—as we all hope *you* do, of course.

labia majora and minora

Time to brush up on your Latin. *Labia* translates to lips. *Majora* and *minora* mean big and little, respectively. Thus, when you peer at a woman's genitals, you see one set each of big and little lips.

The labia majora are the ones that form the outer part of her oyster shell. Unless she's shorn clean, their outer surfaces are covered with pubic hair. When she's aroused, they swell noticeably and get a puffy sort of feel.

The labia minora are the ones you spy when she parts her legs widely. In crude colloquial terms, they're sometimes called piss flaps because they enclose her urethra, the hole from which she urinates. They also form a cover for her vaginal opening.

Her little lips are too often overlooked in the mad stampede for the clitoris. Too bad, because they're packed with nerve endings and highly sensitive to a knowing touch. They also contain an opening called the vestibule, through which a lubricant is secreted to ease your passage into paradise valley.

You can put this insider knowledge to use next time you're headlong into foreplay or even giving her a massage. Gently use your fingertips to knead her lips. Squeeze and tug her labia minora softly, pulling them outward and rolling each one delicately between your fingers.

libido

A Freudian term for our sex drives and instincts.

Famed psychiatrist Sigmund Freud believed that the libido is the most basic and powerful human drive and that it develops in several stages: oral, anal, and phallic. The oral stage occurs in infancy, when children are interested in sucking and other mouth-related activities, such as spitting up on you. Freud labeled the period when children are toilet training, between the ages of 2 and 3, the anal stage. And finally, as youngsters enter pubescence and discover their genitalia, they go through what Freud called the phallic stage.

Contemporary psychology has jiggled Freud's beliefs, as his theories are focused primarily on biology and downplay other factors like cultural and social influences. Modern shrinks agree that the biological side is important: Hormones influence the basic human drive to reproduce and affect how we feel pleasure. But the way in which you act on those drives and emotions is determined in large part by your childhood experiences, family beliefs, and surrounding societal values. In other words, as with most things sexual, libido is determined by both the physical and the mental.

love

Shakespeare wrote 154 sonnets on the subject; Woody Allen made 34 films about it in 35 years; Barry White explored the feeling on 33 albums. There's been a lot of talk about love, and no one has ever gotten it completely right. Of course, that won't keep us from taking a stab at it, however inept that stab may be.

Love is a deep and abiding attraction based on trust, desire, admiration, and respect, all of which are mutual. So much for the clinical definition. Part of the problem with love is that it is many things all wrapped up in one thin word.

We expect love to be unchanging; it's not. We demand love to be impervious to all affronts; it isn't. We insist that love be the balm for all wounds; it can't be.

That's not to take away from the powerful force that actually is love. We just need to let it be what it is, rather than what we misconceive it to be. So, then, expect love to change. You'll want to roar from the rooftops when you first fall in love. Over time, that passion will mellow; love will become a quieter, more thoughtful thing—not necessarily better or worse, just different. It's the difference between a summer storm and a breeze that carries the smell of autumn.

Know, too, that love is not invincible. If you do enough crappy things to each other over time, love will die—or be overwhelmed by so much hurt that what you feel mostly about each other, despite the love, is sadness. Common decency is the water that nourishes love's roots. Neither will love make all the wrongs in the world right. Anyone who has a difficult, challenging child knows this. You can love the little beast all you want—he'll still be a beast. But you'll love him anyway if you don't expect love to turn him into something he's not.

We can tell you how we feel on the subject, but don't let your inquiry stop there. In fact, let this be your foremost accomplishment in life: to know that every year brings you a greater understanding of that crazy thing called love.

marriage

Don't believe the doom and gloom coming from some misguided quarters of the population. Guys in barrooms and holier-than-thou preachers love to disparage the state of American wedlock. But two Harris polls beg to differ: Of the 1,000 polled each time, more than 95 percent of those who were married said they felt good about their marriages. Less than 5 percent said otherwise.

And some researchers believe that men, particularly, are better off married than single. Wedded guys have longer lives, better health, and higher earnings than single men. More to the point of this book, they also have more gratifying sex lives. For one thing, they have sex more often than bachelors do, simply because there's always a woman right there next to them in bed. And all that boot knocking may actually be behind some of marriage's other benefits, since having sex on a regular basis contributes to a healthier prostate, better-quality sperm, less stress, less chance of becoming impotent, and an expanded sense of well-being.

This is not to say that the marital bed is a bed of roses. If you honor your marriage vows, it's always the same woman right there next to you, and familiarity and routine can be the death of sex. This is due in part to a psychological phenomenon called sensory adaptation. You know what it is, even if you haven't heard the term before. It's when a stimulus that is constant and unchanging simply begins to disappear over time. Like when you jump into a cold lake: Eventually, it doesn't feel so chilly. Or when you live next to a pulp mill: After a while, you don't notice that your neighborhood smells like a dog fart. The entire human nervous system evolved to notice change and contrast in the world and to ignore nonessential background noise.

Since the average couple beds each other some 2,640 times over the course of a 25-year marriage, it's a challenge of the highest order to keep things full of change and contrast for that many rounds of nuptial nookie. Your wife becomes white noise, bursting back into your sensory awareness only when she takes off her ratty old nightshirt and puts on that skimpy, hot-pink number.

So go buy her an electric-blue number and a majestic-purple number—and pick up a pair of silky black Skivvies for yourself. Set up a pseudocampsite in the middle of the living room once in a while. Encourage her to style her hair differently now and then (instead of griping when she comes home with a new hairdo). Go down on her while she's talking on the phone to a telemarketer. (Did a woman ever have a better reason for brushing off a nuisance call?) Do all these things and more to keep your conjugal union intense, to keep it varied, and to make sure your senses don't have a chance to fatigue.

Throughout this book, there are lots of other tips and suggestions to help you. Keep reading and put our advice to good use. Otherwise, you may find yourself in one of the 40 to 50 percent of marriages that end in divorce.

meeting women

When looking for a woman, you do all the (supposedly) right things. You frequent the nightclubs, chat up the tight-bodies at the gym, and even let your mom set you up on blind dates. Yet the best opportunity for hooking up with a compatible mate may come along in a chance encounter: You spy an amazing woman in a public place and can't keep your eyes off her. A quick finger check reveals no glittering rings. So, naturally, you do nothing. You let the moment slip by. You just stand there and, in an instant, your potential soul mate walks out the sliding door . . . crosses the parking lot . . . puts her groceries in the trunk . . . starts her car . . . and drives away, never to be seen again.

We know; we've done it ourselves, many times. By the time you scan your brain for something to say and pluck up the courage to act, the moment has passed. An old adage tells us that luck favors those who are prepared. So be a Boy Scout.

That means that the most important thing to do when running into the supermarket is simply appear presentable. You don't have to put on a top hat and tails; just look clean. Otherwise, though you're a wonderful guy, she may not be able to get past the fact that your hairy nipple is poking through the tear in your oil-caked sweatshirt. Also make it a habit to run a comb through your hair before leaving the house.

When you do approach her, give up on trying to sound witty, clever, and erudite. You'll freeze up or sound rehearsed. Say something open-ended and matter-of-fact. If you're in the cereal aisle: "It's hard to find cereal that's good for you, yet doesn't taste like sawdust." If she responds with a smile and a comment, extend your hand and say, "Hi, my name is Bruno." (Do this only if your name is Bruno.)

Still too complicated? Try, "I was trying to think of a great way to start a conversation with you, but I couldn't. So I thought I'd just say hello." She'll most likely appreciate the no-bull approach.

If the two of you hit it off and she seems interested, offer her your business card or e-mail address. Don't ask for her number; she's not likely to feel comfortable giving it out to a guy she just met. Count it as a plus if she offers up her e-mail address. From there on out, it's up to her.

ménage à trois

A French phrase that literally translates into "household of three." In the strictest sense, it describes a living arrangement between a married couple and an extra man or woman who has a sexual relationship with one of the spouses. More commonly, it refers to a threesome.

While a ménage à trois is a favorite fantasy of many men (and women), in practice it's a different story. The Kinsey Institute for Research in Sex, Gender, and Reproduction, in Bloomington, Indiana, says that only about 3 percent of married men and 1 percent of married women have had sex with one other partner while the spouse was present. And the majority of those folks said that they've done it only once.

If you are thinking of having a ménage à trois, remember that it is never something you want to spring on your partner or decide to do when both of you are drunk or stoned. It requires serious discussion to avoid any morning-after regrets.

missionary position

This is to sex what Wonder bread is to the sandwich: serviceable, reasonably appetizing, a little bland after repeated use. (That's not to say that it can't be your favorite.) It is, of course, the traditional man-on-top-between-the-woman's-legs position.

In case Regis asks you on nationwide television someday, here's the origin of the term: European conquerors forbade their Polynesian colonial charges from having sex in any other fashion, deeming all other positions barbaric and pagan. It does have a bit of the conquering theme to it, what with the man on top, in control.

But it can also be a very intimate, loving position. It allows you to gaze into her eyes and kiss her freely. It can be very relaxing for her since you're often the one doing most of the work.

To spice things up, try placing your legs to the outsides of hers. This forces you higher up on her pelvis and puts you in greater contact with her clitoris. Or suggest that she hook her ankles over your shoulders. This variation allows you deeper inside her and stimulates the back wall of her vagina. Go easy here; it can be painful if you propel yourself like a battering ram.

The missionary position is not for all men, all the time. Especially if you've been watching your bellies burgeon over the years, having your gut pressing down on hers is far from erotic for either of you.

nymphomania

Excessive sexual desire in a female. That's the official *Webster's* definition. To which we might reply, "Define *excessive*." Or, "Yeah, so what's the problem?"

Seriously, who decides these things? Nymphomania is a concept that has confounded us through the ages, probably because female sexual desire has so long been suppressed, cloaked in shame, or otherwise misunderstood.

The ancient Greeks called it "uterine fury." (They said this in ancient Greek, of course.) In the 19th century, some American doctors were not above removing the clitorises of women they considered nymphomaniacs; some foreign cultures still do this as a matter of course. The famed sex researcher Alfred Kinsey is reported to have flippantly remarked that a nympho is a woman who "wants sex more than you do." Today, we use the word with equal parts reverence and condescension.

The thing is, our feelings about it are pretty hard to pin down. It's a cultural archetype representing both our fear of and fascination with female sexuality. We want a woman who shudders with desire for us, but we don't want her to overwhelm us sexually. We want to be the object of her passion, but we don't want that passion to spill over to other men.

That said, there are those (of both sexes) who *are* out of control sexually. If a woman engages in compulsive sexual activity without regard to consequences and without satisfaction, she's got a problem. It's like eating compulsively or washing your hands compulsively. She's just using sex as her compulsive vehicle.

one-night stand

Falling into bed with a woman you just met is great . . . until you wake up the next morning. It's not only that your standards tend to drop considerably as last call approaches—hence the phrase *any port in a storm* (and its less-flattering morning-after bookend, *coyote ugly*). It's that many people find it pretty tough to have sex with no strings attached. And if you're one of those people who thinks one-night stands are totally depersonalized sex, you may want to think again. By its very nature, can sexual intercourse truly be depersonalized?

So now you have two choices: creep out like, well, a creep—or handle it like a decent guy. Your first task come daybreak is to listen closely to what she says. She may well think that the two of you made an awful mistake. Don't be defensive.

Second, it's important to leave nothing behind—make sure you take your wallet, your tie, and so forth. Make it clear that you enjoyed meeting her, but that there's no future beyond the past. If you knew going in that this was a one-time gig, don't tell her you'll call her, and don't say you'll see her around. False hopes lead to hurt feelings.

Finally, don't be surprised if you end up feeling a bit more attached to her than you expected to. (It's a myth that women are the only ones who want sex to lead somewhere.) This brings us to another don't: Don't, under any circumstances, be surprised if she's the one who wants a clean break. Essentially, the two of you went into this looking for a form of mutual masturbation. Be prepared to leave it at that. You have no right to force the issue just because you woke up smitten.

oral sex

We always knew we were ahead of our time. Way back before the sexual revolution, when oral sex was still listed in medical and psychiatric books as a deviant act, we knew better. We can thank the feminist movement, however, for bringing a positive change in attitudes about fellatio and cunnilingus.

Today, almost as many women as men view oral sex as a normal part of lovemaking. Younger women, in particular, have an even more casual attitude about oral sex than men their own age. A survey of 600 college students found that only 37 percent of the female respondents would say that they had "had sex" with someone to whom they'd given a blow job, while 44 percent of male respondents said they would define giving or receiving such favors as "having sex."

All this means that you're much more likely than your grandfather was to find a partner who's willing to give head—*and* to expect you to return the favor. Here's what you need to know to improve the odds still further.

- When she's going down on you, always warn her before you come. Whether she spits or swallows, she'll appreciate the, uh, heads-up. It'll give her a second to prepare, so she'll be less likely to gag and more likely to want to come back for more.

- Keep in mind that being on the receiving end of oral sex is the only way some women can reach orgasm. (Let's face it, we'd say that, too, if it meant getting more head.) So try to hang in there until her moans turn into all-out screams and she begins digging her fingernails into your skin. Oh, and follow the same rule you hope she does: no biting.

- As for that post-cunnilingus kiss, not every woman likes the taste of her own secretions. (You're not wild about yours, are you?) Your best bet is to slowly work your way back up. If she turns her head when you zero in, nibble her neck instead. Then go brush your teeth and give your face a quick once-over with soap and water.

orgasm

To too many of us, an orgasm can be as simple as a *National Geographic* article on seminude tribal peoples and a couple tosses of the hand.

That's ejaculation. And while no one is disparaging the pleasant feeling of ejaculation, it pales mightily compared to the sensation of orgasm. What's the difference? In the case of orgasm, we encourage you to think globally and act locally. Orgasm begins with the same sort of activity that brings on ejaculation. It just doesn't stop there.

Unlike ejaculation, orgasm is an all-over feeling. It swallows your entire body and soul, not just your groin. Your breathing rate, heartbeat, and blood pressure rise. Let it build even more, and your whole body can spasm and thrash, from your toes to your lips. You doubt us? Ever see the full-body rapture a woman often goes through during orgasm? Yours can be just as powerful if you expect more than mere ejaculation during lovemaking.

One of the easiest ways to experience true orgasm is to put off ejaculation for a while when you're in the midst of passion. Each time you feel yourself nearing the brink, back off. Stop thrusting for a bit and slow things down. If you're too close, you may even want to pull out and concentrate just on kissing for a few minutes. Each time you relax and let the momentum build, your orgasmic threshold gets a tad higher. When you're finally ready to unleash, waves of oceanic pleasure will carry both of you to new lands. Or at least make the old land seem a little bit brighter.

ovaries

If there's a physical center to womanhood, it's the ovaries. Either that, or the television studio where Oprah's audience sits.

Almond-shaped glands the size of large walnuts, a woman's two ovaries sit sheltered in her lower abdomen, one on either side of her uterus. (Speaking of nuts: If manhood had been her destiny, the tissue that became her ovaries would've formed testicles, instead.)

Ovaries do three important things: They produce the hormones estrogen and progesterone, which shape a woman's sexual characteristics (quite nicely, we might add). They cause the walls of her uterus to thicken with blood-rich cells and create a hospitable spot for a fertilized egg. And they produce eggs like those from which we all sprang.

A woman is born with about one million undeveloped egg cells, or follicles, but her body absorbs more than half of those during childhood. When she reaches puberty, 300 to 400 of the remaining follicles begin to mature into eggs at the usual rate of one a month. Her two ovaries generally alternate the egg-laying duties monthly. Unlike those of her counterparts in the henhouse, though, a woman's eggs are nowhere near large enough to scramble. Each of the little tykes is only one-tenth of a millimeter in diameter.

Every menstrual cycle, that month's mature, fertile egg floats out of its ovary and into the corresponding fallopian tube. If it hooks up with a healthy, hardy sperm, the result is a tax deduction. If it doesn't, it's expelled from the woman's body during her period.

ovulation

This is her other "time of the month." It's when her ovaries release an egg that's ready and waiting to be fertilized. Depending on your present intentions, it's either a time of dread or a chance to give her a—ahem—standing ovulation.

Yes, the only time she can get pregnant is during ovulation. But that's not a guarantee that she *will* conceive. Even under ideal circumstances, the chance of conception tops out at around 20 percent in any given month.

There are kits you can buy at many drugstores that will tell you if she's in those fertile few days. If you're trying to put a bun in her oven, having sex several times within that window of opportunity will boost your chances.

If, on the other hand, you're trying to evade ovulation, let us wish you the best of luck. First off, you'd do well to take leave of the misconception that ovulation occurs only in the middle of her cycle. It can—and does—take place at any point in the month, even rarely *during* menstruation.

penis

Ah, yes. The tallywhacker. The master of ceremonies. Old Blind Bob. The upstanding citizen. Big Jim and his twins. He who is exactly, gloriously, one arm's length away.

How much do you really know about your penis? Sure, you know his name, likes, dislikes, and favorite foods, but there's a lot more to him than that. Your penis is anything but the simple device it seems like from the outside. Consider first that it performs two seemingly contradictory functions: urination and fertilization. Thus it's involved in both the elimination of life's waste products and the very production of life itself. How it does this is a marvel of nature.

The penis comprises one long tube—the urethra—surrounded by three inflatable cylinders, all wrapped up in a surprisingly tough sheath of elastic tissue. Capping it off is what's known as the glans, or head. Sensitive nerve endings abound in this nut-shaped tip. In uncircumcised guys, a fold of skin called the foreskin covers the glans.

Extending from the bladder to the tip of the penis, the urethra carries urine or ejaculate, depending on your most pressing need at the moment. The urethra is surrounded by the corpus spongiosum, one of the three inflatable cylinders. The other, larger cylinders are called the corpora cavernosa. All three cylinders are made of a spongelike material filled with blood vessels and tiny chambers. When you have sexy thoughts, your brain sends signals to these cylinders, which begin filling with blood, making your penis stand at attention.

Your brain also signals the prostate, a walnut-size organ located beneath the bladder. This little guy releases the bulk of the fluid in which your sperm swim. The bladder neck squeezes shut the part of the urethra connected to the bladder, so only semen gets through to the target. (This also explains why it's so difficult to get a good urine stream going right after sex.) When you're done, the valves that drain the cylinders relax, allowing the blood to flow out of the penis, returning it to its floppy state.

performance anxiety

You've shown up for the big game, but left your bat at home. Trust us, it's happened to a lot of guys—almost everybody at some point, in fact, whether we admit it or not. That's the price we pay for having a penis that's required to stand tall in order to complete the sex act.

Some therapists call this spectatoring, and for good reason. Essentially, an anxious fellow is watching himself perform (or trying to perform) rather than being fully involved in the moment. He's so worried about not being able to get the job done that, as an ironic result, he removes himself from the very sensations that *would* shiver his timber.

Try to take a fatalistic approach to it all. Simply assume that, at one time or another, you won't be able to get it up. The only question then is, What do you do when that happens?

Fortunately, we have an answer: Immediately stop the stampede toward penetration. Focus instead on pleasing one another in alternate ways. Dwell over her breasts, or parts farther south, with your tongue. Give her a massage. Let her massage you. Take a break and just talk for a while. Make a concerted decision *not* to have intercourse.

You know something? You'll actually come out of this a better lover. If you expand your repertoire of skills beyond mere intercourse, you'll have one very devoted fan in bed next to you.

period

Common slang for menstruation (other popular terms include *friend, curse, on the rag, that time of the month*). It's when she changes into her lackluster "period panties" so she doesn't wreck the tiger-striped thong you bought her last Valentine's Day.

Let's face it, not menstruating is one of the great things about being a man. Imagine if you bled out of the end of your peter every month. Imagine having to stock cotton condoms in your desk drawer. Imagine having to suddenly excuse yourself in the midst of an important meeting to rush to the john and wash out the scarlet stain that's started to leak across the crotch of your pants. There's a good reason women begrudge our not having to go through this a dozen times a year.

Add to that the fact that a woman's period has been surrounded by myth and misinformation since the dawn of history. Some cultures—ancient and not so ancient—felt that women were unclean during this time and forbade any sort of contact with a menstruating woman.

Though we're a bit more enlightened these days, some men and women are still wary of getting it on during menstruation. Too bad, because aside from the added cleanup, it's a great time to have sex. In fact, some women are hornier during their periods than at any other time of the month.

If you decide to take advantage of her increased interest in you, realize that even though she may be really randy, her natural lubrication may be limited, especially if she uses tampons. (They *are* superabsorbent, after all.) Spend extra time kissing and caressing, and use a good lubricant. It's also a good idea to wear a condom, especially if you don't know her HIV status.

pornography

Originally, it meant writings about prostitutes. Today, it means videos, pictures, writings, and other media intended to cause sexual arousal. While the word is used interchangeably with *obscenity,* pornography is not a legal term, just a popular one.

The question of when pornography becomes obscene—and hence illegal—is an ongoing conundrum. Congress passed the first antipornography law in 1873, with the US Post Office granting a man named Anthony Comstock enormous power to snoop through people's mail in search of smut.

Books ranging from James Joyce's *Ulysses* to Henry Miller's *Tropic of Cancer* had been banned in the United States because they were regarded as obscene. More recently, music lyrics have been the source of controversy, from the Rolling Stones' song "Let's Spend the Night Together" to 2 Live Crew's "Nasty as They Wanna Be" album.

Pornography became a truly big business with the advent of videocassettes that enabled folks to take home copies of *Debbie Does Dallas* with the same ease with which they rent *Honey, I Shrunk the Kids.* The industry did $3.62 billion in rentals and sales in 2006, the last year for which figures were available. And the Internet has provided even easier access to porn, with 28,258 people viewing online porn every second.

The overwhelming majority of skin flicks are made in the San Fernando Valley area of Los Angeles. Here's a shock: Guys are the biggest audience. It's estimated that of adult videos rented, 71 percent are by lone (and lonely?) male customers, 19 percent by women accompanied by men, 7 percent by male couples, 2 percent by women alone, and less than 1 percent by female couples.

U.S. obscenity law now states that material can be deemed obscene only if its dominant theme appeals to a "prurient interest" in sex, if the material affronts contemporary community standards relating to the depiction of sexual matters, and if the material has no serious literary, artistic, political, or scientific value. Lawmakers across the country have worked hard to find loopholes in this Supreme Court–mandated definition. They've also grappled with how to impose restrictions on the proliferation of porn on the Internet—and on children's access to it—without hampering free expression.

Defenders of the right to view porn point to countries such as Denmark, Holland, and Germany, which have repealed obscenity laws with no discernible ill effect. President Reagan's Meese Commission also found no causal link between sexually explicit materials and sexually aggressive behavior. Indeed, there are no studies showing any such connection in any American communities. However, strong conservative views in the United States continue to keep porn obscenity laws in effect for the foreseeable future.

premature ejaculation

Defining what it means to "come too soon" is, shall we say, a slippery subject. The usual meaning is the inability to delay orgasm for more than a very short period after entering your partner. Then again, some women insist that any guy who comes before they do has ejaculated "prematurely." This, of course, prompts questions of its own: How long should it take for a woman to come? And how long should a guy have to wait? These questions, in turn, lead to other questions having more to do, perhaps, with sexual politics than with pleasure. In fairness to the fair sex, the bottom line is that regardless of how and when you come, you owe it to your partner to maximize your contribution to her satisfaction. How you help her get there is up to the two of you.

In any case, textbook premature ejaculation is a common problem. (For the record, it wouldn't be if we were, say, apes. Other mammals routinely ejaculate faster than you can say "ejaculate.") And several reasons are commonly cited as to why some men have quicker triggers than others. Performance anxiety. Stress. Hypersensitive penises. Even a learned response—a vestige of boyhood masturbation, wherein rapid-fire ejaculation was the norm.

How to fix this? Sex experts recommend two closely related methods: squeeze and start-stop. In the first, your partner stimulates you until you're just about there, then one of you simply firmly squeezes the glans, or head, of your penis with a thumb and index finger (or with both hands, depending on the sizes of the available fingers and glans), thus thwarting ejaculation. This can be done several times during foreplay to prolong it without causing ejaculation. Once you get better acquainted with your body's moment-by-moment responses, you can use this tactic during intercourse, as well. It works best with the woman on top, because you're stimulated less intensely in this position, so you're better able to last longer. She can lift herself off you when you're too close, too soon.

In the start-stop method, your partner stimulates you until you're near orgasm, then stops. Once your sexual tension is diminished, she resumes. This helps a man to anticipate his point of inevitability and thereby control it. Once you master this, you can also employ the technique during intercourse, again starting, ideally, with the woman on top. (Of course, you can practice either of these without a partner, too. It's just not as much fun.)

Doctors don't recommend using desensitizing creams or gels. They don't help you learn new ways of responding during sex. And if you use them but don't use a condom, they may numb your partner's erogenous zones as well as yours—and then you'll be right back to the coming-before-she-does problem.

Since younger men generally come quicker than their elders do, if you're under 40, consider masturbating before an anticipated sexual encounter. This may reduce your excitement somewhat and give you more self-control. Plus, it ensures that you'll definitely get off, even if your date isn't in the mood to help you.

rough sex

It's a potent female fantasy—though one that's often misinterpreted, with regrettable (and sometimes illegal) results. A woman who hints about making love more aggressively is usually not looking to have sensitive body parts sundered or her head bashed against the nearest bedpost. Rough sex for most women is a role-playing game in which you create the illusion of forcefulness. You tease; you don't draw blood.

It bears repeating that the operative word here is *illusion*. Before you engage in rough sex, you and your partner should mutually agree upon a safe word that means, "Enough." No matter how much you're enjoying yourself or how close you are to coming, if your partner utters the safe word, cease and desist immediately!

That said, you also should be alert to your partner's nonverbal cues about desiring a bolder approach to lovemaking. If you think she's in the mood, you might start by backing her up against a wall—again, not too hard at first— and holding her there tightly. Employ your fingernails and your teeth, but use them as pleasure tools, not weapons. Monitor her response as you gently scrape your nails down her back and nip her neck or breasts. If she doesn't flinch, dig a bit deeper, bite a bit harder. Be a little more forceful in removing her clothing. Again, pay attention to her reaction as you go along.

Arguably the most misunderstood concept in sex is rough intercourse itself. No woman enjoys being jabbed with a fully erect penis when she's not yet lubricated or otherwise ready. The roughness comes in more in the way you move once she's fully aroused and you're actually inside her. Try rocking her hard and fast in a setting where she won't get bruised or rug-burned; a soft mattress is ideal. Gradually increase your pace or force. Here, too, nonverbal cues play a big role. Look for wincing or an attempt on her part to disengage. Learn the difference between a pleasurable moan and a painful groan.

It's a delicate balancing act: You have to learn to push the limits without exceeding them. Further complicating things, different women have different limits. And at different times.

If you're not sure whether your woman is enjoying it or just how hard she wants it, then, by all means, ask her. There's nothing wrong with a well-placed, "Have you had enough yet?" or "Do you like this?" You may even get a breathy, "No, baby, I *love* it," in return.

safe sex

You know as well as we do that to avoid a host of sexually transmitted diseases, you have to wear a condom every time you have sex with a new partner. Trouble is, too many of us consider safe sex just another ritual of early courtship that we can move beyond as a relationship progresses (kind of like leaving each other's company when we have to break wind). Once we begin to feel emotionally secure in a relationship, many of us make the mistake of assuming that our partners are disease-free and monogamous. So we say goodbye to the condoms. And, potentially, we say hello to STDs.

Here's the bottom line: You should always practice safe sex. That's because some STDs (specifically, herpes and genital warts) are difficult to detect through routine tests and can be carried relatively symptom-free, meaning that if you or your partner have them, you may not even know. That said, if condom-free sex is of utmost importance to you, have it only after you're both completely monogamous and you've taken the following steps.

- First, get tested for every imaginable STD. For 6 months thereafter, even if you each get a clean bill of health, you have to remain faithful to each other and, most important, continue using condoms.
- To keep you on track during the 6-month waiting period, keep your condoms where you're most likely to use them: by the bed. Also carry a few with you when you go out. Don't store them in your wallet or back pocket for too long. Heat weakens them, as does extreme cold. Make sure you get the right fit. Too big, and it could slip off. Too small, and it could break. Avoid novelty and lambskin condoms; they don't prevent disease transmission.
- Put on the prophylactic before your penis comes in contact with her fluids, and keep it on until you remove yourself from her. Use it not only for vaginal intercourse but also during anal sex (when the risk of transmitting diseases is highest) and when you're the recipient of oral sex.
- If you go down on her, use a dental dam (available from sex shops) or plastic wrap to cover her genitals.
- Finally, remember to be careful when you take off the condom; don't be sloppy with the semen.
- When the 6-month wait is up, you each have to get another HIV test because the virus doesn't register on tests until 6 months after infection (so if you contracted it less than 6 months before the first test, it wouldn't have shown up then anyway). Remember, if either of you carries the viruses that cause herpes or genital warts, you still may be able to transmit them.

Keep all this in mind even if you both come up clean and agree to remain monogamous. After all, safe sex is better than no sex.

seduction

The best seducers read body language: the way a woman stands, the movements of her hands, the wideness of her eyes, the breadth of her smile. A man who can interpret those signals will have little trouble sweeping her off her feet—and into his bed.

The important thing to recognize about seduction is that it's not just you making a sales pitch; it's a negotiation. At various points along the way, an interested woman throws off certain cues that signal her mounting desire (or her desire to mount you, as the case may be). She expects you to perceive, acknowledge, and act on those cues. So ask her questions about herself, and pay very close attention to her answers—not just what she says but also how she says it. Does she seem to sway toward you for a moment as she tells you that she recently became single again? Or does she just state it matter-of-factly?

This is critical because a woman whose come-hither vibes are ignored starts to feel just as rejected as the woman who asks a man outright to sleep with her and gets turned down. Pretty soon, her pride forces her to put up a wall, to be less demonstrative about her interest. And then the seduction is over.

If the tables are turned and that Venus you met at last Friday night's dart game puts the moves on you, how should you react? If you're interested, reciprocate simply by being yourself. Smile, ask her lots of questions about herself, and let her discover who you are. Enjoy the seduction for what it is: a highly charged erotic buildup that culminates in some kind of connection, be it a phone number exchange or a romp in bed.

sex drive

Next time you bring up sex and a woman complains, "That's all you think about!" point out that men and women have fairly equal libidos, according to studies of the subject. The difference in how the two genders perceive their respective sex drives may occur because of other dynamics that affect male-female relationships, causing us to confuse other factors with low sex drive.

For instance, when you're pissed off at your partner, you probably don't want to get frisky with her. Well, okay, that's not necessarily true; if she's hot, you probably want to nail her anyway. But we can almost guarantee that when *she's* pissed off at *you,* sex won't be uppermost in her mind.

Your woman's sex drive is also strongly influenced by her reproductive cycle. Her libido is highest during the 3 days of her ovulatory phase, which occurs about 8 days after her period ends. She's probably least lustful for the 2 weeks afterward, known as the luteal phase, when her body produces the progesterone that makes her prone to PMS. Some women, however, do feel sexually aggressive in the middle of this phase.

Libido-sapping problems affecting both sexes include diabetes, alcoholism, fatigue, anxiety, and depression. Even some remedies for depression, such as the medications Prozac (fluoxetine hydrochloride) and Zoloft (sertraline), inhibit sexual desire.

The key to keeping your sex drive strong is to stay active and healthy: Continue having sex, eat right, and exercise. Vegetables are the best foods for enhancing virility, because they're rich in vitamins, minerals, and carbohydrates. In addition, you may want to take a good multivitamin.

While your sex drive will begin to decrease after middle age, your woman's may increase postmenopause because she'll no longer have to worry about unintended pregnancy. And both of you may be more sexually motivated, because you'll tend to have fewer family and career responsibilities dampening your sexual energy.

talking dirty

A pastime popular enough to make those 1-900 phone sex numbers a booming business.

Even if your partner is one of those women who's a bit put off by your fondness for heat-of-the-moment obscenities, just remember this: According to the landmark *Janus Report on Sexual Behavior,* more than half of Americans think that a bit of raunchy language during sex is just fine, thank you.

In fact, when it comes to sex, many of us are more at ease using slang terms (including the more than 200 euphemisms for intercourse) than clinical, scientific words. And, for those folks who like it, dirty talk isn't just for the bedroom. Graphically whispering in your girlfriend's ear while you're, say, picking out guavas in the supermarket can jump-start your plans for an evening of great sex.

And if you and your partner have trouble speaking the same sexual language? Here's what sex therapists suggest for bridging the great divide.

- Ask your partner if she has a pet name for her vagina. When she stops laughing, tell her about the childhood nickname you gave your penis. This may amuse her enough to reveal her own secret words or the slang terms she prefers.
- Another exercise is for each partner to make two side-by-side lists, one containing clinical words, the other, the corresponding dirty words. Exchange lists and look for words that you've both picked. Discuss which are the most mutually arousing, then try them in bed later.
- If this still sounds too silly or embarrassing for a face-to-face setting, you might experiment first over the phone or online. The relative anonymity makes it easier for some people to open up. Just don't do any of this in Willowdale, Oregon, where town fathers have enacted a law against a husband uttering profanity while having sex with his wife.

testicles

We seldom call them that, of course. To us, they're balls, nuts, jewels, cojones. And though we think of them primarily in terms of pumping out sperm cells, they also produce testosterone, our hormonal ticket to manhood.

The average testicle weighs less than an ounce. It's oval-shaped, about 1½ inches long, and 1 inch in diameter. For some reason, the left ball is usually a bit bigger, and hangs a little lower, than the right.

Most doctors and sex therapists will tell you not to worry if you don't have balls that'd be the envy of the Merrill Lynch bull. Size doesn't affect your sexual endurance, sex drive, or level of fertility. Yet some studies do appear to show a link between large testicles and promiscuity or infidelity. Robin Baker, PhD, a biologist at the University of Manchester in England, announced in 1997 that men with big balls were likely to have more lovers and more active sex lives than their more modestly endowed counterparts. Baker's studies also suggested that when two pairs of testicles competed for one woman's affections, they were both likely to generate more sperm. Go figure.

trophy wife

A luscious babe—often very blonde, sometimes constructed of silicone and cosmetics—with a wealthy, usually older, husband. In general, a trophy wife is not a man's first wife, but rather a late-arriving accoutrement he attains as he climbs the ladder of success. Think Marla Maples. And her successor, Melania Knauss.

We'll assume that most of you reading this aren't The Donald, but still, there comes a point in your life—maybe around 45 or 50—when you're financially comfortable. Maybe the magic goes out of your life with the woman who's been your companion all those years. And maybe you get attention from cute, younger women at the office. And you start to wonder, "Hmmm. . . . What would it be like to pull a Michael Douglas and hook up with a Catherine Zeta-Jones?"

While you're lingering over that fantasy, here are a few reality checks.

- Realize that you want to share your life with someone who loves *you,* not the size of your 401(k).
- Realize that young women, trophies or not, are going to hear the alarms on their biological clocks. Will you really be up for that?
- Realize that if you have to dump your existing wife in order to effect this change, it's going to cost you, maybe big-time. A woman scorned, and all that.
- Realize that most people, especially friends who enter midlife along with you, are not going to be impressed by a big-breasted

young thang. Sure, they may wink and elbow you on the golf course, making sly references about how hot the sex must be, going along with the joke. Just don't kid yourself. In the end, that's probably how they perceive your latest conquest: as a joke. "So, I see Ted went out and bought himself a wife. . . ." It may seem unfair, but if you have some money and she has some looks, that's how it will be.

All that said, well, if you're just lucky enough to fall in real, true love with a drop-dead gorgeous woman who's also a dynamic lover and a sensitive sweetheart—in other words, if the fundamentals of a good, honest relationship are all in place—damn the torpedoes. Go for it.

turn-offs

Maybe you can't understand why your partner isn't interested in resuming her riding position after a phone call interrupts the action. After all, the call was brief enough. You were gone for 10 minutes, tops. Hell, you're still hard. So why does she roll away rather than climb aboard?

Could it be that she's offended by the fact that you took the call in the first place? Or by the fact that—while you thought maybe it was your boss calling about that important account—it turned out to be your ex-girlfriend?

As any guy who's gone on more than two dates knows entirely too well, there are dozens of things we do that turn women off. Unfortunately, most of this happens beneath our radar: We don't even know we're doing it, and when they point it out to us—something they love doing—we're, like, shocked. "What? I can't scratch my balls at dinner? Geez, it was under the table and all. And your mother was preoccupied with carving the turkey. . . ."

Lots of these problems have to do with what might graciously be called a disconnect in the way men and women regard the homes they share. Maybe a man's home is his castle, but your queen doesn't like you soiling the moat or leaving the drawbridge up. The sight of your filthy, smelly socks under the kitchen table is not going to make her ravenous for sex.

So, too, in the bathroom: She doesn't want to see your beard remnants scattered all over the sink. And hey, believe us when we say we're in your corner, but flush the damn toilet. Each and every time. Okay?

Even more important than keeping the lavatory clean is washing yourself. All over. Especially if you're expecting head. If she does go down on you, don't yank her around by the ears. . . . You're sick of hearing this? Then tell all the other guys you know to stop doing it, because women still complain about it in droves.

Once you're well-scrubbed, remember that a woman generally expects a seduction to amount to more than, "Uh, wanna screw?" Yes, even when she wants it, too. If she's in the mood for a quickie, she'll let you know about it, have no fear.

She'll also let you know if she's not in the mood at all because she's still pissed at you for something you did or didn't do earlier. Sorry, but makeup sex is a misnomer. In most cases, you should attempt it only *after* the issue has been settled and apologies have been offered and accepted. You do not delight a woman by graciously offering her the pleasure of your erection in recompense for your previous sins. You just start a brand-new fight.

If it's kinkiness you're after, don't expect to achieve it by telling her that your regular bedroom routine leaves you cold. This makes her feel very inadequate. Say instead, "I heard about this activity, and I thought you'd be very sexy doing it." Or just pick out something we discuss in this book, and bring it to her attention.

Don't ask, "Did you come?" It's annoying if she did, and it puts pressure on her if she didn't. Just ask her sweetly if she'd like you to keep going.

While you're being sweet, make sure any compliment you give her is really a compliment. We actually know a living, breathing guy who enthusiastically told his wife, "Honey, you don't look nearly as fat in that new hairstyle!"

unwanted advances

It's the stuff of romantic comedies: A guy is attracted to a woman who's not the least bit interested. He spends the entire film either secretly pining for her or pleading for just one date. After 2 hours or months or years of this (in movie time), he finally gives up, a beaten man. Whereupon, due to some magical serendipitous circumstances, she falls into his arms, realizing they were meant for each other all along. They live happily ever after.

Unfortunately, this happens only in Hollywood. In the real-world version of the same scenario, you get fed up with being ignored or rebuffed so often, or she gets fed up with your coming around so much. Or maybe she meets somebody else and gets married before she has a chance to realize that you're Mr. Right.

Which brings us back to these advances. So, how often do you make a move? When does no mean no?

We're told these days that no always means no, but you know better. For instance: You offer to buy a woman a drink. She says, "No, thank you. I'm really sorry; I'm seeing someone." But she says it in a forlorn way that seems to imply she's really sorry that she's seeing someone. It's a classic mixed message. You wonder whether there's a chance she'll say yes, with a bit more coaxing. So you hang around for a while and casually strike up a conversation. She doesn't seem to mind the company.

What do you do next? And what don't you do?

You don't become a pest. (She did turn you down once, after all.) Perhaps the most face-saving tactic at this point is to tell her you're available if she ever wants to get to know you better. Either say that explicitly or drop hints about how she can find you: not just where you work, but also social places that you visit. If you have a business card, this is the time to give it to her. Then tell her you've enjoyed talking to her, and leave.

If a woman doesn't call you or return your messages, that's a pretty clear signal that she's not interested. Sometimes. There are women who just do not call guys. It goes against some sort of programming, or maybe they just read that book *The Rules* one too many times. In any case, understand that there really are women—nice ones—who'll let a perfectly good relationship slip away simply because they've been taught that the man is supposed to take the initiative.

If you do manage to reach her by phone, try the following: "Look, I really like you. I don't want to just go away. But if I'm bugging you, let me know, and I won't call again." If she gives you no opening whatsoever at this point, put her behind you and move on. Bear in mind that many states have stalking-via-telephone statutes.

urinary problems

An umbrella term for a variety of conditions involving the urinary tract, which is made up of the kidneys, ureters, bladder, and urethra. The most common disorders affecting men include urinary tract infections and obstructions. In older men in particular, incontinence and prostate enlargement tend to become more common. Alas, more to dislike about aging.

Urinary tract infections (UTIs) affect millions of men each year; only respiratory infections are more common. You may not have realized that they're so prevalent, because infections in individual organs have different names: an infection of the urethra is called urethritis, a bladder infection is cystitis, and a kidney infection is pyelonephritis.

UTIs usually stem from a urinary blockage caused by an enlarged prostate, a kidney or bladder stone, or a medical procedure involving a catheter. As a result of the blockage, your body can't flush out bacteria and other micro-organisms the way it normally would when you pee. The result is an over-growth of these nasty buggers that causes an infection.

Symptoms usually include cloudy or reddish urine, a painful burning sensation during urination, and the need to go frequently and urgently. The good news is that most infections can be taken care of with antibiotics. (By the way, women also get these infections, and they can be transmitted sexually. So if you or your partner has one, it's a good idea to steer clear of sex until the UTI has cleared up.)

Urinary obstructions can wreak havoc in more ways than those we describe above, especially if the blockage is a kidney stone. Roughly one in seven men will develop a kidney stone in his lifetime. A stone occurs when substances in the urine form small, hard crystals that prevent urine from passing through the urethra. The feeling of a stone passing through your urinary tract can be excruciating (some folks liken it to the pain of childbirth). While most guys are able to pass stones on their own, stubborn cases require medical intervention. And once you've had a stone, you also have a fifty-fifty chance of a recurrence. Some easy preventive measures? Drink lots of fluids, cut back on meat and salt, and eat foods high in potassium, such as baked potatoes, bananas, cantaloupe, and steamed clams.

We know. Just reading this entry is painful in and of itself. And we're not done yet. Although rare, bladder cancer is a particular concern for guys, affecting three times more men than women. Aside from problems urinating, the hallmark symptom is blood in the urine. The most important way to help prevent it? Quit smoking. Your body gets rid of cancer-causing smoke toxins via urine. If you smoke, your bladder literally soaks in these chemicals.

Prostate cancer is the second leading cause of cancer deaths in men, with one in five Americans developing it.

Okay, we've saved the best for last. Six million men in the United States suffer from incontinence, or lack of bladder control. Causes include a weak bladder muscle, an enlarged prostate, nerve injuries, surgery, and diseases like diabetes. Cold medications, antidepressants, and muscle relaxants can also affect your urinary control.

If you have any problems urinating or experience any of the symptoms listed above, be sure to consult with your doctor as soon as possible. Take it from us, this stuff isn't anything to fool around with.

vagina

Ah, the vagina. Source of endless bewilderment, amazement, and many a good locker room joke. And the ultimate in female symbolism.

But don't get too caught up in the idea of a vagina as a symbol of womanliness—you have one, too. Yes, you read right. It's called the *vagina masculina*, or male vagina. It could have been a "real" one, but when you were bouncing around in your mother's womb, testosterone kicked in and turned you into a boy. But your vagina is still there, a piece of tissue dangling uselessly from your bladder. And your would-be hymen is by your prostate.

vasectomy

Mention this to most men, and we react as if we'd just been kicked in our jock-straps. We're just not too thrilled with the idea of sharp and burning objects coming at our most sensitive of areas.

The procedure is, of course, a "permanent" form of male birth control in which the tubes that carry sperm from your testicles are severed and cauterized. That may sound painful and terrifying, but the procedure is actually safe, quick, relatively cheap, and highly effective. It is also quite common. About half a million of our fellow men in the United States have vasectomies each year—and the procedure is usually covered by health insurance.

There are two ways to go about the surgery: with scalpel and without. A scalpel vasectomy involves two small incisions in the scrotum, through which the doc reaches in, cuts out a piece of each vas deferens, and ties off or cauterizes the ends. In the no-scalpel version, he makes a single puncture in the scrotum and uses a special tool to do the same thing. Either way, it's a simple outpatient procedure, and you'll be done in less than a half-hour.

Which should you choose? Your choice, really—but some doctors think the less-complicated, no-scalpel vasectomy should become the method of choice.

A couple of things to bear in mind: Although a vasectomy can be reversed in some cases (that's why we put *permanent* in quotes, above), you need to consider it a lifelong decision. Any good urologist will spend some time counseling you to make sure you're ready for this. Among the things he should ask: Are you old enough? (If you're single and in your twenties, a responsible doc won't snip you. There are just too many reasons for you to change your mind down the road.) Have you sown your seeds? Do you have children, and are you sure you're done?

If all systems are still go, make an appointment for a Friday. You'll need the weekend to ice your twins to make sure there's no undue swelling. And don't expect to hop right back in the saddle: You'll need a few days before you'll feel like having sex. Even when you do feel like it, you'll need to wrap your willy. It takes about 20 ejaculations to clean out any residual sperm.

And forget the myth that your ejaculations will be any different in volume. Sperm make up a microscopic amount of semen. The bulk of it comes from your prostate and seminal vesicles, which are unaffected by the surgery.

vibrator

A sex toy that can either offer external stimulation or serve as a faux phallus that penetrates the vagina or anus. Otherwise known as a woman's best friend.

Vibration causes genitals to engorge, or fill with blood, which intensifies sexual arousal and may lead to orgasm. Because the genitals and all surrounding areas are exquisitely sensitive to vibration, an external vibrator can be placed just about anywhere except the toenails to produce pleasure. And even the toenails might work on the right person. More commonly, women place vibrators on their clits and let them buzz away.

You can find vibrators in a variety of sizes and shapes: from rocketlike dildos to small egg-shaped devices to tiny ones meant to be worn on a fingertip and held in a pleasant place.

Vibrators have traditionally been thought of as something women enjoy using solo. You're going to be wiser than that. Adventurous lovers report excellent results from incorporating vibrators into their lovemaking routines. You can use a vibrator to get your partner off if you come first during intercourse. It sure reduces the pressure to last forever. Or use a vibrating dildo for anal stimulation during oral sex to enhance the sensation of orgasm. As always, here's our anal-activity mantra: Use a water-based lube, and wash the device thoroughly or slip a latex condom on it before you use it anywhere else.

Never feel competitive with a vibrator or feel that you've failed if your partner suggests using one. Be glad that she's cool enough to use it in front of you. To be sure, a vibrator allows you to do certain things that you couldn't accomplish with your hands or penis alone. Why limit yourself to a few simple appendages?

withholding

The very idea of withholding sex baffles most men. Why would anyone ever want to withhold *sex?* It's like voluntarily giving up air. Or pizza.

The thing is, when a woman in an active relationship withholds sex, it boils down to a straight, old-fashioned power struggle. In passive-aggressive fashion, she typically does it (or *won't* do it, as the case may be) to communicate that something is amiss. She's playing her trump card, getting your attention in the only way she thinks will work.

This keeps you wanting, panting, threatening, maybe even pleading. That's not healthy. And it's damn sure not dignified. While her refusal to put out may solve a short-term problem once in a great while, you're quickly going to tire of the "Guess what I'm mad about now" game.

The two of you need to address the built-up resentment that's causing her to close the barn door. If she withholds sex routinely just to get her way, she needs a therapist, and you need to decide if you want to live with a bully. More likely, though, it's a sign that the rest of your relationship isn't so hot, either. A well-worn adage says that sex begins in the kitchen, and it's true, at least for women. How she feels about your time together outside the bedroom has much to do with her willingness to play inside the boudoir.

In other words, withholding, to her, may be shorthand for, "I need to talk to you." She's trying to get your attention. Give it to her, so both of you don't have to continue going through this.

One final warning: Be careful not to confuse intentional withholding—that is, the sort of gonadal gamesmanship described above—with other, legitimate reasons why she may just not be in the mood for sex. Generally speaking, you should be able to tell the difference. But it never hurts to broach the subject in a tactful, nonthreatening way.

X-rated

Although it now screams of sweaty sex scenes and cheesy soundtracks, the original X rating wasn't devised for hardcore porn. It was intended to warn parents that a mainstream Hollywood release had too much violence, adult language, and lust to be acceptable for folks under age 17.

In the 1960s, the Motion Picture Association of America (MPAA) began to notice that as social codes became looser, so did the content of films. The first mildly profane phrase to enter the cinema—"hump the hostess"—caused a stir during the 1966 release of *Who's Afraid of Virginia Woolf?* A few months later, *Blow-Up* got another rise out of the organization as the first wide-release movie to put naked bodies up on the big screen. After that, the MPAA decided it was time to crack down and create a rating system that let parents know when to keep their children out of the theaters.

Late in 1968, the motion picture industry adopted the following letter guidelines: G, or general rating, for all audiences; M, for mature audiences; R, for restricted audiences, wherein theaters barred unsupervised children under 16; and the infamous X for those films that could be viewed by no one under 17. The association trademarked all of its ratings except the X, which any company could affix to its film without undergoing the rating process.

By 1990, the rising pornography industry had successfully swiped the X rating, adding XX and XXX, thereby giving the original label even naughtier connotations. The MPAA then changed its X rating to NC-17.

yeast infection

A vaginal overgrowth of the yeast organism *Candida albicans*—and yet another reason to be glad you're not a woman.

But before you get too thankful, consider that you can contract candida from an infected woman if she doesn't stop you from getting too close. You're more likely to pick up a case if you are obese, have diabetes, are uncircumcised, or take a lot of antibiotics.

So before you take the plunge, pay special attention to the appearance of her vagina. If it's unusually red and sore (or you catch her scratching down there), think twice. And if she's oozing something that looks a lot like cottage cheese, you'll want to put your pants back on.

If you're still not sure—and as humorist Dave Barry likes to say, we are not making this up—take a quick whiff: If she smells more like a warm loaf of sourdough than like a pleasant seashore, she may have the fungus. The odor of a yeast infection strongly resembles that of fresh-baked bread.

More unsettling news: If you do catch candida, you'll likely notice white fungus growing on the head of your penis. And still more: It can appear anywhere else that your skin folds and traps sweat—under your elbows, behind your knees, between your toes. You can even get it in your mouth. The oral version of a yeast infection, called thrush, is sometimes contracted through cunnilingus.

A yeast infection sometimes ping-pongs back and forth between partners. To break the cycle, pick up an over-the-counter antiyeast cream, like Micatin antifungal cream, usually found near the athlete's foot or jock itch medications. Don't use the athlete's foot preparations on your penis, as they can be irritating. If you need a more potent prescription, or if the infection appears in your mouth, see your doctor.

zinc

One of the most important nutrients for proper sexual function. Low levels of this mineral can weaken the reproductive system, dampen sex drive, and even delay sexual maturation in prepubescent males.

Studies show that 10 to 15 percent of infertile adult males have low zinc levels. Such deficiencies seem to wear down the swimming strength of sperm—the little guys just don't have enough gusto to rocket up the fallopian tube and penetrate the egg.

Since semen contains high concentrations of zinc, frequent ejaculation can make you lose too much of the mineral. Your body may even respond by reducing your sexual drive.

Prolific sex *is* good for prostate health, not to mention mental health. So go ahead and let it fly on a regular basis—just make sure you think zinc. Eat foods like oysters, liver, steak, crab, wheat germ, black-eyed peas, chickpeas, and miso. Also, check the labeling of your multivitamin to see if it's fortified with zinc. Some are, some aren't.

INDEX

Underscored page references indicate boxed text or tables.